SERIES EDITOR: ALAN SMITH

Modular Maths for Edexcel

Mechanics 1

Second Edition

◆ DAVID O'MEARA

◆ PAT BRYDEN, JOHN BERRY, TED GRAHAM, DAVID HOLLAND, ROGER PORKESS

Hodder & Stoughton

A MEMBER OF THE HODDER HEADLINE GROUP

Acknowledgements

We are grateful to the following companies, institutions and individuals who have given permission to reproduce copyright material in this book. Every effort has been made to trace and acknowledge ownership of copyright. The publishers will be glad to make suitable arrangements with any copyright holders whom it has not been possible to contact.

Photos:
p7, left © John Cox/Life File
p7, centre © Graham Buchan/Life File
p7, right © B&C Alexander
p28 © Ruth Nossek
p31 © Andrew Ward/Life File
p43 © David Cumming, Eye Ubiquitous/CORBIS
p60 © Topham Picturepoint – Korea 1950
p64 © Science Photo Library
p65 © Action-Plus Photographic
p67 © Jeremy Hoare/Life File
p73 © NASA
p77, top © N.P.G., London – Sir Isaac Newton
p77, bottom © Matt Fullerty
p80 © Jeremy Hoare/Life File
p102 © Colorsport
p132 © J Allan Cash Photolibrary

Orders: please contact Bookpoint Ltd, 130 Milton Park, Abingdon, Oxon OX14 4SB.
Telephone: (44) 01235 827720, Fax: (44) 01235 400454.
Lines are open from 9.00–6.00, Monday to Saturday, with a 24 hour message answering service.
You can also order through our website www.madaboutbooks.co.uk.

British Library Cataloguing in Publication Data
A catalogue record for this title is available from The British Library

ISBN 0 340 885297

First published 2000
Second edition published 2004

Impression number	10 9 8 7 6 5 4 3 2 1
Year	2010 2009 2008 2007 2006 2005 2004

This work includes material adapted from the MEI Structured Mathematics series.

Cover photo from The Image Bank/Getty Images
Typeset by Tech-Set Ltd, Gateshead, Tyne & Wear.
Printed in Great Britain for Hodder & Stoughton Educational, a division of Hodder Headline Plc, 338 Euston Road, London NW1 3BH by Martins the Printers Ltd.

EDEXCEL ADVANCED MATHEMATICS

The Edexcel course is based on units in the four strands of Pure Mathematics, Mechanics, Statistics and Decision Mathematics. The first unit in each of these strands is designated AS, and so is Pure Mathematics: Core 2; all others are A2.

The units may be aggregated as follows:

3 units	AS Mathematics
6 units	A Level Mathematics
9 units	A Level Mathematics + AS Further Mathematics
12 units	A Level Mathematics + A Level Further Mathematics

Core 1 and 2 are compulsory for AS Mathematics, and Core 3 and 4 must also be included in a full A Level award.

Examinations are offered by Edexcel twice a year, in January (most units) and in June (all units). All units are assessed by examination only; there is no longer any coursework in the scheme.

Candidates are not permitted to use electronic calculators in the Core 1 examination. In all other examinations candidates may use any legal calculator of their choice, including graphical calculators.

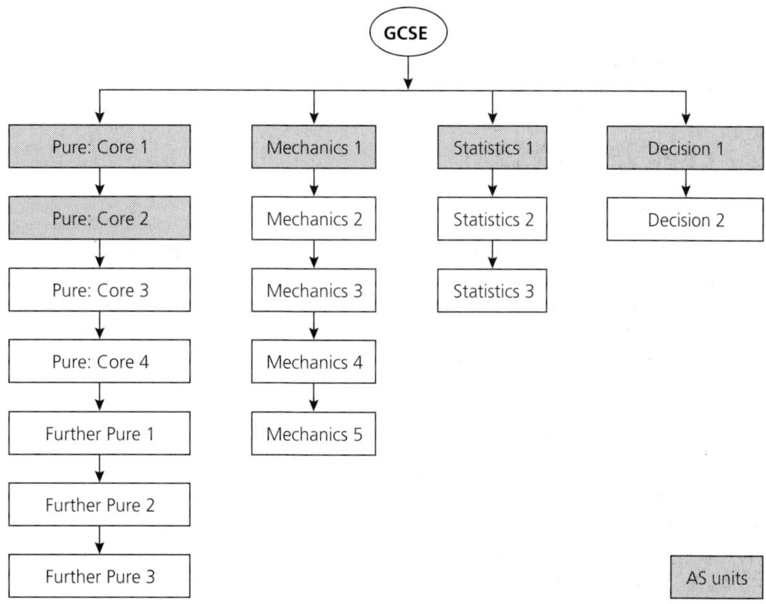

INTRODUCTION

This is the first book in a series written to support the Mechanics units in the Edexcel Advanced Mathematics scheme. It has been adapted from the successful series written to support the MEI Structured Mathematics scheme, and has been substantially edited and rewritten to provide complete coverage of the new Edexcel Mechanics 1 unit.

Throughout the series the emphasis is on understanding and applying a wide variety of mathematical skills, and particularly on the application of mathematics to modelling.

There are nine chapters in this book. They are presented in the same order as the specification, although many teachers will wish to study them in a different order. Cross-references have been reduced to the minimum to make this possible. Full answers are included.

After a short introduction on mathematical modelling, the vectors chapter introduces this fundamental topic with particular reference to displacement, velocity and acceleration. The kinematics chapter develops graphical techniques and finishes with the constant acceleration formulae.

Newton's laws are the subject of the next two chapters. They are applied to single particles in Chapter 4 and to connected particles in Chapter 5. The use of the principle of conservation of momentum in one dimension only is covered in the next chapter.

Statics is the subject of the last three chapters. Triangles (or polygons) of forces are covered in Chapter 7, together with the methods of resolving forces. Coulomb's laws of friction occupy Chapter 8, and the last chapter starts the coverage of the principle of moments. This topic is studied in more detail in *Mechanics 2*.

Throughout the book you will require the use of a calculator. Computer packages and graphics calculators may be helpful in clarifying new ideas, but you should remember that certain calculator restrictions may be enforced by the examination board.

I would like to thank the many people who have helped in the preparation and checking of material. Special thanks to Pat Bryden, John Berry, Ted Graham, David Holland and Roger Porkess, who wrote the original MEI edition, and to Terry Heard for his help and suggestions.

David O'Meara

Contents

Chapter one

MATHEMATICAL MODELS

Hereafter, when they come to model heaven
And calculate the stars, how they will wield
The mighty frame, how build, unbuild, contrive
To save appearances.

John Milton, Paradise Lost

SETTING UP A MATHEMATICAL MODEL

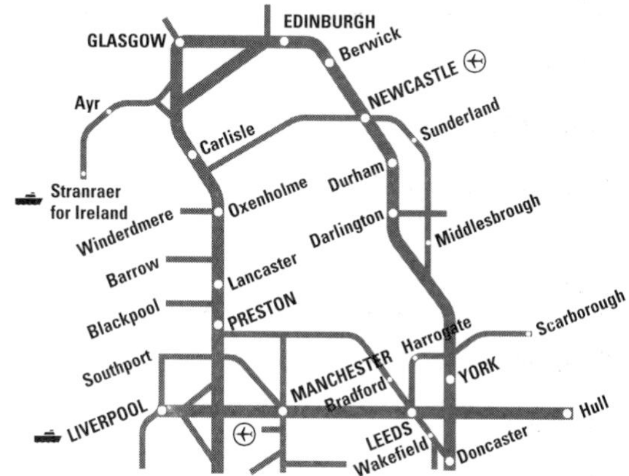

FIGURE 1.1 *Northern Great Britain's Main Railways*

The figure shows part of the map of the main railway lines of northern Great Britain. Which of the following statements can you be sure of just by looking at this map? Which of them might be important to a visitor from abroad?

(a) Darlington is on the line from York to Durham.
(b) Carlisle is nearer to Glasgow than it is to Newcastle.
(c) Leeds is due east of Manchester.
(d) The quickest way from Leeds to Glasgow is via York.

This is a *diagrammatic model* of the railway system which gives essential though by no means all the information you need for planning train journeys. You can be sure about the places a line passes through but distances and directions are only approximate and if you compare this map with an ordinary map you will see that statements (b) and (c) are false. You will also need further information from timetables to plan the best way to get from Leeds to Glasgow.

MAKING SIMPLIFYING ASSUMPTIONS

When setting up a model, you first need to decide what is essential. For example, what would you take into account and what would you ignore when considering the motion of a car travelling from Bristol to London?

You will need to know the distance and the time taken for parts of the journey, but you might decide to ignore the dimensions of the car and the motion of the wheels. You would then be using the idea of a *particle* to model the car. *A particle has no dimensions.*

You might also decide to ignore the bends in the road and its width and so treat it as a *straight line with only one dimension.* A length along the line would represent a length along the road in the same way as a piece of thread following a road on a map might be straightened out to measure its length.

You might decide to split the journey up into parts and assume that the speed is constant over these parts.

The process of making decisions like these is called *making simplifying assumptions* and is the first stage of setting up a *mathematical model* of the situation.

DEFINING THE VARIABLES AND SETTING UP THE EQUATIONS

The next step in setting up a mathematical model is to *define the variables* with suitable units. These will depend on the problem you are trying to solve. Suppose you want to know where you ought to be at certain times in order to maintain a good average speed between Bristol and London. You might define your variables as follows:

- the total time since the car left Bristol is t hours
- the distance from Bristol at time t is x km
- the average speed up to time t is $v\,\mathrm{km\,h^{-1}}$.

Then, at Newbury $t = t_1$ and $x = x_1$; etc.

You can then *set up equations* and go through the mathematics required to solve the problem. Remember to check that your answer is sensible. If it isn't, you might have made a mistake in your mathematics, or your simplifying assumptions might need reconsideration.

The theories of mechanics that you will learn about in this course, and indeed any other studies in which mathematics is applied, are based on mathematical models of the real world. When necessary, these models can become more complex as your knowledge increases.

COMMONLY USED MODELS

Particle

A particle has no dimensions, but does have mass. We very often treat a more complex object as a particle at the centre of mass of the object. The car in the journey above could well be treated as a particle if we simply wanted to estimate the journey time. It would, however, be incorrect to treat it as a particle if we were considering how to pack the luggage into the car. We might treat a person parachuting out of an aircraft as a particle if we were trying to predict their landing spot, but we would not do so if we were designing the parachute. An aircraft might be treated as a particle by air traffic control while it was circling waiting to land, but its dimensions become important while it is queuing on the ground waiting to take off.

The particle is the simplest model that we use.

Lamina

A lamina is a plane or part of a plane with mass but no thickness. It is the ultimate thin sheet. No actual laminas exist, just as no actual lines exist – they must have some thickness, but we use the zero thickness model when either they are very thin, or their thickness is unimportant. We may well treat a tray with some items on it as a lamina with some particles attached. Signposts and pictures are other examples where a lamina may well be the right model, but it would probably not be right to treat a person as a lamina.

It is possible to model more complex structures (e.g. a box) as a set of laminas.

Rigid body

A rigid body is usually three-dimensional. *Rigid* means that it does not change shape. In practice, of course, everything changes shape when a load is applied to it. When we treat a body as rigid it means that we are neglecting that change, either because it is too small to notice, or because it does not affect the problem.

Most bodies are treated as rigid in the first stages of mechanics.

Rod

A rod is a rigid, one-dimensional body. It is, in effect, an infinitely thin stick. It may be light, uniform, or non-uniform.

A *light* rod or any other body has no mass. In practice, this means that the mass is much less than the other masses involved in the problem. A ruler pushing a book might well be treated as a light rod, as might the handle of a mop. A first model of a bicycle might treat the frame as being made of light rods.

A *uniform* rod or any other body has mass which is distributed evenly. If the body has a centre which is obvious from symmetry, then we can put a single mass at the centre to represent the whole body. We might treat a ladder as a uniform rod, with the mass at the centre, or the top of a table as a uniform lamina.

Other properties of a uniform body are also the same all over the body, for example density or roughness.

Non-uniform is the opposite of uniform: the mass is not distributed evenly. A first model of a tree trunk might treat it as a uniform rod, but a better model might well treat it as non-uniform, as it is thicker at the bottom than the top. In this case we need to be told or to find out more before we can progress. In practice we need to know the centre of mass, which can be calculated by methods which will be found in *Mechanics 2*, or measured by balancing or measuring forces.

String

Mathematical string is not used for tying up parcels. It is however a good approximation to have in mind when string is mentioned. It can pull along its length only. The tension is the same at all points along the string – particularly at the ends. It cannot push or produce a sideways force. It is usually treated as light, as its mass is very small compared to the other masses involved, and it will be in a straight line if there is any tension in it at all. It can be inextensible or elastic.

Inextensible string does not change length when it is under load. Real inextensible string does not exist, of course, but provided the change in length is small then we can ignore it. This means that objects attached to a string's ends must have the same velocity along its length, although they are free to move sideways. We might treat the spokes of a bicycle wheel as inextensible strings.

Elastic strings do change length under load, and are dealt with in *Mechanics 3*.

Surfaces

Surfaces can be any shape, but commonly we come across planes, spheres and cylinders.

A *smooth* surface has no friction. This is not achievable in practice, so we are neglecting the friction when we treat a surface as smooth. An ice rink comes fairly close to being a smooth plane, and there are various experimental devices which reduce friction to a very small amount and which can be treated as being smooth. Smooth surfaces only produce a force at right angles to the surface.

A *rough* surface does have friction. Friction is a force parallel to the surface which tends to stop relative motion. The recognition of the force of friction was one of the great steps forward in mechanics. There is a full treatment in Chapter 8.

Pulley

A pulley is used to change the direction of a string. Those familiar with the sea may well call them *blocks*. At this level they are all light, smooth pulleys. For these their own mass is neglected, and they are assumed to have good bearings which do not change the tension in the string which passes over them. Good quality pulleys come fairly close to achieving this, but there is always some friction.

Bead

A bead is effectively a particle with a hole in it. It can be threaded on to a string or a wire and will move along it but cannot leave it. It may be light or have a mass. It may also be smooth or rough. Most often it is smooth, and then the force on it is perpendicular to the wire. Beads that you find on strings of beads are good approximations to the theoretical beads found in mechanics. In diagrams beads are usually drawn as a small circle or ellipse around the wire.

Wire

A wire is very much like real fence wire, except that it is treated as being infinitely thin. It is rigid, unlike a string, and can produce a sideways force. Theoretical wire does not change shape under load.

Peg

A peg is the theoretical equivalent of a nail. Things can rest on it, and strings can be led round it. It is usually smooth, which means that the tension in a string around it does not change. We usually treat the peg as being a point, with no dimensions and no particular shape. It is usually shown in diagrams as a small circle.

EXERCISE 1A

Mathematical modelling pervades the whole course. You may well want to come back to this exercise when you have had more experience of mathematical modelling.

For each of the following situations

(a) suggest a suitable model

(b) list any modelling assumptions that you would make.

Notice that you should *not* attempt a complete solution.

1 A person drops a coin.

2 A person drops a single sheet of paper.

3 A rope is led over a pulley, and two monkeys start climbing the rope, one on each side.

4 A ship is tied up with several ropes.

5 A cricketer hits a ball over the boundary.

6 A comet orbits close to the sun.

7 A tray is used to carry several glasses.

8 A child slides down a slide in a playground.

9 An ice-hockey puck is hit across the ice.

10 A yo-yo is being used to do tricks.

Key points

Commonly used modelling terms

inextensible	does not change length
negligible	small enough to ignore
light	negligible mass
particle	negligible dimensions
bead	a particle with a hole
smooth	negligible friction
rough	does have friction
uniform	the same throughout
lamina	a plane with mass

Chapter two

VECTORS IN MECHANICS

But the principal failing occurred in the sailing
And the bellman, perplexed and distressed,
Said he *had* hoped, at least, when the wind blew due East,
That the ship would *not* travel due West!

Lewis Carroll, The Hunting of the Snark

ADDING VECTORS

If you walk 12 m east and then 5 m north, how far and in what direction will you be from your starting point?

A bird is caught in a wind blowing east at $12\,\mathrm{ms}^{-1}$ and flies so that its speed would be $5\,\mathrm{ms}^{-1}$ north in still air. What is its actual velocity?

A sledge is being pulled with forces of 12 N east and 5 N north. What single force would have the same effect?

All these questions involve vectors – displacement, velocity and force. When you are concerned only with the *magnitude and direction* of these vectors, the three problems can be reduced to one. They can all be solved using the same vector techniques.

Displacement vectors

The instruction 'walk 12 m east and then 5 m north' can be modelled mathematically using a scale diagram, as in figure 2.1. The arrowed lines AB and BC are examples of vectors.

We write the vectors as $\overrightarrow{AB}$ and $\overrightarrow{BC}$. The arrow above the letters is very important as it indicates the direction of the vector. $\overrightarrow{AB}$ means from A to B. $\overrightarrow{AB}$ and $\overrightarrow{BC}$ are examples of *displacement vectors*. Their lengths represent the magnitude of the displacements.

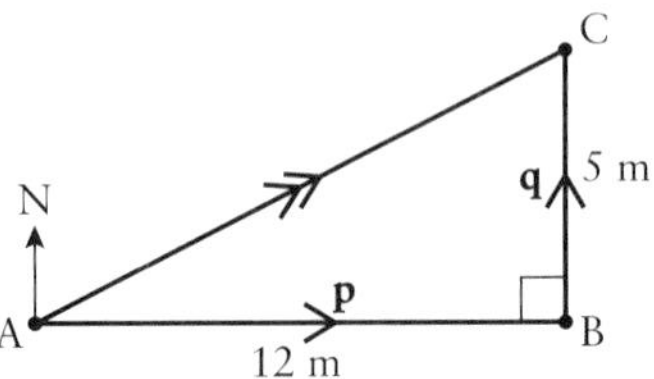

Figure 2.1

It is often more convenient to use a single letter to denote a vector. For example in textbooks and exam papers you might see the displacement vectors $\overrightarrow{AB}$ and $\overrightarrow{BC}$ written as **p** and **q** (i.e. in bold print). When writing these vectors yourself, you should underline your letters, for example $\underline{p}$ and $\underline{q}$.

The magnitudes of **p** and **q** are then shown as |**p**| and |**q**| or *p* and *q* (in ordinary print). These are *scalar* quantities.

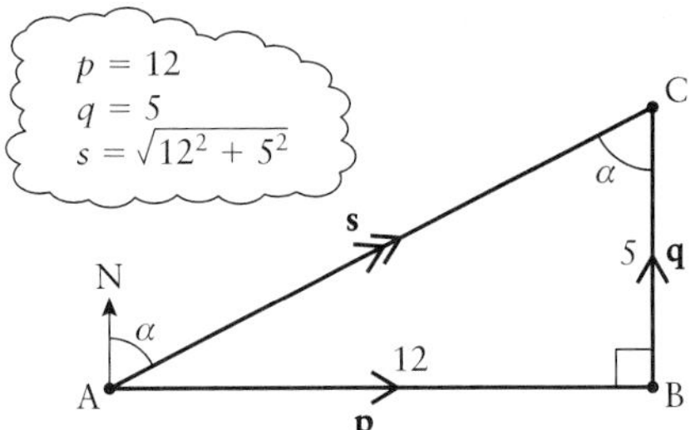

Figure 2.2

The combined effect of the two displacements $\overrightarrow{AB}$ (= **p**) and $\overrightarrow{BC}$ (= **q**) is $\overrightarrow{AC}$ and this is called the *resultant vector*. It is marked with two arrows to distinguish it from **p** and **q**. The process of combining vectors in this way is called *vector addition*. We write $\overrightarrow{AB} + \overrightarrow{BC} = \overrightarrow{AC}$ or $\mathbf{p} + \mathbf{q} = \mathbf{s}$.

You can calculate the resultant using Pythagoras' theorem and trigonometry.

In triangle ABC $\quad \text{AC} = \sqrt{12^2 + 5^2} = 13$

and $\quad \tan\alpha = \dfrac{12}{5}$

$$\alpha = 67^\circ \text{ (to the nearest degree).}$$

The distance from the starting point is 13 m and the direction is 067°.

VELOCITY AND FORCE

The other two problems that began this chapter (see page 7) are illustrated in these diagrams.

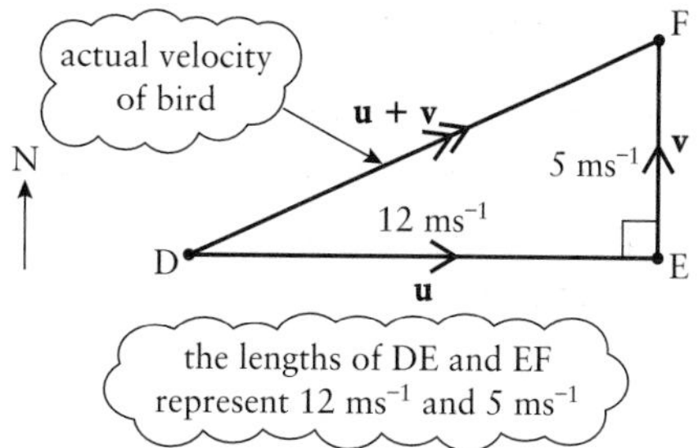

FIGURE 2.3

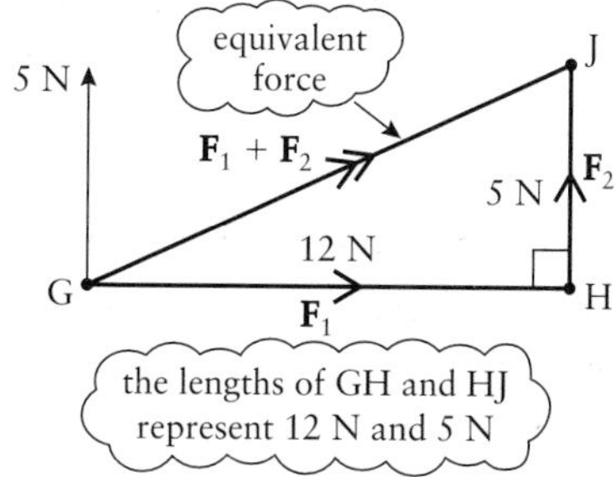

FIGURE 2.4

When $\overrightarrow{DE}$ represents the velocity (**u**) of the wind and $\overrightarrow{EF}$ represents the velocity (**v**) of the bird in still air, the vector $\overrightarrow{DF}$ represents the resultant velocity, **u** + **v**.

In figure 2.4, the vector $\overrightarrow{GJ}$ represents the equivalent (resultant) force. You know that it acts at the same point as the children's forces, but its magnitude and direction can be found using the triangle GHJ which is similar to the two triangles, ABC and DEF.

FREE VECTORS

Free vectors have magnitude and direction only. All vectors which are in the same direction and have the same magnitude are equal.

If the vector **p** represents a velocity of $3\,\text{km}\,\text{h}^{-1}$ north-east, what do –**p** and 2**p** represent?

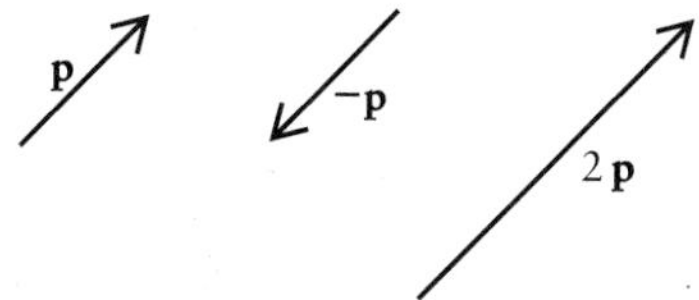

FIGURE 2.5

The vector $-\mathbf{p}$ has the same magnitude as $\mathbf{p}$ but is in the opposite direction. The vector $2\mathbf{p}$ is in the same direction as $\mathbf{p}$ but has twice its magnitude.

To add several vectors, draw them end-to-end with the arrows following each other as in figure 2.6. The resultant is the vector which joins the start of the first vector to the end of the last one and forms the last side of a polygon. Notice its direction.

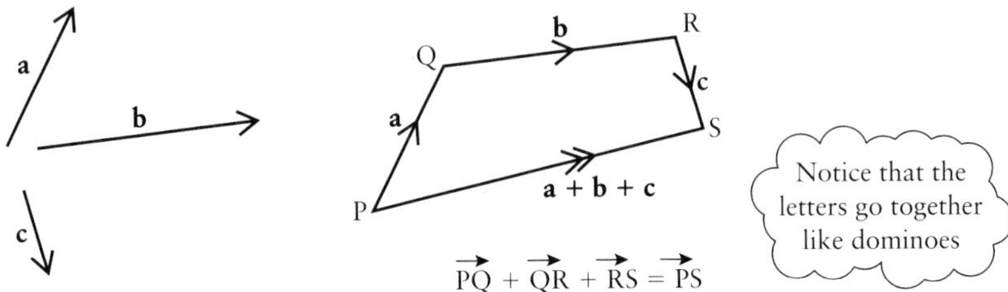

FIGURE 2.6

EXAMPLE 2.1

The diagram shows several vectors.

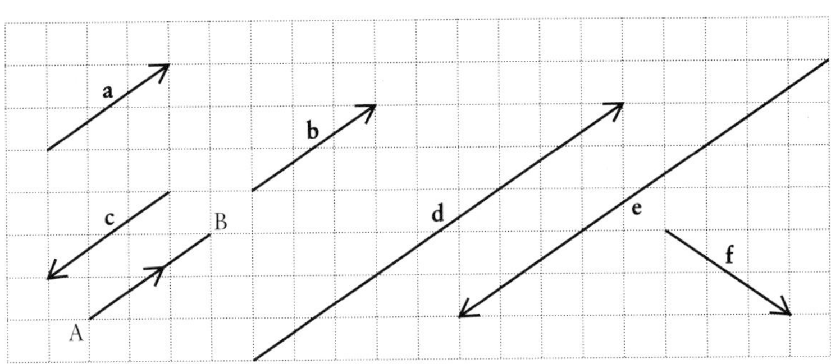

FIGURE 2.7

(a) Write each of the other vectors in terms of the vector **a**.

(b) Draw scale diagrams to show

(i) $\mathbf{a} + \mathbf{f}$

(ii) $\mathbf{a} - \mathbf{f}$

(iii) $2\mathbf{c} + \mathbf{f}$

(iv) $\mathbf{a} + \mathbf{f} + \mathbf{c}$

Solution

(a) $\mathbf{b} = \mathbf{a}$, $\overrightarrow{AB} = \mathbf{a}$, $\mathbf{c} = -\mathbf{a}$, $\mathbf{d} = 3\mathbf{a}$, $\mathbf{e} = -3\mathbf{a}$.
The vector **f** cannot be written in terms of **a** but $|\mathbf{f}| = |\mathbf{a}|$.

(b) Using vector addition the solutions are as shown in figure 2.8.

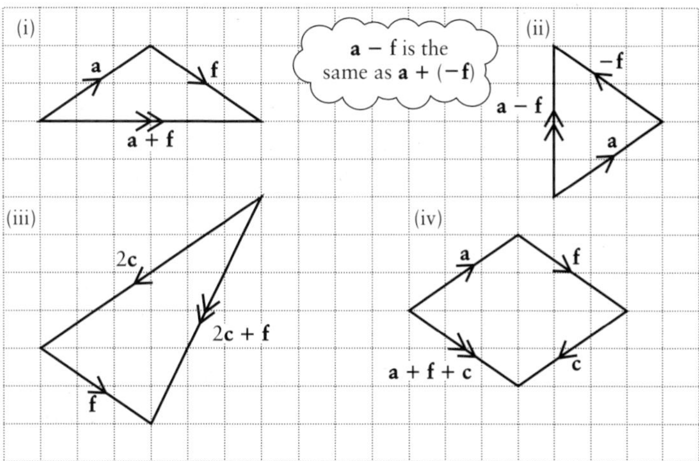

FIGURE 2.8

ADDING PARALLEL VECTORS

You can add parallel vectors by thinking of them as positive and negative, or by drawing diagrams as in Example 2.2.

EXAMPLE 2.2

The vector **p** is 10 units north-west and **q** is 6 units north-west.

(a) Describe the vector **p** – **q** and write the answer in terms of **p**.

(b) Write **p** + **q** and **q** – **p** in terms of **p**.

(c) The vector **s** is 5 units south-east. What is **p** + 2**s**?

Solution

(a) The diagram shows the vectors **p**, **q** and **p** – **q**.

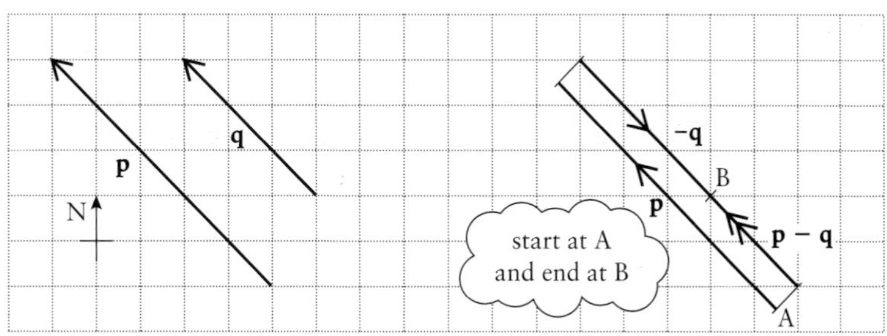

FIGURE 2.9

p – **q** is in the direction of **p** and of magnitude 10 – 6 = 4 units.

p – **q** = 0.4 **p**

(b) **p** + **q** is (10 + 6) = 16 units NW so **p** + **q** = 1.6 **p**

q – **p** is (6 – 10) = –4 units NW or 4 units SE, so **q** – **p** = –(**p** – **q**) = –0.4 **p**

(c) **s** = –0.5 **p** so **p** + 2**s** = 0**p** = 0

Note We use **0** (in bold) and not 0 (in ordinary type) on the right-hand side of this expression to show that the quantity is still a vector.

EXERCISE 2A

1 The diagram shows several vectors.
Write each of the other vectors in terms of **a** or **b**. How are **a** and **b** related?

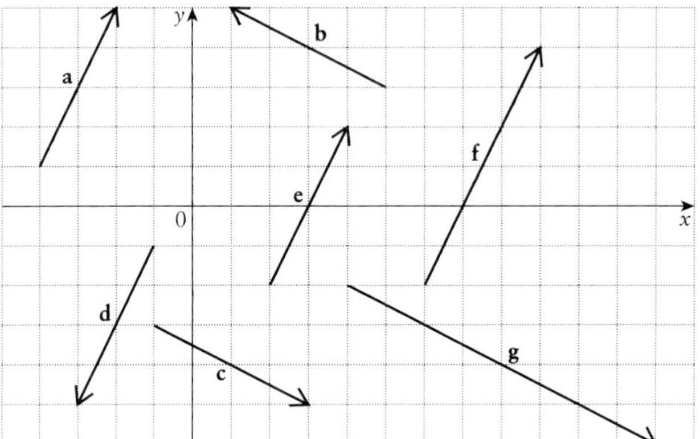

2 A child climbs up the ladder attached to a slide and then slides down. What three vectors model the displacement of the child during this activity?

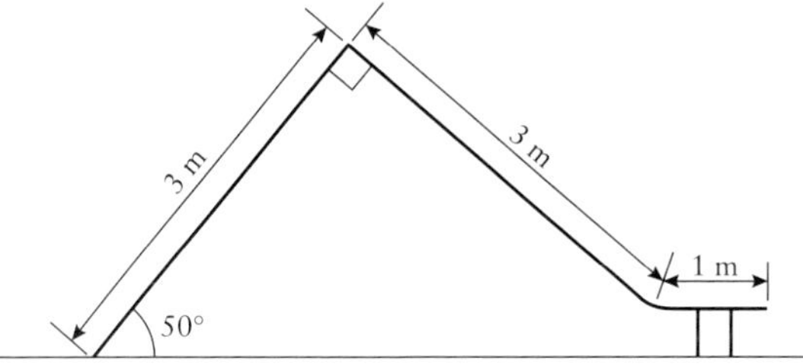

3 A child runs up and down a train. If the child runs at $2\,\text{ms}^{-1}$ and the train moves at $30\,\text{ms}^{-1}$, what are the resultant velocities of the child?

4 A girl rows at $5\,\text{ms}^{-1}$ in still water. What is her resultant velocity if she rows

(a) in the same direction as a current flowing at $3\,\text{ms}^{-1}$?

(b) in the opposite direction to the same current?

(c) in the opposite direction to a current flowing at $8\,\text{ms}^{-1}$?

5 A crane moves a crate from the ground 10 m vertically upward, then 6 m horizontally and 2 m vertically downward. Draw a scale diagram of the path of the crate. What single translation would move the crate to its final position from its initial position on the ground?

COMPONENTS OF A VECTOR

So far you have added two vectors to make one resultant vector. Alternatively, it is often convenient to write one vector in terms of two others called *components*.

The vector **a** in the diagram can be split into two components in an infinite number of ways. All you need to do is to make **a** one side of a triangle. It is most sensible, however, to split vectors into components in convenient directions and these directions are usually perpendicular.

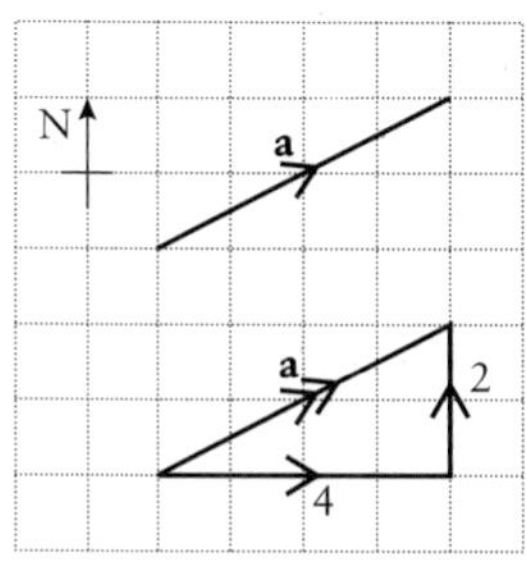

FIGURE 2.10

Using the given grid, **a** is 4 units east combined with 2 units north.

UNIT VECTORS i AND j

You can write **a** in figure 2.10 as 4**i** + 2**j** where **i** represents a vector of one unit to the east and **j** a vector of one unit to the north. **i** and **j** are called *unit vectors*.

When using the standard Cartesian coordinate system, **i** is a vector of one unit along the x axis and **j** is a vector of one unit along the y axis. Any other vector drawn in the xy plane can then be written in terms of **i** and **j**.

You may define the unit vectors **i** and **j** to be in *any* two perpendicular directions if it is convenient to do so.

EXAMPLE 2.3

The four vectors **a**, **b**, **c** and **d** are shown in the diagram.

(a) Write them in component form.

(b) Draw a diagram to show 2**c** and −**d** and write them in component form.

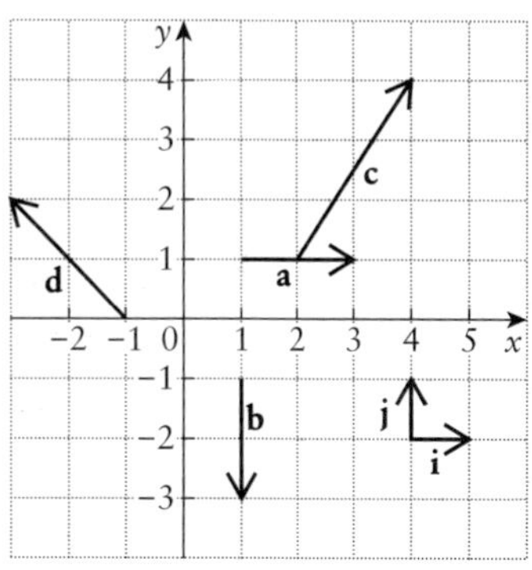

FIGURE 2.11

Solution

(a) **a** = 2**i** **b** = −2**j**

c = 2**i** + 3**j** **d** = −2**i** + 2**j**

(b) 2**c** = 2(2**i** + 3**j**)

= 4**i** + 6**j**

−**d** = −(−2**i** + 2**j**)

= 2**i** − 2**j**

FIGURE 2.12

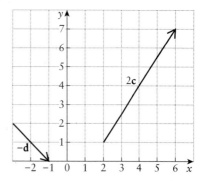

Equal vectors and parallel vectors

When two vectors, **p** and **q**, are *equal* then they must be equal in both magnitude and direction. If they are written in component form their components must be equal.

So if $\quad \mathbf{p} = a_1\mathbf{i} + b_1\mathbf{j}$

and $\quad \mathbf{q} = a_2\mathbf{i} + b_2\mathbf{j}$

then $\quad a_1 = a_2$ and $b_1 = b_2$.

Thus in two dimensions, the statement $\mathbf{p} = \mathbf{q}$ is the equivalent of two equations (and in three dimensions, three equations).

If **p** and **q** are *parallel but not equal*, they make the same angle with the x axis.

Then $\quad \dfrac{b_1}{a_1} = \dfrac{b_2}{a_2}$ or $\dfrac{a_1}{a_2} = \dfrac{b_1}{b_2}$

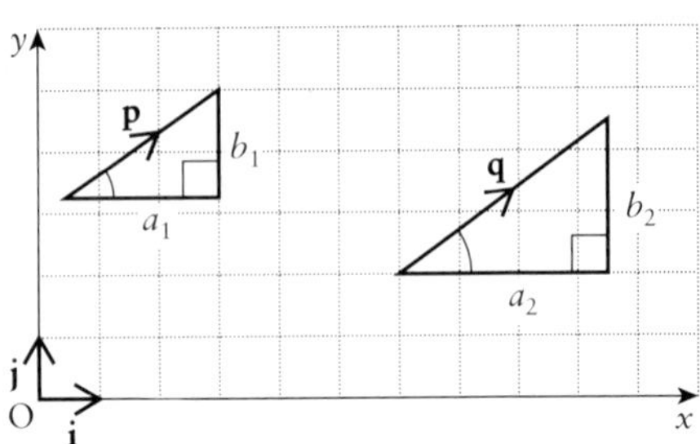

Figure 2.13

Position vectors

When an object is modelled as a particle or a point moving in space its *position* is its *displacement relative to a fixed origin*.

In figure 2.14 the vector **a** (or $\overrightarrow{OA}$) is called the *position vector* of A.

If a point P has coordinates (3, 2) and **i** and **j** are in the directions of the x and y axes, the position of the point P is

$$\overrightarrow{OP} = 3\mathbf{i} + 2\mathbf{j}.$$

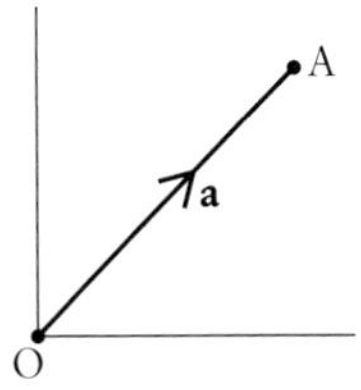

Figure 2.14

Adding vectors in component form

In component form, addition and subtraction of vectors is simply carried out by adding or subtracting the components of the vectors.

EXAMPLE 2.4

Two vectors **a** and **b** are given by **a** = 2**i** + 3**j** and **b** = –**i** + 4**j**.

Find the vectors **a** + **b** and **a** – **b**.

Solution

$$\mathbf{a} + \mathbf{b} = (2\mathbf{i} + 3\mathbf{j}) + (-\mathbf{i} + 4\mathbf{j})$$
$$= 2\mathbf{i} - \mathbf{i} + 3\mathbf{j} + 4\mathbf{j}$$
$$= \mathbf{i} + 7\mathbf{j}$$

$$\mathbf{a} - \mathbf{b} = (2\mathbf{i} + 3\mathbf{j}) - (-\mathbf{i} + 4\mathbf{j})$$
$$= 2\mathbf{i} + \mathbf{i} + 3\mathbf{j} - 4\mathbf{j}$$
$$= 3\mathbf{i} - \mathbf{j}$$

Note

When **a** and **b** are the position vectors of points A and B, the vector **a** – **b** is equal to the displacement vector $\overrightarrow{BA}$ as shown in the diagram.

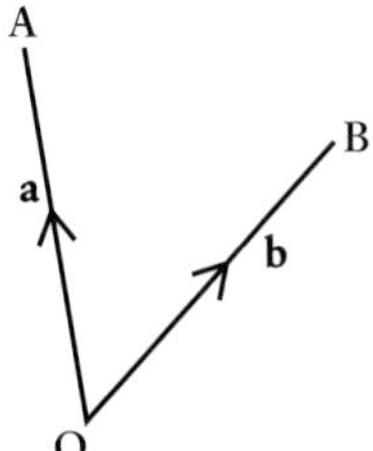

FIGURE 2.15

EXERCISE 2B

1 The diagram shows a grid of 1 m squares. A person walks first east and then north. How far should the person walk in each of these directions to travel

(a) from A to B?

(b) from B to C?

(c) from A to D?

2 Write the vectors in the diagram in terms of unit vectors **i** and **j**.

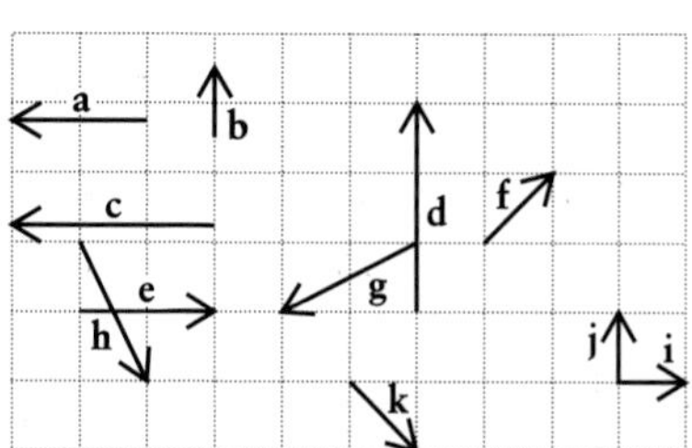

3 Given that $\mathbf{a} = 2\mathbf{i} - \mathbf{j}$ and $\mathbf{b} = \mathbf{i} + 4\mathbf{j}$ what are the coordinates of the point with position vector $3\mathbf{a} - 2\mathbf{b}$?

4 Four vectors are given in component form by $\mathbf{a} = 3\mathbf{i} + 4\mathbf{j}$, $\mathbf{b} = 6\mathbf{i} - 7\mathbf{j}$, $\mathbf{c} = -2\mathbf{i} + 5\mathbf{j}$ and $\mathbf{d} = -5\mathbf{i} - 3\mathbf{j}$.

Find the vectors:

(a) $\mathbf{a} + \mathbf{b}$ **(b)** $\mathbf{b} + \mathbf{c}$ **(c)** $\mathbf{c} + \mathbf{d}$

(d) $\mathbf{a} + \mathbf{b} + \mathbf{d}$ **(e)** $\mathbf{a} - \mathbf{b}$ **(f)** $\mathbf{d} - \mathbf{b} + \mathbf{a}$

5 A, B and C are the points (1, 2), (5, 1) and (7, 8).

(a) Write down in terms of $\mathbf{i}$ and $\mathbf{j}$ the position vectors of these three points.

(b) Find the component form of the displacements $\overrightarrow{AB}$, $\overrightarrow{BC}$ and $\overrightarrow{CA}$.

(c) Draw a diagram to show the position vectors of A, B and C and your answers to part (b).

6 A, B and C are the points (0, −3), (2, 5) and (3, 9).

(a) Write down in terms of $\mathbf{i}$ and $\mathbf{j}$ the position vectors of these three points.

(b) Find the displacements $\overrightarrow{AB}$ and $\overrightarrow{BC}$.

(c) Show that the three points all lie on a straight line.

7 A, B, C and D are the points (4, 2), (1, 3), (0, 10) and (3, d).

(a) Find the value of d so that DC is parallel to AB.

(b) Find a relationship between $\overrightarrow{BC}$ and $\overrightarrow{AD}$. What is ABCD?

8 Three vectors $\mathbf{a}$, $\mathbf{b}$ and $\mathbf{c}$ are given by $\mathbf{a} = \mathbf{i} + \mathbf{j}$, $\mathbf{b} = \mathbf{i} + 2\mathbf{j}$ and $\mathbf{c} = 3\mathbf{i} - 4\mathbf{j}$. R is the end-point of the displacement $2\mathbf{a} + 3\mathbf{b} + \mathbf{c}$ and (1, 2) is the starting point. What is the position vector of R?

9 Given the vectors $\mathbf{p} = 3\mathbf{i} - 5\mathbf{j}$ and $\mathbf{q} = -\mathbf{i} + 4\mathbf{j}$ find the vectors $\mathbf{x}$ and $\mathbf{y}$ where

(a) $2\mathbf{x} - 3\mathbf{p} = \mathbf{q}$ **(b)** $4\mathbf{p} - 3\mathbf{y} = 7\mathbf{q}$

10 The vectors $\mathbf{x}$ and $\mathbf{y}$ are defined in terms of a and b as $\mathbf{x} = a\mathbf{i} + (a + b)\mathbf{j}$ and $\mathbf{y} = (6 - b)\mathbf{i} - (2a + 3)\mathbf{j}$. Given that $\mathbf{x} = \mathbf{y}$, find the values of a and b.

THE MAGNITUDE AND DIRECTION OF VECTORS WRITTEN IN COMPONENT FORM

At the beginning of this chapter the magnitude of a vector was found by using Pythagoras' theorem (see page 8). The directions used bearings, measured clockwise from the north.

When the vectors are in an xy plane, a mathematical convention is used for direction. Starting from the x axis, angles measured anticlockwise are positive and angles in a clockwise direction are negative as in figure 2.16.

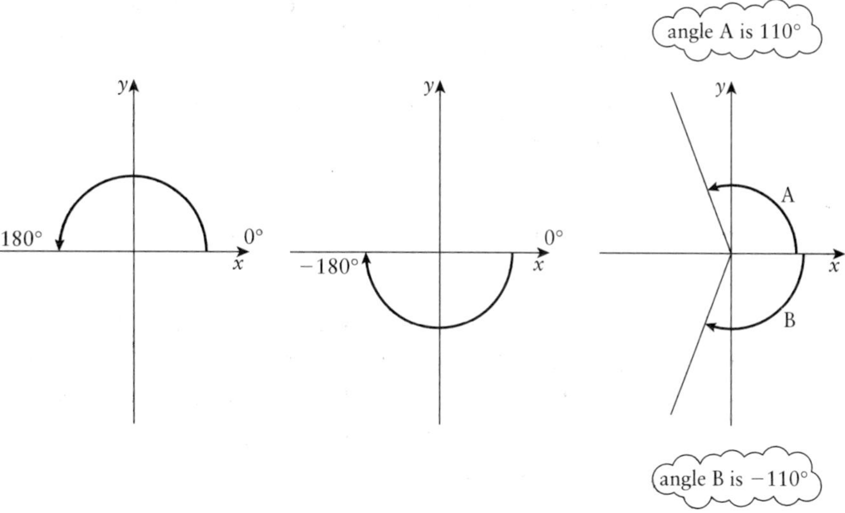

FIGURE 2.16

Using the notation in figure 2.17, the magnitude and direction can be written in general form.

Magnitude of the vector $|a_1\mathbf{i} + a_2\mathbf{j}| = \sqrt{a_1{}^2 + a_2{}^2}$

Direction $\tan\theta = \dfrac{a_2}{a_1}$

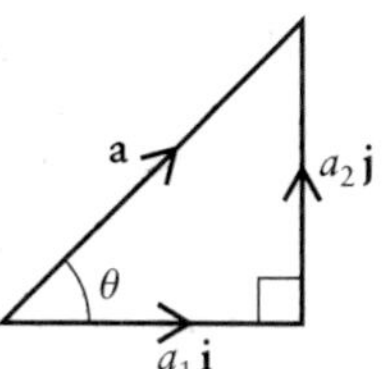

FIGURE 2.17

EXAMPLE 2.5

Find the magnitude and direction of the vectors $4\mathbf{i} + 3\mathbf{j}$, $4\mathbf{i} - 3\mathbf{j}$, $-4\mathbf{i} + 3\mathbf{j}$ and $-4\mathbf{i} - 3\mathbf{j}$ in the xy plane.

Solution First draw diagrams so that you can see which lengths and acute angles to find.

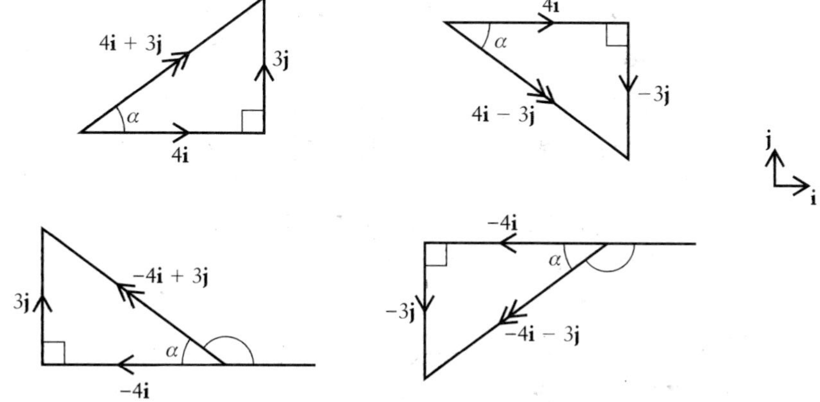

FIGURE 2.18

The vectors in each of the diagrams have the same magnitude and using Pythagoras' theorem, the resultants all have magnitude $\sqrt{4^2 + 3^2} = 5$.

The angles α are also the same size in each diagram and can be found using

$$\tan\alpha = \frac{3}{4}$$

$$\alpha = 37^\circ$$

The angles the vectors make with the **i** direction specify their directions:

$4\mathbf{i} + 3\mathbf{j}$	37°
$4\mathbf{i} - 3\mathbf{j}$	-37°
$-4\mathbf{i} + 3\mathbf{j}$	$180^\circ - 37^\circ = 143^\circ$
$-4\mathbf{i} - 3\mathbf{j}$	-143°

EXERCISE 2C

Make use of sketches to help you in this exercise.

1 Find the magnitude and direction of each of these vectors.

(a) $\mathbf{a} = 2\mathbf{i} + 3\mathbf{j}$

(b) $\mathbf{v} = 5\mathbf{i} - 12\mathbf{j}$

(c) $\mathbf{F} = -4\mathbf{i} + \mathbf{j}$

(d) $\mathbf{u} = -3\mathbf{i} - 6\mathbf{j}$

2 Find the magnitude and direction of:

(a) $6\mathbf{i} - 8\mathbf{j}$ **(b)** $-4\mathbf{i} - 8\mathbf{j}$ **(c)** $-\mathbf{i} - 2\mathbf{j}$.

3 Write the sum, $\mathbf{F}_1 + \mathbf{F}_2$, of the two forces $\mathbf{F}_1 = 10\mathbf{i} + 40\mathbf{j}$ N and $\mathbf{F}_2 = 20\mathbf{i} - 10\mathbf{j}$ N in component notation and then find its magnitude and direction.

4 Write the sum of the three forces $\mathbf{F}_1 = -\mathbf{i} + 5\mathbf{j}$ N, $\mathbf{F}_2 = 2\mathbf{i} - 10\mathbf{j}$ N and $\mathbf{F}_3 = -2\mathbf{i} + 7\mathbf{j}$ N in component notation and then find its magnitude and direction.

RESOLVING VECTORS

A vector has magnitude 10 units and it makes an angle of 60° with the **i** direction. How can it be represented in component form?

In the diagram:

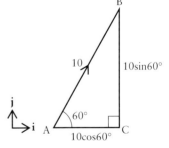

$$\frac{AC}{AB} = \cos 60^\circ \qquad \text{and} \qquad \frac{BC}{AB} = \sin 60^\circ$$

$$AC = AB\cos 60^\circ \qquad BC = AB\sin 60^\circ$$

$$= 10\cos 60^\circ \qquad = 10\sin 60^\circ$$

FIGURE 2.19

The vector can then be written as $10\cos 60^\circ\,\mathbf{i} + 10\sin 60^\circ\,\mathbf{j} = 5\mathbf{i} + 8.66\mathbf{j}$ (to 3 sf).

In a similar way, any vector **a** with magnitude a which makes an angle α with the **i** direction can be written in component form as

$$\mathbf{a} = a\cos\alpha\mathbf{i} + a\sin\alpha\mathbf{j}.$$

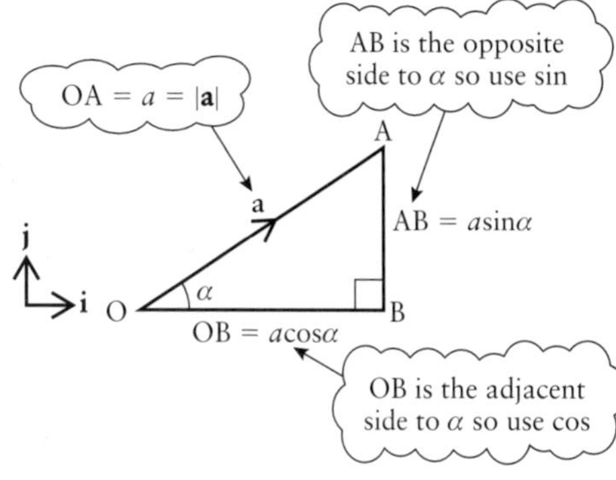

FIGURE 2.20

When α is an obtuse angle, this expression is still true. For example, when $\alpha = 120°$ and $a = 10$,

$$\begin{aligned}\mathbf{a} &= a\cos\alpha\,\mathbf{i} + a\sin\alpha\,\mathbf{j}\\ &= 10\cos 120°\mathbf{i} + 10\sin 120°\mathbf{j}\\ &= -5\mathbf{i} + 8.66\mathbf{j}\end{aligned}$$

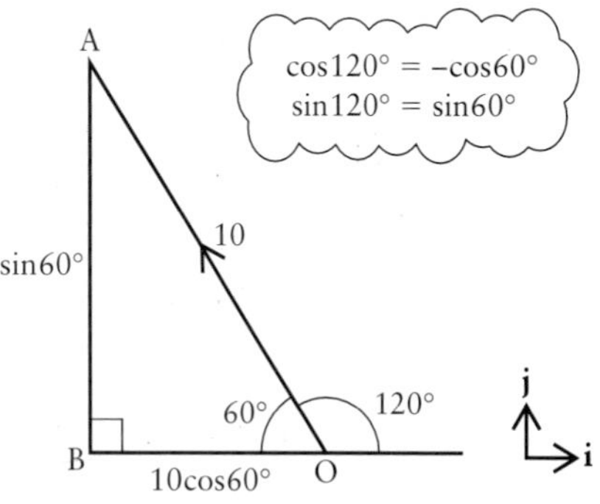

FIGURE 2.21

EXAMPLE 2.6

Two forces **P** and **Q** have magnitudes 4 and 5 in the directions shown in the diagram.

Find the magnitude and direction of the resultant force **P** + **Q**.

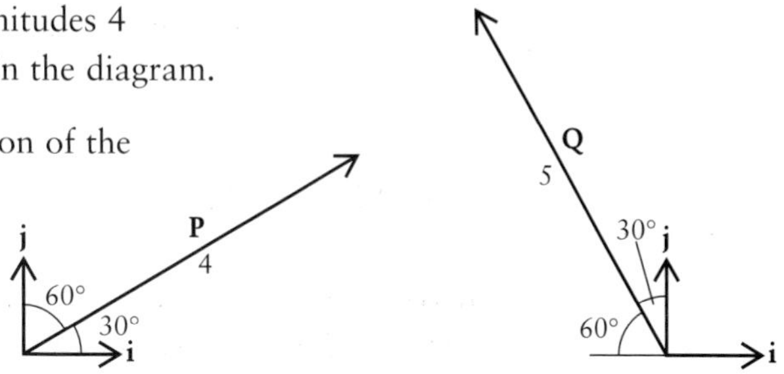

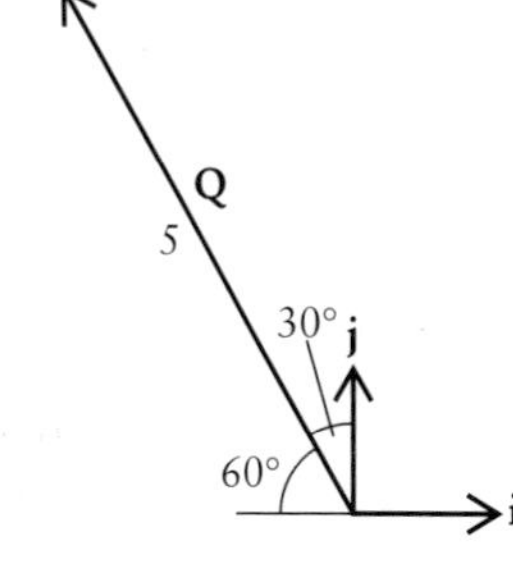

FIGURE 2.22

Solution

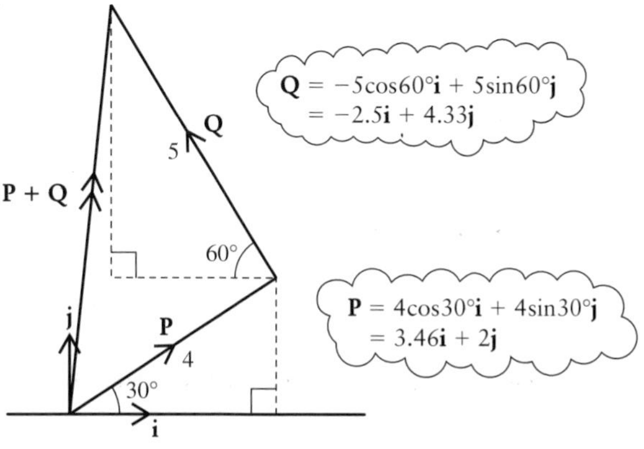

$\mathbf{Q} = -5\cos 60°\mathbf{i} + 5\sin 60°\mathbf{j} = -2.5\mathbf{i} + 4.33\mathbf{j}$

$\mathbf{P} = 4\cos 30°\mathbf{i} + 4\sin 30°\mathbf{j} = 3.46\mathbf{i} + 2\mathbf{j}$

FIGURE 2.23

$$\mathbf{P} + \mathbf{Q} = (3.46\mathbf{i} + 2\mathbf{j}) + (-2.5\mathbf{i} + 4.33\mathbf{j})$$
$$= 0.96\mathbf{i} + 6.33\mathbf{j}$$

This resultant is shown in the figure 2.24.

Magnitude $|\mathbf{P} + \mathbf{Q}| = \sqrt{0.96^2 + 6.33^2}$
$= \sqrt{40.99}$
$= 6.4$

Direction $\tan\theta = \dfrac{6.33}{0.96}$
$= 6.59$
$\theta = 81.4^\circ$

The force $\mathbf{P} + \mathbf{Q}$ has magnitude 6.4 and direction 81.4° relative to the positive x direction.

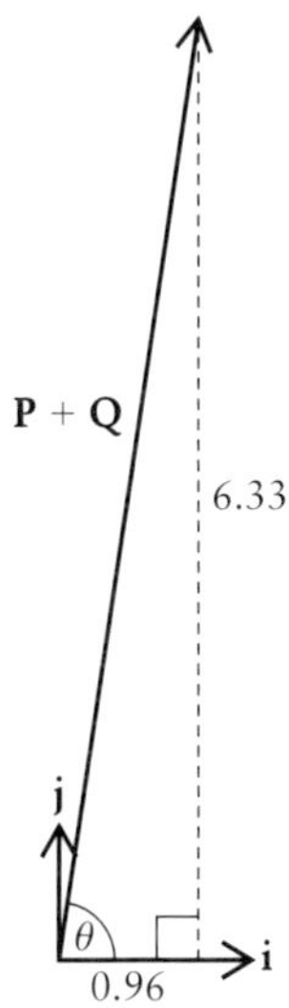

FIGURE 2.24

EXERCISE 2D

1 Write down the following vectors in component form in terms of **i** and **j**.

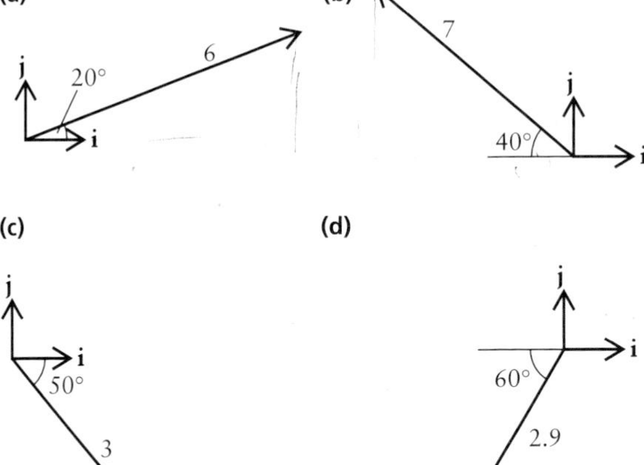

2 Draw a diagram showing each of the following displacements. Write each in component form using unit vectors **i** and **j** in directions east and north respectively.

(a) 130 km, bearing 060°

(b) 250 km, bearing 130°

(c) 400 km, bearing 210°

(d) 50 miles, bearing 300°

3 A boat has a speed of $4\,\text{km}\,\text{h}^{-1}$ in still water and sets its course north-east in an easterly current of $3\,\text{km}\,\text{h}^{-1}$. Write each velocity in component form using unit vectors **i** and **j** in directions east and north and hence find the magnitude and direction of the resultant velocity.

4 A boy walks 30 m north and then 50 m south-west.

(a) Draw a diagram to show the boy's path.

(b) Write each displacement in component form.

(c) In which direction should he walk to get directly back to his starting point?

5 (i) Write down each of the following vectors in terms of **i** and **j**.

(ii) Find the resultant of each set of vectors in terms of **i** and **j**.

(a)

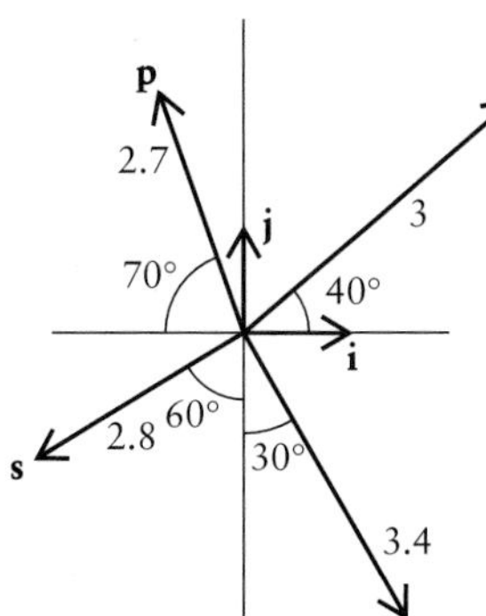

(b)

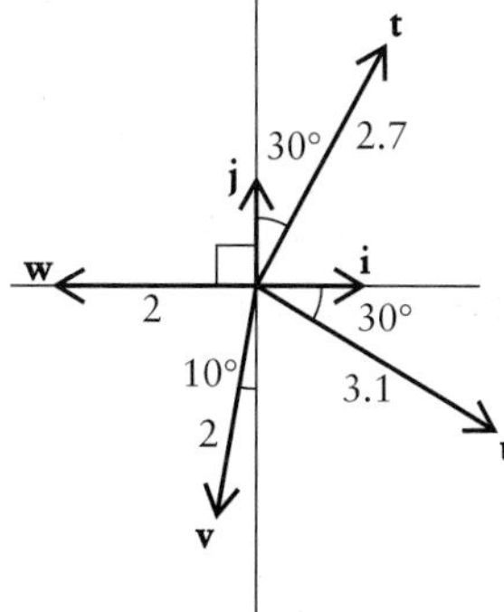

6 (a) Find the distance and bearing of Sean relative to his starting point if he goes for a walk with the following three stages.

Stage 1: 600 m on a bearing 030°

Stage 2: 1 km on a bearing 100°

Stage 3: 700 m on a bearing 340°

(b) Shona sets off from the same place at the same time as Sean. She walks at the same speed but takes the stages in the order 3–1–2.

(c) How far apart are Sean and Shona at the end of their walks?

7 The diagram shows the journey of a yacht.

Express $\overrightarrow{OA}$, $\overrightarrow{AB}$ and $\overrightarrow{OB}$ as vectors in terms of **i** and **j**, which are unit vectors east and north respectively.

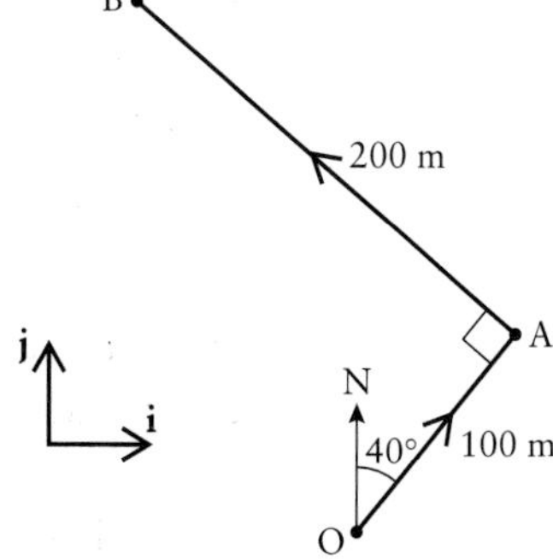

8 An aircraft is travelling from Plymouth to London at 200 km h^{-1} on a bearing of 075°. Due to fog the aircraft changes direction to fly to Birmingham on a bearing of 015°.

(a) Show the velocity vectors and the change in velocity on a diagram.

(b) Write down the components of the change in velocity in terms of unit vectors in directions east and north.

9 A plane completes a journey in three stages. The displacements at each stage, in kilometres, are $3000\mathbf{i} + 4000\mathbf{j}$, $1000\mathbf{i} + 500\mathbf{j}$ and $300\mathbf{i} - 1000\mathbf{j}$, where $\mathbf{i}$ and $\mathbf{j}$ are unit vectors in directions east and north respectively.
Express the total journey as a distance and a bearing.

CONNECTING VELOCITY AND DISPLACEMENT

The rule that *distance* = *speed* × *time* works in two dimensions also, but becomes **displacement** = **velocity** × time, providing the velocity is constant.

You have to work with the two components together. Two objects are in the same place if both components of their positions are the same at the same time.

In the same way, change in **velocity** = **acceleration** × time, providing the acceleration is constant.

You will, of course, not be able to use both these formulae in the same question.

EXAMPLE 2.7

Jack and Jill are playing hockey on a pitch which may be treated as a horizontal plane. At time $t = 0$, Jack is at the origin, and Jill is at the point with position vector $33\mathbf{i} + 24\mathbf{j}$ m. Jack runs with velocity $2\mathbf{i} + 3\mathbf{j}\,\text{ms}^{-1}$, and Jill runs with velocity $-\mathbf{i} + 2\mathbf{j}\,\text{ms}^{-1}$. Jack hits the ball with velocity $10\mathbf{i} + 10\mathbf{j}\,\text{ms}^{-1}$.

(a) Write down expressions for the position vectors of Jack and Jill at any later time t.
(b) Verify that Jill receives the ball after 3 s.

Immediately Jill receives the ball, she hits it back to Jack.

(c) What velocity should Jill give to the ball if Jack receives the pass 2 s later?

Solution

(a) Displacement = velocity × time,
so Jack is at position $(2\mathbf{i} + 3\mathbf{j}) \times t = 2t\mathbf{i} + 3t\mathbf{j}$ m.
Jill is at position $33\mathbf{i} + 24\mathbf{j} + (-\mathbf{i} + 2\mathbf{j})t = (33 - t)\mathbf{i} + (24 + 2t)\mathbf{j}$ m.

(b) At time $t = 3$, Jill is at position $(33 - 3)\mathbf{i} + (24 + 6)\mathbf{j} = 30\mathbf{i} + 30\mathbf{j}$ m.
The ball is at position $(10\mathbf{i} + 10\mathbf{j}) \times 3 = 30\mathbf{i} + 30\mathbf{j}$, which is the same.

(c) Jack receives the ball at time $t = 5$, and is then at position $10\mathbf{i} + 15\mathbf{j}$ m.
So the ball requires a displacement of $-20\mathbf{i} - 15\mathbf{j}$ m.

Since velocity $= \dfrac{\text{displacement}}{\text{time}}$,

the velocity required $= \dfrac{-20\mathbf{i} - 15\mathbf{j}}{2}$

$= -10\mathbf{i} - 7.5\mathbf{j}\,\text{ms}^{-1}$.

EXAMPLE 2.8

A bicycle has a velocity given by $10\mathbf{i}\,\text{ms}^{-1}$. Ten seconds later, its velocity is $6\mathbf{i} + 8\mathbf{j}\,\text{ms}^{-1}$. Find its average acceleration.

Solution The change in velocity $= (6\mathbf{i} + 8\mathbf{j}) - 10\mathbf{i} = -4\mathbf{i} + 8\mathbf{j}\,\text{ms}^{-1}$.

So the acceleration $= \dfrac{-4\mathbf{i} + 8\mathbf{j}}{10} = -0.4\mathbf{i} + 0.8\mathbf{j}\,\text{ms}^{-2}$.

PARALLEL VECTORS

Vectors are parallel if their components are in the same ratio. One must be a multiple of the other.

EXAMPLE 2.9

Two forces $\mathbf{F}_1$ and $\mathbf{F}_2$ act on a particle. $\mathbf{F}_1 = 4\mathbf{i} - 6\mathbf{j}\,\text{N}$ and $\mathbf{F}_2 = \lambda\mathbf{i} + \mu\mathbf{j}\,\text{N}$. Given that the resultant is parallel to $2\mathbf{i} + \mathbf{j}$, show that $\lambda - 2\mu = -16$.

Solution The resultant is $(4\mathbf{i} - 6\mathbf{j}) + (\lambda\mathbf{i} + \mu\mathbf{j}) = (4 + \lambda)\mathbf{i} + (-6 + \mu)\mathbf{j}$,

so $\dfrac{4 + \lambda}{-6 + \mu} = \dfrac{2}{1}$.

Cross multiplying,

$$1(4 + \lambda) = 2(-6 + \mu)$$
$$4 + \lambda = -12 + 2\mu$$
$$\lambda - 2\mu = -16$$

EXAMPLE 2.10

From Folkestone to Cap Gris Nez can be represented by the vector $30\mathbf{i} - 20\mathbf{j}\,\text{km}$. A cross-channel swimmer can swim at $3\,\text{km h}^{-1}$. Ignoring currents, what should be the velocity in component form?

Solution The displacement has magnitude $\sqrt{30^2 + 20^2} = \sqrt{1300}$ km.

A unit vector in the same direction is $\dfrac{(30\mathbf{i} - 20\mathbf{j})}{\sqrt{1300}} = \dfrac{(3\mathbf{i} - 2\mathbf{j})}{\sqrt{13}}$.

The velocity we require has magnitude 3, and so is

$3 \times \dfrac{(3\mathbf{i} - 2\mathbf{j})}{\sqrt{13}} = \left(\dfrac{9}{\sqrt{13}}\right)\mathbf{i} - \left(\dfrac{6}{\sqrt{13}}\right)\mathbf{j}\,\text{km h}^{-1}$.

EXERCISE 2E

1 Find a vector of magnitude 8 parallel to the vector $6\mathbf{i} - 8\mathbf{j}$.

2 A footballer is at the origin, and wishes to pass the ball to another footballer who is initially at the point with position vector $12\mathbf{i}$ m, and who is moving with velocity $\mathbf{i} + 2\mathbf{j}$ m s^{-1}. The pass is to take 3 s. What velocity should the footballer give to the ball?

3 Two ships, A and B, are steaming close together. Initially A is at the origin, and has velocity $2\mathbf{i} - 4\mathbf{j}$ m s^{-1}. B starts at the point with position vector $100\mathbf{i} - 300\mathbf{j}$ m, and has velocity $4\mathbf{i} + \mathbf{j}$ m s^{-1}. At time $t = 0$, a small boat sets off from A with velocity $5\mathbf{i} - 2\mathbf{j}$ m s^{-1}.

(a) Show that the boat reaches B after 100 s.

The boat immediately turns round to return to A. The return journey should take 200 s.

(b) At what velocity should the boat travel?

4 A dog is chasing a rabbit. At time $t = 0$, the dog is at the point with position vector $15\mathbf{i} + 4\mathbf{j}$ m, and has velocity $-3\mathbf{i} + 4\mathbf{j}$ m s^{-1}. The rabbit starts at the origin and has velocity $2\mathbf{i} + 3\mathbf{j}$ m s^{-1}. If neither changes velocity, does the dog catch the rabbit?

5 The vector $\mathbf{a} = 3\mathbf{i} + 2\mathbf{j}$, and $\mathbf{b} = \lambda\mathbf{i} + \mu\mathbf{j}$. The vector $\mathbf{a} + \mathbf{b}$ is parallel to $7\mathbf{i} + 3\mathbf{j}$.

(a) Show that $3\lambda - 7\mu = 5$.

(b) Given that $\mathbf{b}$ is parallel to $\mathbf{i} + \mathbf{j}$, find λ and μ.

6 A radio-controlled model aircraft starts at point (50, 60) and has velocity $5\mathbf{i} + 6\mathbf{j}$ m s^{-1}. The controller is at the origin, and has a range of 200 m. For how long a time can the controller keep control of the aircraft if no change is made to the velocity?

EXERCISE 2F

Examination-style questions

1 The vector $\mathbf{a} = -2\mathbf{i} + 3\mathbf{j}$, and $\mathbf{b} = \lambda\mathbf{i} + \mu\mathbf{j}$. In addition, $\mathbf{c} = \mathbf{a} + \mathbf{b}$ and is parallel to the vector $\mathbf{i} + 2\mathbf{j}$.

(a) Find the angle between $\mathbf{a}$ and the vector $\mathbf{i}$.

(b) Show that $2\lambda - \mu = 7$.

(c) Given that $\mathbf{b}$ is parallel to $4\mathbf{i} + \mathbf{j}$, find λ and μ.

2 The vector $\mathbf{a} = 3\mathbf{i} - 2\mathbf{j}$, and $\mathbf{b} = \lambda\mathbf{i} + \mu\mathbf{j}$. In addition, $\mathbf{c} = \mathbf{a} + \mathbf{b}$ and is parallel to the vector $7\mathbf{i} + 2\mathbf{j}$.

(a) Find the angle between $\mathbf{a}$ and the vector $\mathbf{i}$.

(b) Show that $2\lambda - 7\mu + 20 = 0$.

(c) Given that $\mathbf{b}$ is parallel to $\mathbf{i}$, find (to 3 sf) the magnitude of $\mathbf{c}$.

3 A yacht is sailing a race around a triangular course. The first leg is 20 nautical miles on a bearing of 139°, and the second leg is 15 nautical miles on a bearing of 257°.

(a) Express each leg in component form, taking **i** to be one nautical mile due east, and **j** to be one nautical mile due north.

(b) The third leg takes the yacht back to the start. Find the bearing and length of this leg.

4 A dog is running around in a field. It starts at the origin, and first runs 50 m on a bearing of 067°. Next it runs 70 m on a bearing of 212°, and then 100 m on a bearing of 293°. Take **i** to be 1 m east and **j** to be 1 m north.

(a) Express each displacement in component form.

(b) Find the final position of the dog in component form.

(c) How far is the dog from the origin, and in what direction?

5 A snooker table may be modelled as a portion of a horizontal plane bounded by the lines $y = -2$, $y = 2$, $x = -1$ and $x = 1$. During the course of a game, the white ball is at the point (−0.5, −1.5) and is struck with velocity **i** + **j** towards a red ball. 0.5 s later it strikes the red ball.

(a) Where does the collision take place?

After the collision, the red ball has velocity −0.2**i** + 0.6**j**, and the white ball has velocity 1.2**i** + 0.4**j**.

(b) Show that the red ball reaches a pocket at the point (−1, 2).

(c) Where does the white ball strike the cushion given by the line $x = 1$?

6 A spacecraft is moving in a plane. At time $t = 0$, its velocity is 8000**i** + 3000**j** ms^{-1}. 10 hours later its velocity is 7280**j** + 3360**j** ms^{-1}.

(a) Find its acceleration (assumed constant), in component form.

(b) Find the angle the acceleration makes with the vector **i**.

7 Two small boats, A and B, are sailing on a sea which may be treated as being a horizontal plane. A starts from the origin and has a constant velocity of 3**i** − 5**j** km h^{-1}. B starts from the point with position vector 10**i** + 15**j** km, and has a constant velocity of 2**i** + 6**j** km h^{-1}.

(a) Write down an expression for the position vector of each boat at time t hours.

(b) Show that the distance, d km, between the boats is given by the expression $d^2 = 122t^2 + 310t + 325$.

(c) The boats can maintain radio contact until the distance between them is 50 km. For how long a time can they do so?

8 Penny and Rachel are playing netball. At time $t = 0$, Penny is at the origin and Rachel is at the point with position vector 2**i** − 2**j** m. Rachel has velocity **i** + 2**j** ms^{-1}. Penny throws the ball with velocity 2**i** + **j** ms^{-1}.

(a) Write down the position vectors of Rachel and of the ball at time t s.

(b) Verify that Rachel receives the ball after 2 s.

Immediately after passing the ball, Penny starts moving with velocity **i** + **j** ms^{-1}. Rachel passes the ball back as soon as she receives it, and this pass takes 1 s.

(c) What velocity did Rachel give to the ball?

9 A shepherd has two dogs, Left and Right. All start at the origin, and the shepherd stays there throughout. At time $t = 0$, Right is sent off and runs with a constant velocity of $3\mathbf{i} + 5\mathbf{j}\,\text{m s}^{-1}$. At time $t = 10$, Left is sent off and runs with a constant velocity of $-2\mathbf{i} + 6\mathbf{j}\,\text{m s}^{-1}$.

(a) Find the angle which Right's velocity makes with the vector **i**.

(b) Write down the position vector of Right at time t s.

(c) Write down the position vector of Left at time t s, where $t > 10$.

(d) Find the time (to 3 sf) when the two dogs are 70 m apart.

10 Justin and Melanie are planning a move in a game of korfball. Justin will start with the ball at the point with position vector $-2\mathbf{i} - 3\mathbf{j}$ m. Melanie will start at the point with position vector $2\mathbf{i} - 2\mathbf{j}$ m, moving with velocity $-\mathbf{i} + \mathbf{j}\,\text{m s}^{-1}$. Justin will immediately give the ball a velocity of $3\mathbf{i} + 2\mathbf{j}\,\text{m s}^{-1}$, and then move with velocity $2\mathbf{i} + \mathbf{j}\,\text{m s}^{-1}$.

(a) Draw a sketch of the planned move.

(b) Show that Melanie will receive the ball after 1 s.

Melanie will then run with the ball for another second, and then pass the ball back to Justin. This pass is to take a further second.

(c) Find the velocity which Melanie must give to the ball.

11 Two forces $\mathbf{F}_1 = (2\mathbf{i} + 3\mathbf{j})$ N and $\mathbf{F}_2 = (\lambda\mathbf{i} + \mu\mathbf{j})$ N, where λ and μ are scalars, act on a particle. The resultant of the two forces is **R**, where **R** is parallel to the vector $\mathbf{i} + 2\mathbf{j}$.

(a) Find, to the nearest degree, the acute angle between the line of action of **R** and the vector **i**.

(b) Show that $2\lambda - \mu + 1 = 0$.

Given that the direction of $\mathbf{F}_2$ is parallel to **j**,

(c) find, to 3 significant figures, the magnitude of **R**.

[Edexcel]

12 A particle P moves in a straight line with constant velocity. Initially P is at the point A with position vector $(2\mathbf{i} - \mathbf{j})$ m relative to a fixed origin O, and 2 s later it is at the point B with position vector $(6\mathbf{i} + \mathbf{j})$ m.

(a) Find the velocity of P.

(b) Find, in degrees to one decimal place, the size of the angle between the direction of motion of P and the vector **i**.

Three seconds after it passes B the particle P reaches the point C.

(c) Find, in m to one decimal place, the distance OC.

[Edexcel]

13 Two helicopters P and Q are moving in the same horizontal plane. They are modelled as particles moving in straight lines with constant speeds. At noon P is at the point with position vector $(20\mathbf{i} + 35\mathbf{j})$ km with respect to a fixed origin O At time t hours after noon the position vector of P is $\mathbf{p}$ km. When $t = \frac{1}{2}$ the position vector of P is $(50\mathbf{i} - 25\mathbf{j})$ km. Find

(a) the velocity of P in the form $(a\mathbf{i} + b\mathbf{j})\,\text{km h}^{-1}$

(b) an expression for $\mathbf{p}$ in terms of t.

At noon Q is at O and at time t hours after noon the position vector of Q is $\mathbf{q}$ km. The velocity of Q has magnitude $120\,\text{km h}^{-1}$ in the direction of $4\mathbf{i} - 3\mathbf{j}$. Find

(c) an expression for $\mathbf{q}$ in terms of t

(d) the distance, to the nearest km, between P and Q when $t = 2$.

[Edexcel]

KEY POINTS

A **vector** has both magnitude and direction.

Vectors may be represented in either magnitude–direction form or in component form.

Magnitude–direction form	**Component form**
Magnitude r, direction θ	$a_1\mathbf{i} + a_2\mathbf{j}$
where $r = \sqrt{a_1^2 + a_2^2}$	$a_1 = r\cos\theta$
and $\tan\theta = \dfrac{a_1}{a_2}$	$a_2 = r\sin\theta$

When two or more vectors are added, the **resultant** is obtained.
Vector addition may be done graphically or algebraically.

$$\mathbf{p} + \mathbf{q} = (p_1 + q_1)\mathbf{i} + (p_2 + q_2)\mathbf{j}$$

Multiplication by a scalar:

$$n(a_1\mathbf{i} + a_2\mathbf{j}) = na_1\mathbf{i} + na_2\mathbf{j}$$

The **position vector** of a point P is $\overrightarrow{OP}$, its displacement from a fixed origin.

Equal vectors have equal magnitude and are in the same direction.

$$p_1\mathbf{i} + p_2\mathbf{j} = q_1\mathbf{i} + q_2\mathbf{j} \quad \Rightarrow \quad p_1 = q_1 \quad \text{and} \quad p_2 = q_2$$

Displacement = velocity × time

Velocity = acceleration × time

Chapter three

KINEMATICS OF A PARTICLE

The whole burden of philosophy seems to consist in this – from the phenomena of motions to investigate the forces of nature.

Isaac Newton

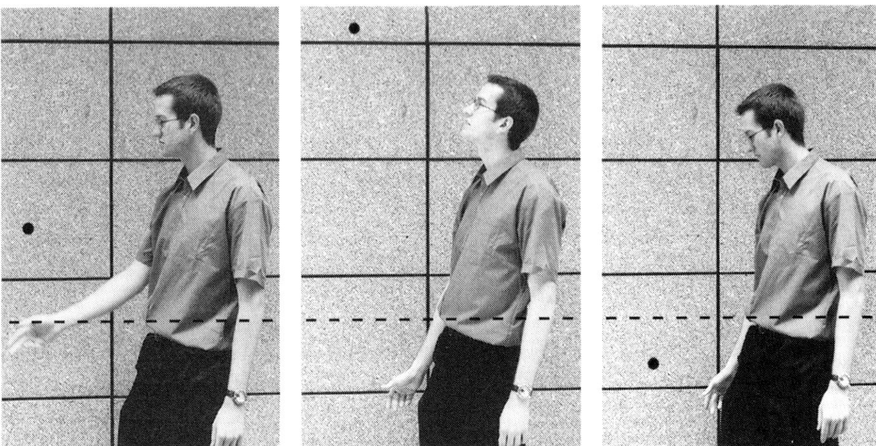

THE LANGUAGE OF MOTION

Throw a small object such as a marble straight up in the air and think about the words you could use to describe its motion from the instant just after it leaves your hand to the instant just before it hits the floor. Some of your words might involve the idea of direction. Other words might be to do with the position of the marble, its speed or whether it is slowing down or speeding up. Underlying many of these is time.

DIRECTION

The marble moves as it does because of the gravitational pull of the earth. We understand directional words such as up and down because we experience this pull towards the centre of the earth all the time. The *vertical* direction is along the line towards or away from the centre of the earth.

In mathematics a quantity which has only size, or magnitude, is called a *scalar*. One which has both magnitude and a direction in space is called a *vector*.

DISTANCE, POSITION AND DISPLACEMENT

The total *distance* travelled by the marble at any time does not depend on its direction. It is a scalar quantity.

Position and displacement are two vectors related to distance; they have direction as well as magnitude. Here their direction is up or down and you decide which of these is positive. When up is taken to be positive, down is negative.

The *position* of the marble is then its distance above a fixed origin, for example the distance above the place it first left your hand.

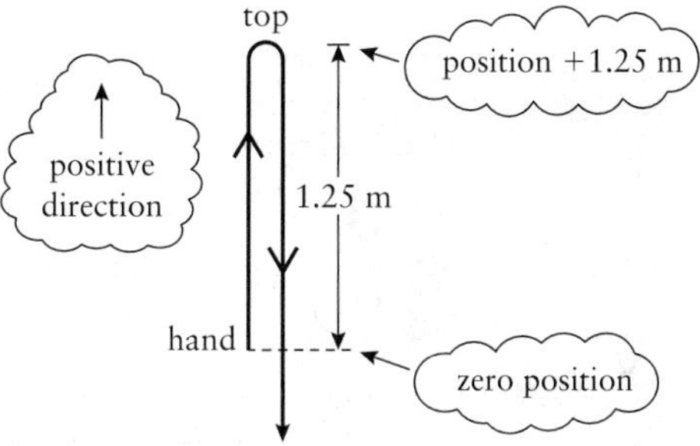

FIGURE 3.1

When it reaches the top, the marble might have travelled a distance of 1.25 m. Relative to your hand its position is then 1.25 m upwards or + 1.25 m.

At the instant it returns to the same level as your hand it will have travelled a total distance of 2.5 m. Its *position*, however, is zero upwards.

A position is always referred to a fixed origin but a *displacement* can be measured from any position. When the marble returns to the level of your hand, its displacement is zero relative to your hand but −1.25 m relative to the top.

DIAGRAMS AND GRAPHS

In mathematics, it is important to use words precisely, even though they might be used more loosely in everyday life. In addition, a picture in the form of a diagram or graph can often be used to show the information more clearly.

Figure 3.2 is a *diagram* showing the direction of motion of the marble and relevant distances. The direction of motion is indicated by an arrow. Figure 3.3 is a *graph* showing its position above the level of your hand against the time. Notice that it is *not* the path of the marble.

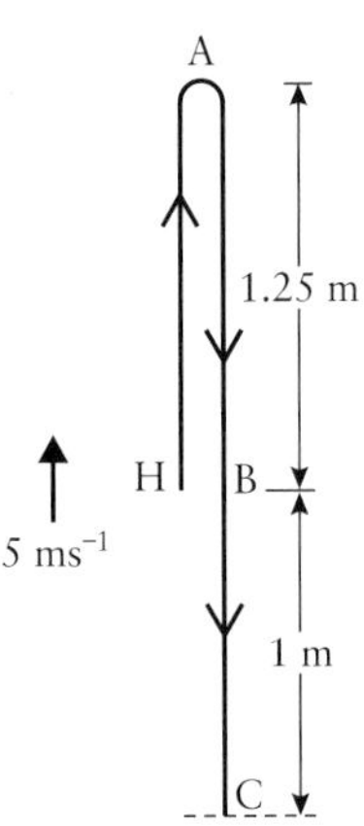

FIGURE 3.2

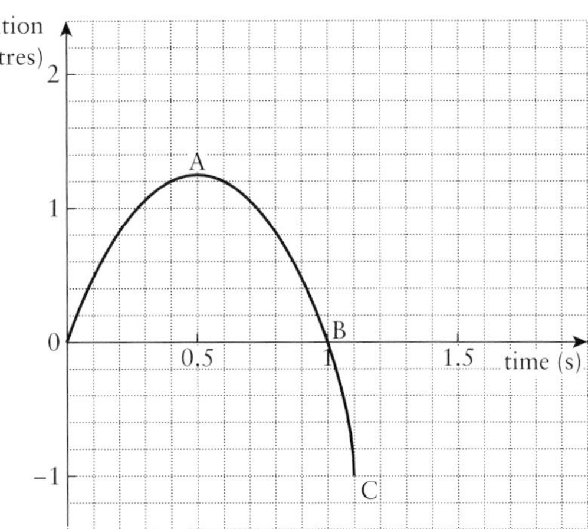

FIGURE 3.3

Note

When drawing a graph it is very important to specify your axes carefully. Graphs showing motion usually have time along the horizontal axis. Then you have to decide where the origin is and which direction is positive on the vertical axis. In the graph in figure 3.3 the origin is at hand level and upwards is positive. The time is measured from the instant the marble leaves your hand.

NOTATION AND UNITS

As with most mathematics, you will see in this book that certain letters are commonly used to denote certain quantities. This makes things easier to follow. Here the letters used are:

- s, h, x, y and z for position
- t for time measured from a starting instant
- u and v for velocity
- a for acceleration.

The S.I. (Système International d'Unités) unit for *distance* is the metre (m), that for *time* is the second (s) and that for *mass* the kilogram (kg). Other units follow from these so speed is measured in metres per second, written ms^{-1}. S.I. units are used almost entirely in this book but occasional references are made to imperial and other units.

EXERCISE 3A

1 When the origin for the motion of the marble (see figure 3.2) is on the ground, what is its position

(a) when it leaves your hand?

(b) at the top?

2 A boy throws a ball vertically upwards so that its position y m at time t s is as shown in the graph.

(a) Write down the position of the ball at times $t = 0$, 0.4, 0.8, 1.2, 1.6 and 2.

(b) Calculate the displacement of the ball relative to its starting position at these times.

(c) What is the total distance travelled
(i) during the first 0.8 s
(ii) during the 2 s of the motion?

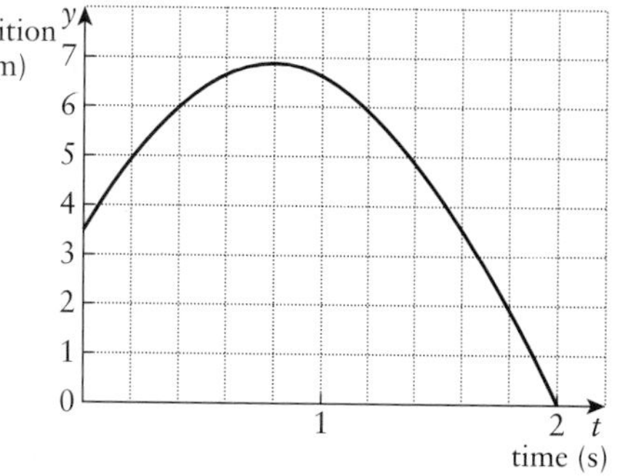

3 The position of a particle moving along a straight horizontal groove is given by $x = 2 + t(t - 3)$ $(0 \leqslant t \leqslant 5)$ where x is measured in metres and t in seconds.
(a) What is the position of the particle at times $t = 0, 1, 1.5, 2, 3, 4$ and 5?
(b) Draw a diagram to show the path of the particle, marking its position at these times.
(c) Find the displacement of the particle relative to its initial position at $t = 5$.
(d) Calculate the total distance travelled during the motion.

4 For each of the following situations sketch a graph of position against time. Show clearly the origin and the positive direction.
(a) A stone is dropped from a bridge which is 40 m above a river.
(b) A parachutist jumps from a helicopter which is hovering at 2000 m. She opens her parachute after 10 s of free fall.
(c) A bungee jumper on the end of an elastic string jumps from a high bridge.

SPEED AND VELOCITY

Speed is a scalar quantity and does not involve direction. *Velocity* is the vector related to speed; its magnitude is the speed but it also has a direction. When an object is moving in the negative direction, its velocity is negative.

Amy has to post a letter on her way to college. The post box is 500 m east of her house and the college is 2.5 km to the west. Amy cycles at a steady speed of 10 ms^{-1} and takes 10 s at the post box to find the letter and post it.

The diagram shows Amy's journey using east as the positive direction. The distance of 2.5 km has been changed to metres so that the units are consistent.

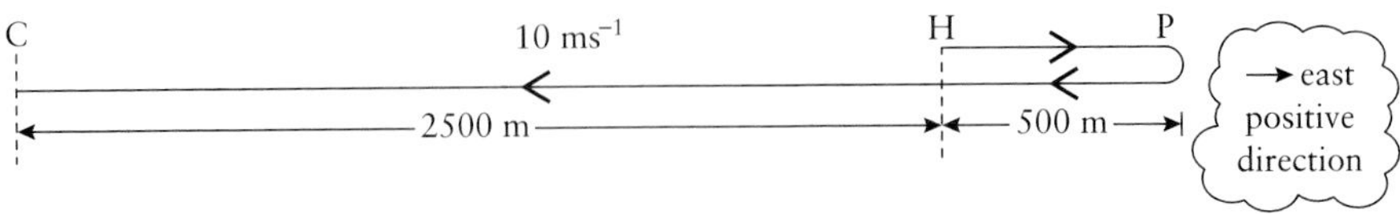

FIGURE 3.4

After she leaves the post box Amy is travelling west so her velocity is negative. It is $-10\,\text{ms}^{-1}$.

The distances and times for the three parts of Amy's journey are:

Home to post box	500 m	$\frac{500}{10}$ =	50 s
At post box	0 m		10 s
Post box to college	3000 m	$\frac{3000}{10}$ =	300 s

These can be used to draw the position–time graph using home as origin as in figure 3.5.

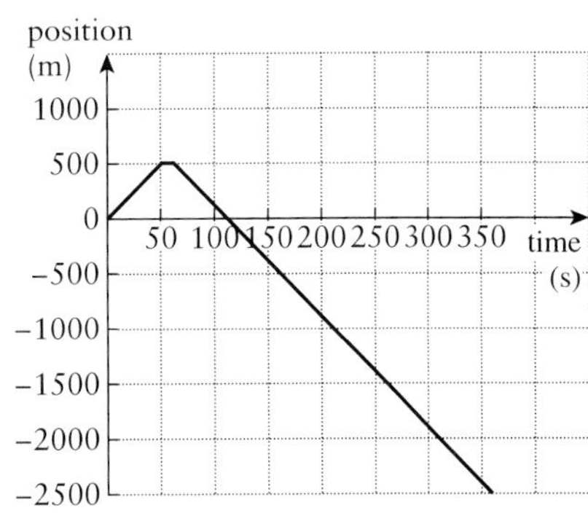

FIGURE 3.5

The velocity is the rate at which the position changes.

Velocity is represented by the gradient of the position–time graph.

Figure 3.6 shows the velocity–time graph.

Note

By drawing the graphs below each other with the same horizontal scales, you can see how they correspond to each other.

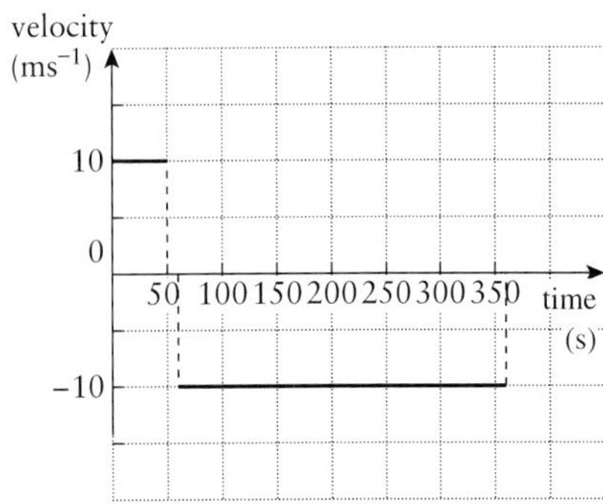

FIGURE 3.6

DISTANCE–TIME GRAPHS

Figure 3.7 shows the distance–time graph of Amy's journey. It differs from the position–time graph because it shows how far she travels irrespective of her direction. There are no negative values.

The gradient of this graph represents Amy's speed rather than her velocity.

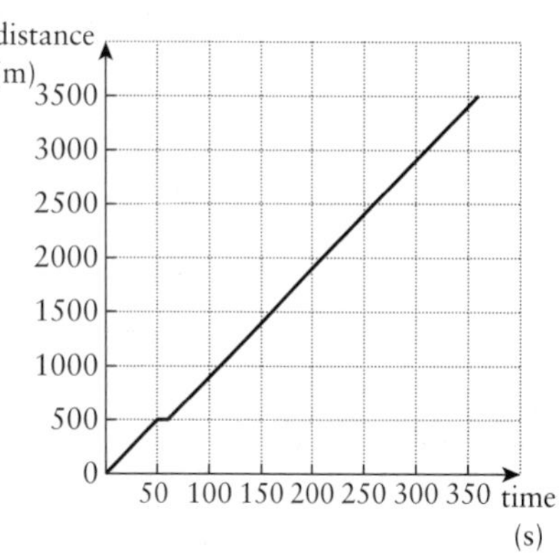

FIGURE 3.7

AVERAGE SPEED AND AVERAGE VELOCITY

You can find Amy's average speed on her way to college by using the definition

$$\text{average speed} = \frac{\text{total distance travelled}}{\text{total time taken}}$$

When the distance is in metres and the time in seconds, speed is found by dividing metres by seconds and is written as m s^{-1}. So Amy's average speed is

$$\frac{3500\,\text{m}}{360\,\text{s}} = 9.72\,\text{m s}^{-1}$$

Amy's average velocity is different. Her displacement from start to finish is −2500 m so

$$\text{average velocity} = \frac{\text{displacement}}{\text{time taken}}$$

$$= \frac{-2500}{360} = -6.94\,\text{m s}^{-1}$$

The college is in the negative direction

If Amy had taken the same time to go straight from home to college at a steady speed, this steady speed would have been $6.94\,\text{m s}^{-1}$.

VELOCITY AT AN INSTANT

The position–time graph for a marble thrown straight up into the air at $5\,\text{ms}^{-1}$ is curved because the velocity is continually changing.

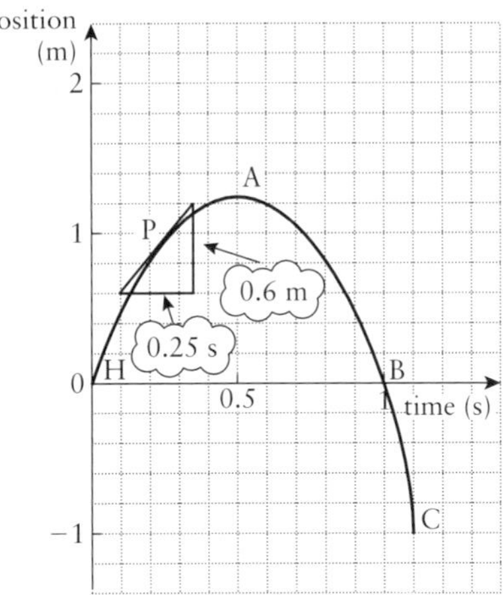

FIGURE 3.8

The velocity is represented by the gradient of the position–time graph. When a position–time graph is curved like this you can find *the velocity at an instant* of time by drawing a tangent as in figure 3.8.

The velocity at P is approximately

$$\frac{0.6}{0.25} = 2.4\,\text{ms}^{-1}$$

The velocity–time graph is shown in figure 3.9.

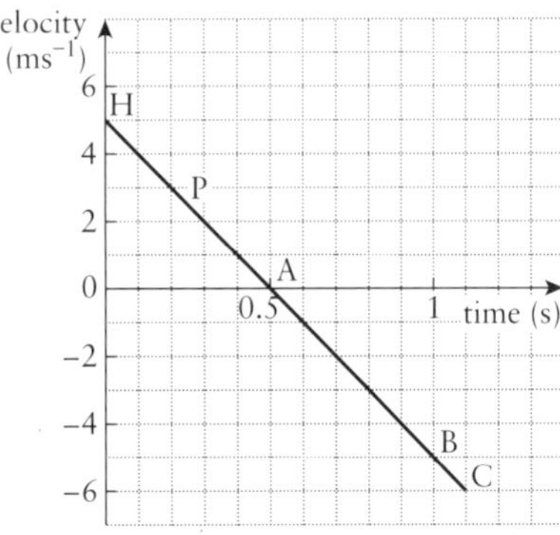

FIGURE 3.9

What is the velocity at H, A, B and C? The speed of the marble increases after it reaches the top. What happens to the velocity?

At the point A, the velocity and gradient of the position–time graph are zero. We say the marble is *instantaneously at rest*. The velocity at H is positive because the marble is moving in the positive direction (upwards). The velocity at B and at C is negative because the marble is moving in the negative direction (downwards).

EXERCISE 3B

1 Draw a speed–time graph for Amy's journey on page 32.

2 The distance–time graph shows the relationship between distance travelled and time for a person who leaves home at 9.00 am, walks to a bus stop and catches a bus into town.

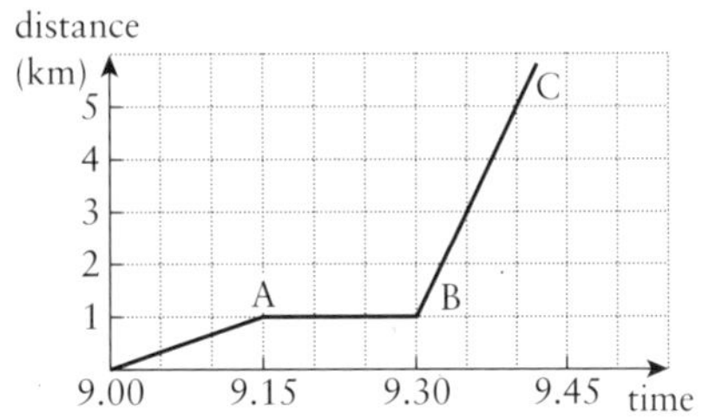

(a) Describe what is happening during the time from A to B.

(b) The section BC is much steeper than OA; what does this tell us about the motion?

(c) Draw the speed–time graph for the person.

(d) What simplifications have been made in drawing these graphs?

3 For each of the following journeys find

(a) 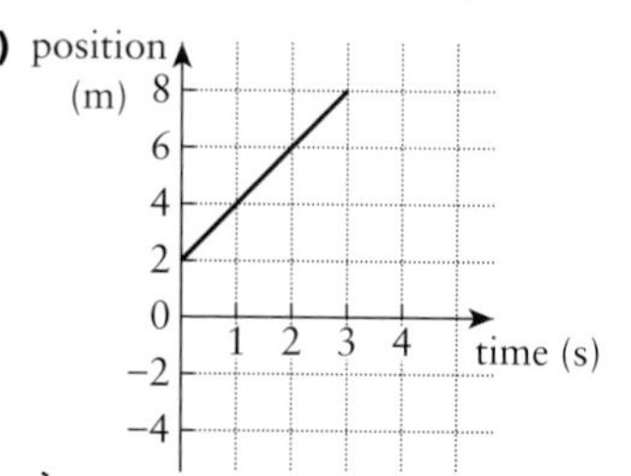

(b) 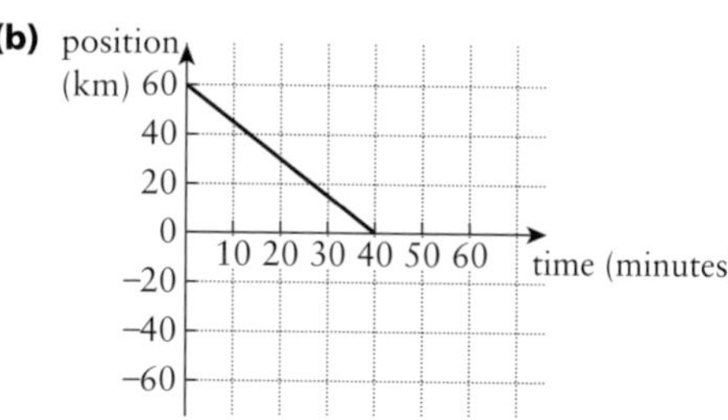

(c) 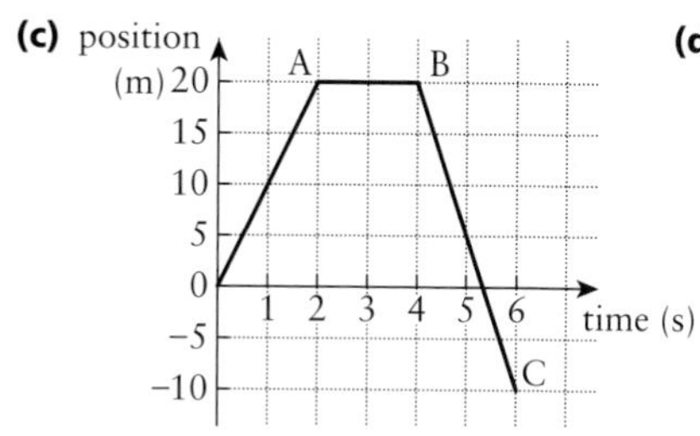

(d) 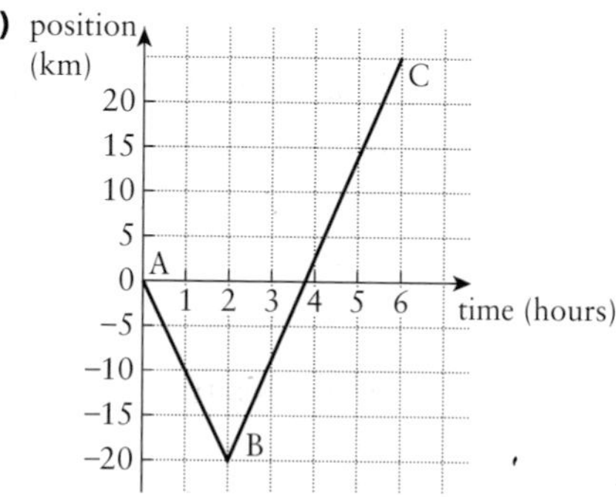

(i) the initial and final positions

(ii) the total displacement

(iii) the total distance travelled

(iv) the velocity and speed for each part of the journey

(v) the average velocity for the whole journey

(vi) the average speed for the whole journey.

4 An aircraft flies from London to Toronto, a distance of 3560 miles at an average speed of 800 mph. It returns at an average speed of 750 mph. Find the average speed for the round trip.

ACCELERATION

In everyday language, the word 'accelerate' is usually used when an object speeds up and 'decelerate' when it slows down. The idea of deceleration is sometimes used in a similar way by mathematicians but in mathematics the word *acceleration* is used whenever there is a change in velocity, whether an object is speeding up, slowing down or changing direction. Acceleration is *the rate at which the velocity changes*.

Over a period of time

$$\text{average acceleration} = \frac{\text{change in velocity}}{\text{time}}$$

Acceleration is represented by the gradient of a velocity–time graph. It is a vector and can take different signs in a similar way to velocity. This is illustrated by Tom's cycle journey which is shown in figure 3.10.

Tom turns on to the main road at $4\,\text{ms}^{-1}$, accelerates uniformly, maintains a constant speed and then slows down uniformly to stop when he reaches home.

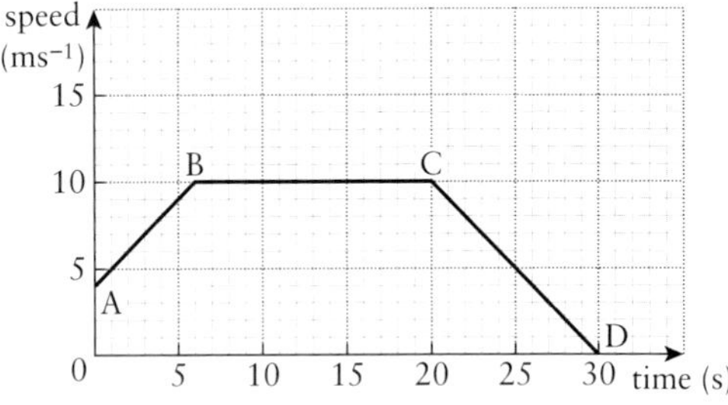

FIGURE 3.10

Between A and B, Tom's velocity increases by $(10 - 4) = 6\,\text{ms}^{-1}$ in 6 seconds, that is by 1 metre per second every second. This acceleration is written as $1\,\text{ms}^{-2}$ (one metre per second squared) and is the gradient of AB.

From B to C acceleration $= 0\,\text{ms}^{-2}$ ← There is no change in velocity

From C to D acceleration $= \dfrac{(0 - 10)}{(30 - 26)} = -2.5\,\text{ms}^{-2}$

From C to D, Tom is slowing down while still moving in the positive direction towards home, so his acceleration, the gradient of the graph, is negative.

THE SIGN OF ACCELERATION

Think again about the marble thrown up into the air with a speed of $5\,\text{ms}^{-1}$.

Figure 3.11 represents the velocity when *upwards* is taken as the positive direction and shows that the velocity *decreases* from $+5\,\text{ms}^{-1}$ to $-5\,\text{ms}^{-1}$ in 1 second.

This means that the gradient, and hence the acceleration, is *negative*. It is $-10\,\text{ms}^{-2}$.

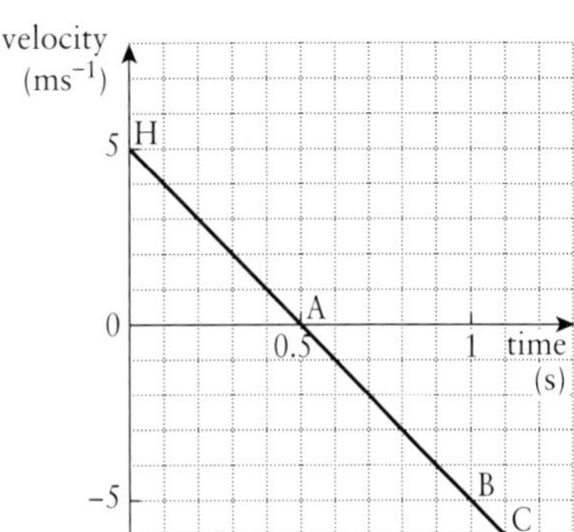

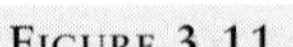
FIGURE 3.11

EXERCISE 3C

1 **(a)** Calculate the acceleration for each part of the following journey.

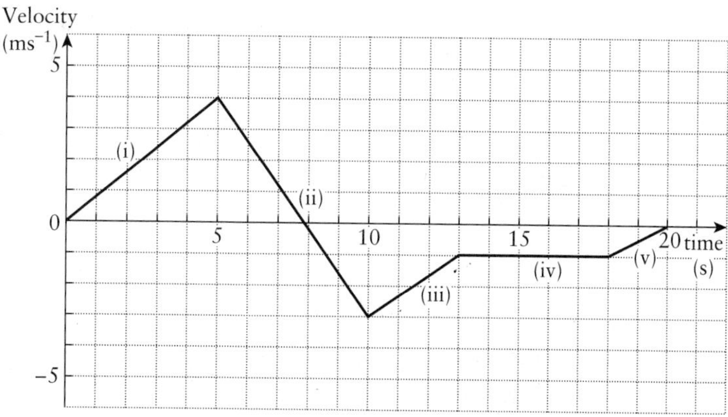

(b) Use your results to sketch an acceleration–time graph.

2 A particle moves so that its position x metres at time t seconds is $x = 2t^3 - 18t$.

(a) Calculate the position of the particle at times $t = 0, 1, 2, 3$ and 4.

(b) Sketch a graph of the position against time.

(c) State the times when the particle is at the origin and describe the direction in which it is moving at those times.

3 A train on a Cornish branch line takes 45 minutes to complete its 15 mile trip. It stops for 3 minutes at each of 7 stations during the trip.

(a) Calculate the average speed of the train.

(b) What would be the average speed if the stop at each station was reduced to 2 minutes?

4 When Louise is planning car journeys she reckons that she can cover distances along main roads at roughly 60 mph and those in towns at 20 mph.

(a) Find her average speed for each of the following journeys.

(i) 20 miles to London and then 10 miles across town

(ii) 150 miles to the coast and then 2 miles in town

(iii) 20 miles to London and then 20 miles across town

(b) In what circumstances would her average speed be 40 mph?

5 A lift travels up and down between the ground floor (G) and the roof garden (R) of a hotel. It starts from rest, takes 5 s to increase its speed uniformly to 2 ms^{-1}, maintains this speed for 5 s and then slows down uniformly to rest in another 5 s. In the following questions, use upwards as positive.

(a) Sketch a velocity–time graph for the journey from G to R.

On one occasion the lift stops for 5 s at R before returning to G.

(b) Sketch a velocity–time graph for this journey from G to R and back.

(c) Calculate the acceleration for each 5 s interval. Take care with the signs.

(d) Sketch an acceleration–time graph for this journey.

6 A film of a dragster doing a 400 m run from a standing start yields the following positions at 1 second intervals.

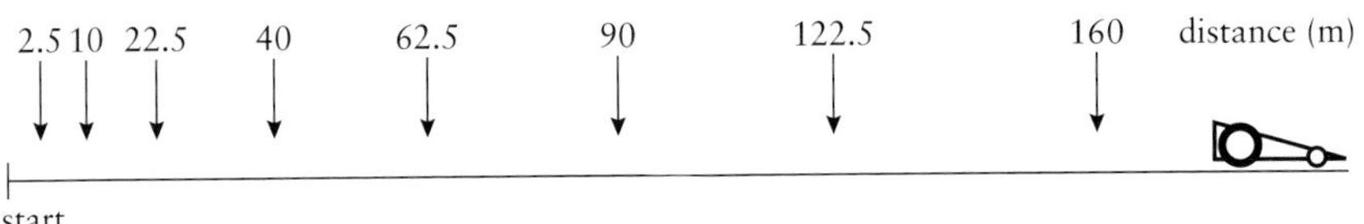

(a) Draw a displacement–time graph of its motion.

(b) Use your graph to help you to sketch

(i) the velocity–time graph

(ii) the acceleration–time graph.

Using areas to find distances and displacements

These distance–time and speed–time graphs model the motion of a stone falling from rest.

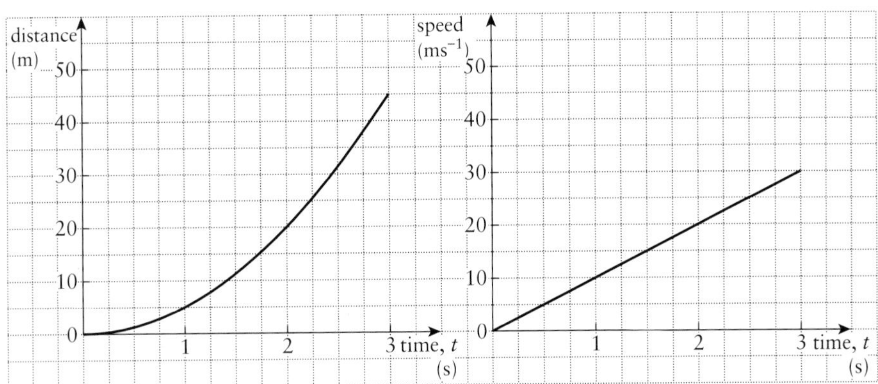

Figure 3.12

Calculate the area between the speed–time graph and the x axis from

(a) $t = 0$ to 1 **(b)** $t = 0$ to 2 **(c)** $t = 0$ to 3.

Compare your answers with the distance that the stone has fallen, shown on the distance–time graph, at $t = 1$, 2 and 3. What conclusions do you reach?

The area between a speed–time graph and the x axis represents the distance travelled.

There is further evidence for this if you consider the units on the graphs. Multiplying metres per second by seconds gives metres. A full justification relies on the calculus methods you will learn in *Mechanics 2*.

Finding the area under speed–time graphs

Many of these graphs consist of straight-line sections. The area is easily found by splitting it up into triangles, rectangles or trapezia.

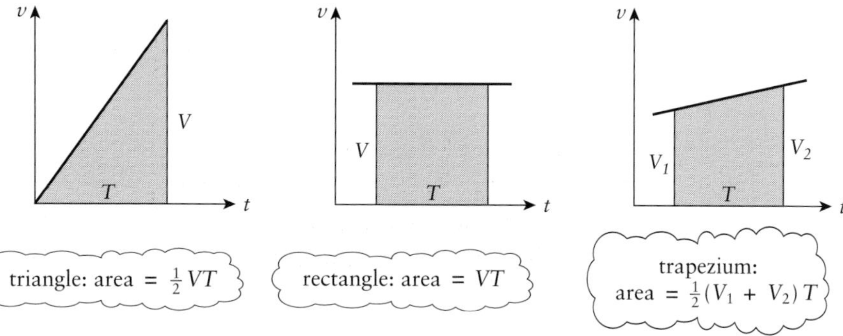

Figure 3.13

EXAMPLE 3.1

The graph shows Tom's journey from the time he turns on to the main road until he arrives home. How far does Tom cycle?

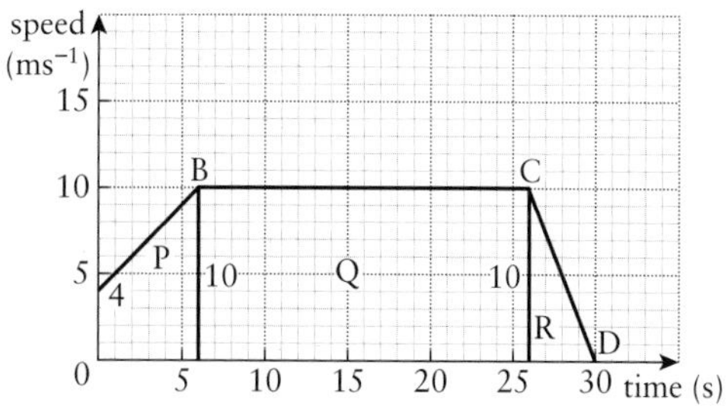

Figure 3.14

Solution The area under the speed–time graph is found by splitting it into three regions.

P	trapezium:	area = $\frac{1}{2}(4 + 10) \times 6 = 42\,\text{m}$
Q	rectangle:	area = $10 \times 20 = 200\,\text{m}$
R	triangle:	area = $\frac{1}{2} \times 10 \times 4 = 20\,\text{m}$
		total area = $262\,\text{m}$

Tom cycles 262 m.

The area between a velocity–time graph and the x axis

EXAMPLE 3.2

David walks east for 6 s at $2\,\mathrm{ms^{-1}}$ then west for 2 s at $1\,\mathrm{ms^{-1}}$. Draw

(a) a diagram of the journey

(b) the speed–time graph

(c) the velocity–time graph.

Interpret the area under each graph.

Solution (a) David's journey is illustrated below.

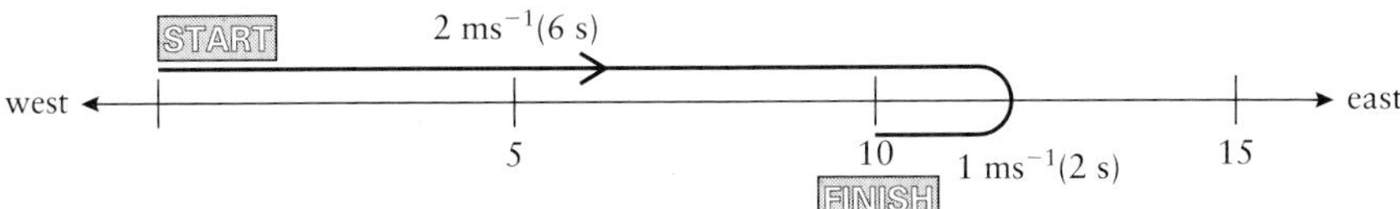

FIGURE 3.15

(b) Speed–time graph

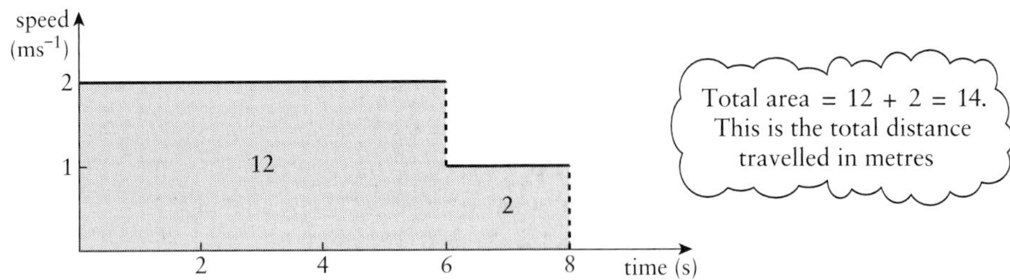

FIGURE 3.16

(c) Velocity–time graph

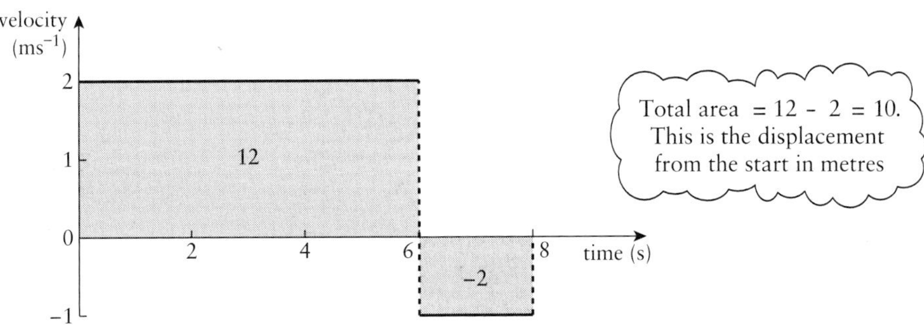

FIGURE 3.17

The area between a velocity–time graph and the x axis represents the change in position, that is the displacement.

When the velocity is negative, the area is below the axis and represents a displacement in the negative direction, west in this case.

EXAMPLE 3.3

On the London Underground, Oxford Circus and Piccadilly Circus are 0.8 km apart. A train accelerates uniformly to a maximum speed when leaving Oxford Circus and maintains this speed for 90 s before decelerating uniformly to stop at Piccadilly Circus. The whole journey takes 2 minutes. Find the maximum speed.

Solution The sketch of the speed–time graph of the journey shows all the information available with suitable units. The maximum speed is $v\,\text{ms}^{-1}$.

The area is $\frac{1}{2}(120 + 90) \times v = 800$

$$v = \frac{1600}{210}$$

$$= 7.619$$

The maximum speed of the train is $7.6\,\text{ms}^{-1}$.

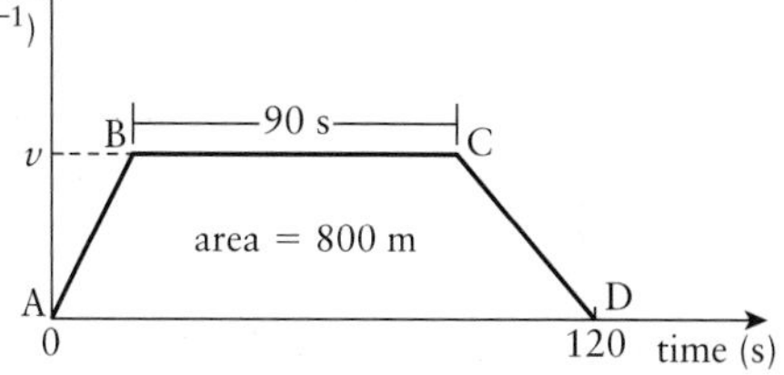

FIGURE 3.18

EXERCISE 3D

1 The graphs show the speeds of two cars travelling along a street.

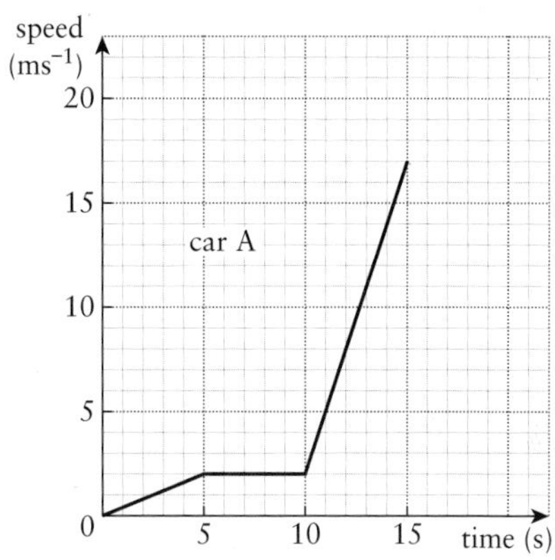

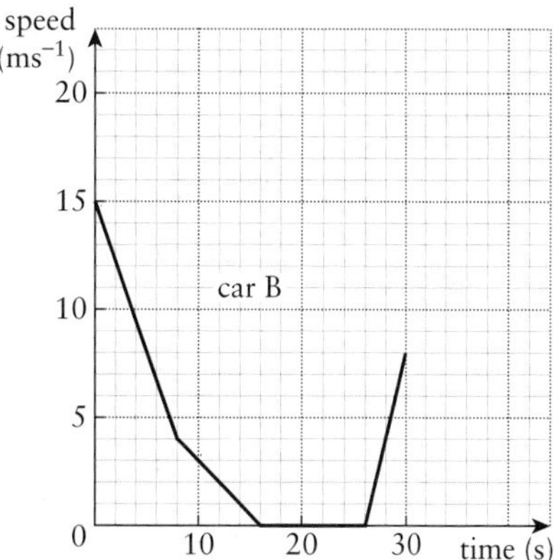

For each car find

(a) the acceleration for each part of its motion

(b) the total distance it travels in the given time

(c) its average speed.

2 The graph shows the speed of a lorry when it enters a very busy motorway.

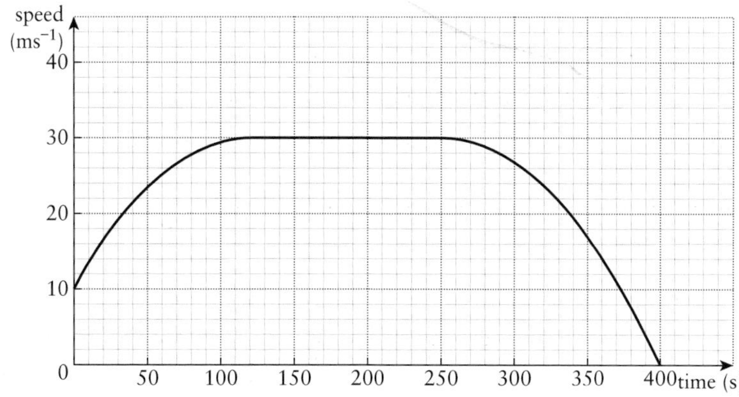

(a) Describe the journey over this time.

(b) Use a ruler to make a tangent to the graph and hence estimate the acceleration at the beginning and end of the period.

(c) Estimate the distance travelled and the average speed.

3 A train leaves a station where it has been at rest and picks up speed at a constant rate for 60 s. It then remains at a constant speed of $17\,\text{ms}^{-1}$ for 60 s before it begins to slow down uniformly as it approaches a set of signals. After 45 s it is travelling at $10\,\text{ms}^{-1}$ and the signal changes. The train again increases speed uniformly for 75 s until it reaches a speed of $20\,\text{ms}^{-1}$. A second set of signals then orders the train to stop, which it does after slowing down uniformly for 30 s.

(a) Draw a speed–time graph for the train.

(b) Use your graph to find the distance that it has travelled from the station.

4 When a parachutist jumps from a balloon stationary above an airfield her speed increases at a constant rate to $28\,\text{ms}^{-1}$ in the first 3 s of her fall. It then decreases uniformly to $8\,\text{ms}^{-1}$ in a further 6 s, remaining constant until she reaches the ground.

(a) Sketch a speed–time graph for the parachutist.

(b) Find the height of the balloon when the parachutist jumps out if the complete jump takes 1 minute.

5 A car is moving at $20\,\text{ms}^{-1}$ when it begins to increase speed. Every 10 s it gains $5\,\text{ms}^{-1}$ until it reaches its maximum speed of $50\,\text{ms}^{-1}$, which it retains.

(a) Draw the speed–time graph of the car.

(b) When does the car reach its maximum speed of $50\,\text{ms}^{-1}$?

(c) Find the distance travelled by the car after 150 s.

(d) Write down expressions for the speed of the car t seconds after it begins to speed up.

6 A train takes 10 minutes to travel from Birmingham New Street to Birmingham International. The train accelerates at a rate of $0.5\,\text{ms}^{-2}$ for 30 s. It then travels at a constant speed and is finally brought to rest in 15 s with a constant deceleration.

(a) Sketch a velocity–time graph for the journey.

(b) Find the steady speed, the rate of deceleration and the distance from Birmingham New Street to Birmingham International.

7 A train was scheduled to travel at $50\,\text{ms}^{-1}$ for 15 minutes on part of its journey. The velocity–time graph illustrates the actual progress of the train, which was forced to stop because of signals.

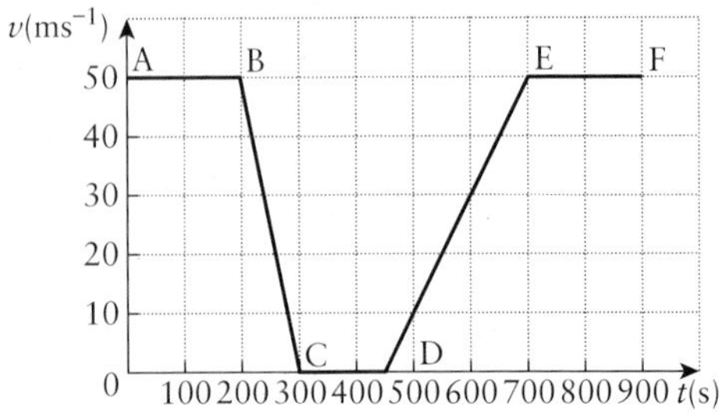

(a) Without carrying out any calculations, describe what was happening to the train in each of the stages BC, CD and DE.
(b) Find the deceleration of the train while it was slowing down and the distance travelled during this stage.
(c) Find the acceleration of the train when it starts off again and the distance travelled during this stage.
(d) Calculate by how long the stop will have delayed the train.
(v) Sketch the distance–time graph for the journey between A and F, marking the points A, B, C, D, E and F.

[MEI]

8 A car is travelling at $36\,\text{km}\,\text{h}^{-1}$ when the driver has to perform an emergency stop. During the time the driver takes to appreciate the situation and apply the brakes the car has travelled 7 m ('thinking distance'). It then pulls up with constant deceleration in a further 8 m ('braking distance'), giving a total stopping distance of 15 m.
(a) Find the initial speed of the car in metres per second and the time that the driver takes to react.
(b) Sketch the velocity–time graph for the car.
(c) Calculate the deceleration once the car starts braking.
(d) What is the stopping distance for a car travelling at $60\,\text{km}\,\text{h}^{-1}$ if the reaction time and the deceleration are the same as before?

THE CONSTANT ACCELERATION FORMULAE

This section develops the mathematics required when an object can be modelled as a *particle moving in a straight line with constant acceleration*. In most real situations this is only the case for part of the motion – you wouldn't expect a car to continue accelerating at the same rate for very long – but it is a very useful model to use as a first approximation over a short time.

The velocity–time graph shows part of the motion of a car on a fairground ride as it picks up speed. The graph is a straight line so the velocity increases at a constant rate and the car has a constant acceleration which is equal to the gradient of the graph.

The velocity increases from $4\,\text{ms}^{-1}$ to $24\,\text{ms}^{-1}$ in 10 s so its acceleration is

$$\frac{24-4}{10} = 2\,\text{ms}^{-2}.$$

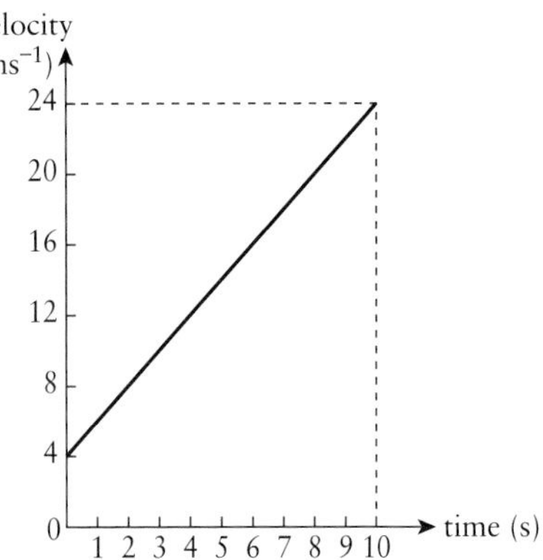

FIGURE 3.19

In general, when the initial velocity is $u\,\text{ms}^{-1}$ and the velocity a time t s later is $v\,\text{ms}^{-1}$, as in figure 3.20, the increase in velocity is $(v-u)\,\text{ms}^{-1}$ and the constant acceleration $a\,\text{ms}^{-2}$ is given by

$$\frac{v-u}{t} = a$$

$$v - u = at$$

so $$v = u + at. \qquad ①$$

The area under the graph represents the distance travelled. For the fairground car, that is represented by a trapezium of area

$$\frac{(4+24)}{2} \times 10 = 140\,\text{m}.$$

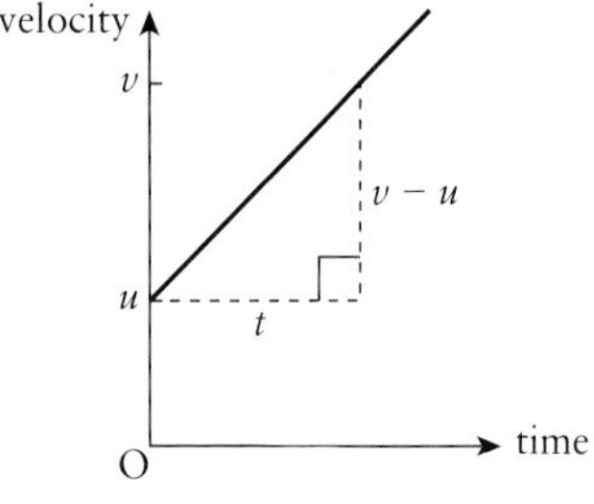

FIGURE 3.20

In the general situation, the area represents the displacement s metres and is

$$s = \frac{(u+v)}{2} \times t \qquad ②$$

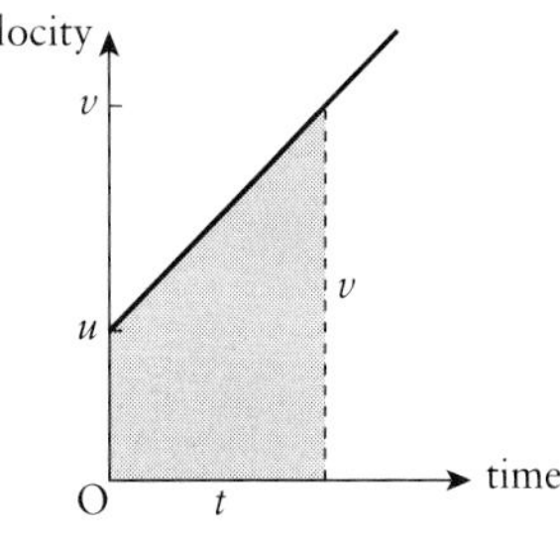

FIGURE 3.21

The two equations, ① and ②, can be used as formulae for solving problems when the acceleration is constant. Check that they work for the fairground ride.

There are other useful formulae as well. For example, you might want to find the displacement, s, without involving v in your calculations. This can be done by looking at the area under the velocity–time graph in a different way, using the rectangle R and the triangle T. In figure 3.22,

$$AC = v \text{ and } BC = u$$

so $$AB = v - u$$

$$= at \quad \text{from equation ①}$$

$$\text{Total area} = \text{area of R} + \text{area of T}$$

so $$s = ut + \tfrac{1}{2} \times t \times at$$

Giving $$s = ut + \tfrac{1}{2}at^2 \quad ③$$

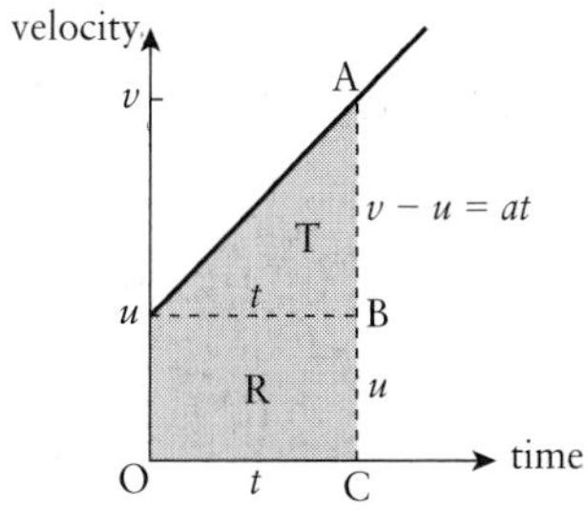

FIGURE 3.22

To find a formula which does not involve t, you need to eliminate t. One way to do this is first to rewrite equations ① and ② as

$$v - u = at \quad \text{and} \quad v + u = \frac{2s}{t}$$

Then multiplying them gives

$$(v - u)(v + u) = at \times \frac{2s}{t}$$

$\Rightarrow$ $$v^2 - u^2 = 2as$$

or $$v^2 = u^2 + 2as \quad ④$$

You might have seen the equations ① to ④ before. They are sometimes called the *uvast* equations or formulae and they can be used whenever an object can be assumed to be moving with *constant acceleration*.

When solving problems it is important to remember the requirement for constant acceleration and also to remember to specify positive and negative directions clearly.

EXAMPLE 3.4

A bus leaving a bus stop accelerates at $0.8\,\text{ms}^{-2}$ for 5 s and then travels at a constant speed for 2 minutes before slowing down uniformly at $4\,\text{ms}^{-2}$ to come to rest at the next bus stop. Calculate

(a) the constant speed
(b) the distance travelled while the bus is accelerating
(c) the total distance travelled.

Solution **(a)** The diagram shows the information for the first part of the motion.

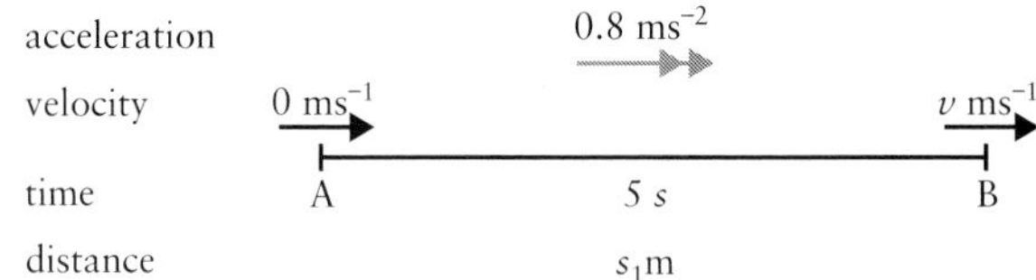

FIGURE 3.23

u	0	$v = u + at$
v	v	$v = 0 + 0.8 \times 5$
a	0.8	$= 4$
s	—	
t	5	The constant speed is $4\,\text{ms}^{-1}$.

Use the suffix because there are three distances to be found in this question

(b) Let the distance travelled be s_1 m.

u	0	$s = ut + \frac{1}{2}at^2$
v	—	$s_1 = 0 \times 5 + \frac{1}{2} \times 0.8 \times 5^2$
a	0.8	$= 10$
s	s_1	
t	5	The bus accelerates over 10 m.

(c) The diagram gives all the information for the rest of the journey.

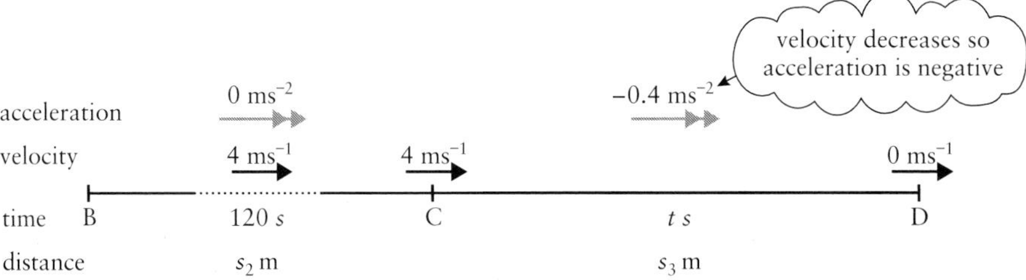

FIGURE 3.24

Between B and C the velocity is constant so the distance travelled is $s_2 = 4 \times 120 = 480$ m.

Let the distance between C and D be s_3 m.

u	4	$v^2 = u^2 + 2as$
v	0	$0^2 = 4^2 + 2 \times (-0.4) \times s_3$
a	−0.4	$0.8 \times s_3 = 16$
s	s_3	$s_3 = 20$
t	—	Distance taken to slow down = 20 m

The total distance travelled is (10 + 480 + 20) m = 510 m

UNITS IN THE *uvast* EQUATIONS

Constant acceleration usually takes place over short periods of time so it is best to use ms^{-2} for this. When you don't need to use a value for the acceleration you can, if you wish, use the *uvast* equations with other units provided they are consistent. This is shown in the next example.

EXAMPLE 3.5

When leaving a town, a car accelerates from 30 mph to 60 mph in 5 s. Assuming the acceleration is constant, find the distance travelled in this time.

Solution

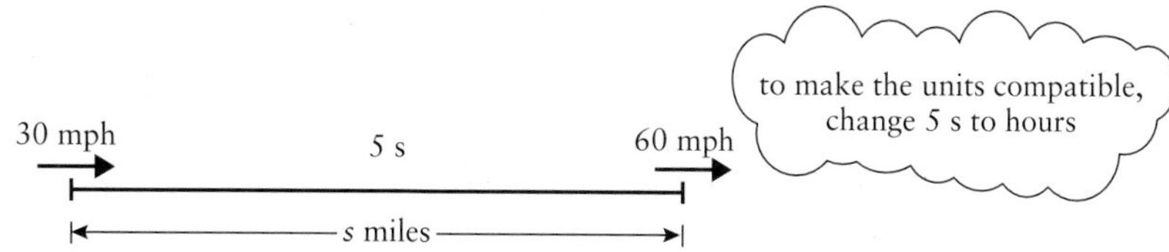

FIGURE 3.25

Let the distance travelled be s miles. Using miles and hours as units, we are given $u = 30$, $v = 60$ and $t = 5 \div 3600$ so we need an equation involving u, v, t and s.

$$s = \frac{(u + v)}{2} \times t$$

$$s = \frac{(30 + 60)}{2} \times \frac{5}{3600} = \frac{1}{16}$$

The distance travelled is $\frac{1}{16}$ mile or 110 yards. (One mile is 1760 yards.)

In Examples 3.4 and 3.5, the bus and the car are always travelling in the positive direction so it is safe to use s for distance. Remember that s is not the same as the distance travelled if the direction changes during the motion.

THE ACCELERATION DUE TO GRAVITY

When a model ignoring air resistance is used, all objects falling freely under gravity fall with the same constant acceleration, $g\,ms^{-2}$. This varies over the surface of the earth. In this book it is assumed that all the situations occur in a place where it is $9.8\,ms^{-2}$ or sometimes $10\,ms^{-2}$ as an approximation. Most answers are given correct to three significant figures so that you can check your working.

EXAMPLE 3.6

A coin is dropped from rest at the top of a building of height 12 m and travels in a straight line with constant acceleration $10\,ms^{-2}$.
Find the time it takes to reach the ground and the speed of impact.

Solution Suppose the time taken to reach the ground is t seconds. Using S.I. units, $u = 0$, $a = 10$ and $s = 12$ when the coin hits the ground, so we need to use a formula involving u, a, s and t.

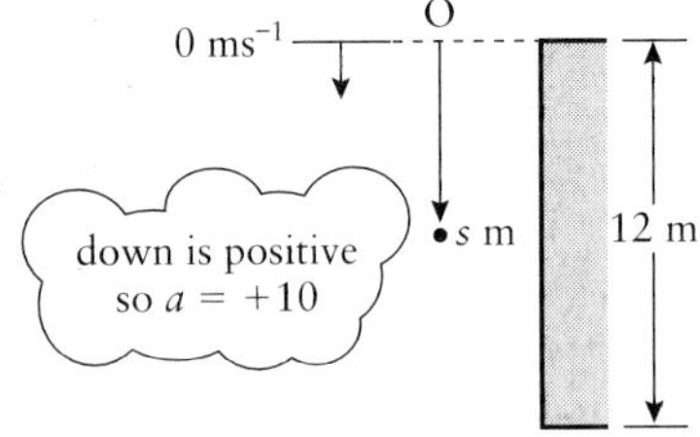

FIGURE 3.26

$$s = ut + \tfrac{1}{2}at^2$$
$$12 = 0 + \tfrac{1}{2} \times 10 \times t^2$$
$$t^2 = 2.4$$
$$t = 1.55$$

To find the velocity, v, a formula involving s, u, a and v is required.

$$v^2 = u^2 + 2as$$
$$v^2 = 0 + 2 \times 10 \times 12$$
$$v^2 = 240$$
$$v = 15.5$$

The coin takes 1.55 s to hit the ground and has speed 15.5 ms^{-1} on impact.

SUMMARY

The equations for *motion with constant acceleration* are

$v = u + at$	s missing	①
$s = \dfrac{(u + v)}{2} \times t$	a missing	②
$s = ut + \frac{1}{2}at^2$	v missing	③
$v^2 = u^2 + 2as$	t missing	④
$s = vt - \frac{1}{2}at^2$	u missing	⑤

When using these equations make sure that the units used are consistent. For example, when the time is t seconds and the distance s metres, any speed involved is in ms^{-1}.

EXERCISE 3E

1 (a) Find v when $u = 10$, $a = 6$ and $t = 2$.
(b) Find s when $v = 20$, $u = 4$ and $t = 10$.
(c) Find s when $v = 10$, $a = 2$ and $t = 10$.
(d) Find a when $v = 2$, $u = 12$, $s = 7$.

2 Decide which equation to use in each of these situations.
(a) Given u, s, a; find v.
(b) Given a, u, t; find v.
(c) Given u, a, t; find s.
(d) Given u, v, s; find t.
(e) Given u, s, v; find a.
(f) Given u, s, t; find a.
(g) Given u, a, v; find s.
(h) Given a, s, t; find v.

3 Assuming no air resistance, a ball has an acceleration of $9.8\,\text{ms}^{-2}$ when it is dropped from a window (so its initial speed, when $t = 0$, is zero). Calculate:
(a) its speed after 1 s and after 10 s
(b) how far it has fallen after 1 s and after 10 s
(c) how long it takes to fall 19.6 m.
(d) Which of these answers are likely to need adjusting to take account of air resistance? Would you expect your answer to be an over- or under-estimate?

4 A car starting from rest at traffic lights reaches a speed of $90\,\text{km h}^{-1}$ in 12 s. Find the acceleration of the car (in ms^{-2}) and the distance travelled. Write down any assumptions that you have made.

5 A top sprinter accelerates from rest to $9\,\text{ms}^{-1}$ in 2 s. Calculate his acceleration, assumed constant, during this period and the distance travelled.

6 A van skids to a halt from an initial speed of $24\,\text{ms}^{-1}$, covering a distance of 36 m. Find the acceleration of the van (assumed constant) and the time it takes to stop.

7 An object moves along a straight line with acceleration $-8\,\text{ms}^{-2}$. It starts its motion at the origin with velocity $16\,\text{ms}^{-1}$.
(a) Write down equations for its position and velocity at time t s.
(b) Find the smallest non-zero time when
(i) the velocity is zero
(ii) the object is at the origin.
(c) Sketch the position–time, velocity–time and speed–time graphs for $0 \leqslant t \leqslant 4$.

FURTHER EXAMPLES

The next two examples illustrate ways of dealing with more complex problems. In Example 3.7, none of the possible equations has only one unknown and there are also two situations, so simultaneous equations are used.

EXAMPLE 3.7

James practises using the stopwatch facility on his new watch by measuring the time between lamp posts on a car journey. As the car speeds up, two consecutive times are 1.2 s and 1 s. Later he finds out that the lamp posts are 30 m apart.

(a) Calculate the acceleration of the car (assumed constant) and its speed at the first lamp post.

(b) Assuming the same acceleration, find the time the car took to travel the 30 m before the first lamp post.

Solution

(a) The diagram shows all the information assuming the acceleration is $a\,\mathrm{ms}^{-2}$ and the velocity at A is $u\,\mathrm{ms}^{-1}$.

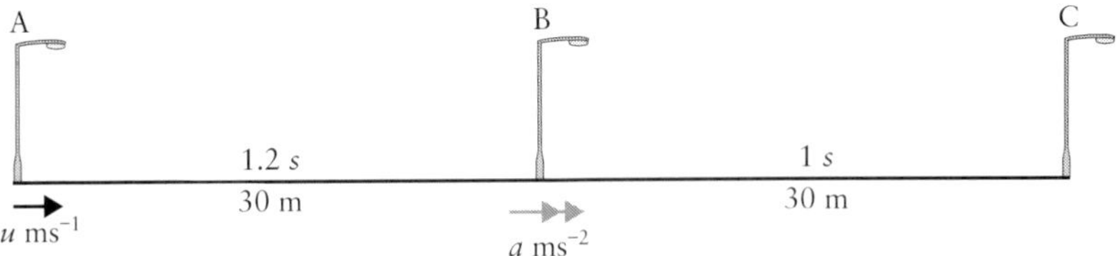

FIGURE 3.27

For AB, $s = 30$ and $t = 1.2$. We are using u and we want a so we use

$$s = ut + \tfrac{1}{2}at^2$$
$$30 = 1.2u + \tfrac{1}{2}a \times 1.2^2$$
$$30 = 1.2u + 0.72a \qquad ①$$

To use the same equation for the part BC would require the velocity at B and this brings in another unknown. It is much better to go back to the beginning and consider the whole of AC with $s = 60$ and $t = 2.2$. Then again using $s = ut + \tfrac{1}{2}at^2$ gives

$$60 = 2.2u + \tfrac{1}{2}a \times 2.2^2$$
$$60 = 2.2u + 2.42a \qquad ②$$

These two simultaneous equations in two unknowns can be solved more easily if they are simplified. First make the coefficients of u integers.

	① × 10 ÷ 12	$25 = u + 0.6a$	③
	② × 5	$300 = 11u + 12.1a$	④
then	③ × 11	$275 = 11u + 6.6a$	⑤

Subtracting gives

$$25 = 0 + 5.5a$$
$$a = 4.545$$

Now substitute 4.545 for a in ③ to find

$$u = 25 - 0.6 \times 4.545 = 22.273$$

The acceleration of the car is $4.55\,\text{ms}^{-2}$ and the initial speed is $22.3\,\text{ms}^{-1}$ (correct to 3 sf).

(b)

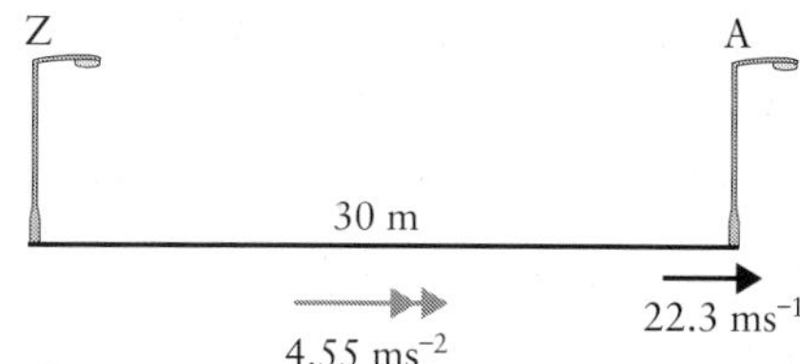

FIGURE 3.28

For this part, we know that $s = 30$, $v = 22.3$ and $a = 4.55$ and we want t so we use the fifth formula.

$$s = vt - \tfrac{1}{2}at^2$$

$$30 = 22.3 \times t - \tfrac{1}{2} \times 4.55 \times t^2$$

$$\Rightarrow \quad 2.275t^2 - 22.3t + 30 = 0$$

Solving this using the quadratic formula gives $t = 1.61$ and $t = 8.19$.

The most sensible answer to this particular problem is 1.61 s.

USING A NON-ZERO INITIAL DISPLACEMENT

What, in the *uvast* acceleration equations, are v and s when $t = 0$?

Putting $t = 0$ gives the *initial values*, u for the velocity and $s = 0$ for the position.

Sometimes, however, it is convenient to use an origin which gives a non-zero value for s when $t = 0$. For example, when you model the motion of a marble thrown vertically upwards you might decide to find its height above the ground rather than from the point from which it was thrown.

What is the effect on the various *uvast* equations if the initial position is s_0 rather than 0?

If the height of the marble above the ground is s at time t and s_0 when $t = 0$, the displacement over time t is $s - s_0$. You then need to replace s in each equation by $(s - s_0)$, which is zero when $t = 0$. Then equations ③ and ④ become

$$s - s_0 = ut + \tfrac{1}{2}at^2 \quad \text{and} \quad v^2 = u^2 + 2a(s - s_0)$$

The next example avoids this in the first part but it is very useful in part (b).

EXAMPLE 3.8

A juggler throws a ball up in the air with initial speed $5\,\text{ms}^{-1}$ from a height of 1.2 m. It has a constant acceleration of $10\,\text{ms}^{-2}$ vertically downwards due to gravity.

(a) Find the maximum height of the ball above the ground and the time it takes to reach it.

At the instant that the ball reaches its maximum height, the juggler throws up another ball with the same speed and from the same height.

(b) Where and when will the balls pass each other?

Solution **(a)** In this example it is very important to draw a diagram and to be clear about the position of the origin. When O is 1.2 m above the ground and s is the height in metres above O after t s, the diagram looks like figure 3.29.

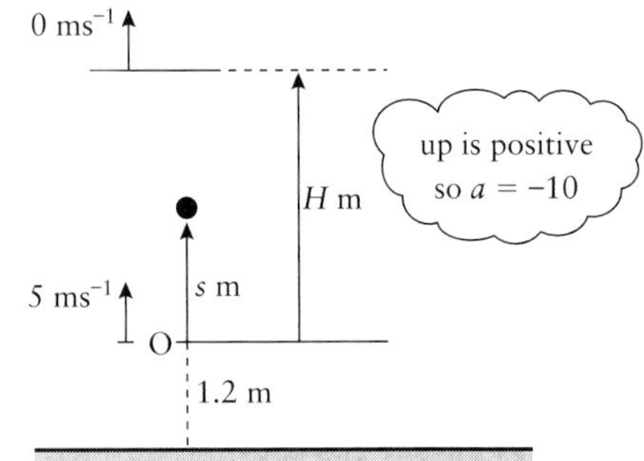

FIGURE 3.29

At the point of maximum height, let $s = H$ and $t = t_1$. ← Use the suffix because there are two times to be found in this question

The ball stops instantaneously before falling so at the top, $v = 0$. The acceleration given is constant, $a = -10$; $u = +5$ and $s = H$.

An equation involving u, v, a and s is required, so using $v^2 = u^2 + 2as$,

$$0 = 5^2 + 2 \times (-10) \times H$$
$$H = 1.25$$

The maximum height of the ball above the ground is 1.25 + 1.2 = 2.45 m.

To find t_1, given $v = 0$, $a = -10$ and $u = +5$ requires a formula in v, u, a and t. Using $v = u + at$,

$$0 = 5 + (-10)\,t_1$$
$$t_1 = 0.5$$

The ball takes half a second to reach its maximum height.

(b) Now consider the motion from the instant the first ball reaches the top of its path and the second is thrown up.

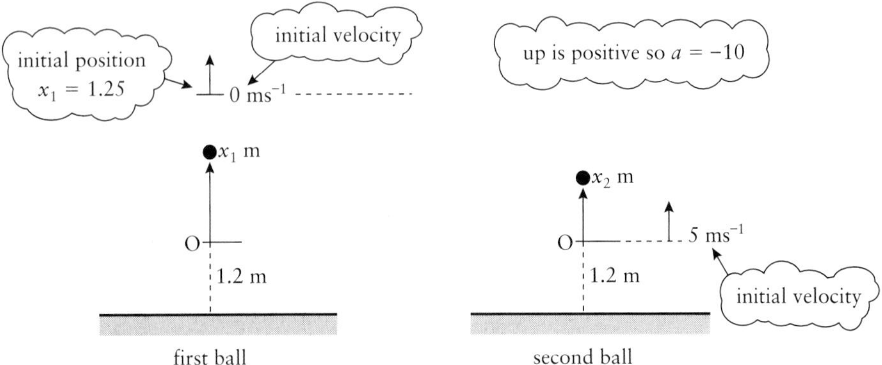

FIGURE 3.30

Suppose that the balls have displacements *above* the origin of x_1 m and x_2 m, as shown in the diagram, at a general time t s after the second ball is thrown up. The initial position of the second ball is 0, but the initial position of the first ball is +1.25 m.

For each ball we know u and a. We want to involve t and s so we use $s - s_0 = ut + \frac{1}{2}at^2$

i.e. $\quad s = ut + \frac{1}{2}at^2 + s_0$

For the first ball:

$$x_1 = 0 \times t + \tfrac{1}{2} \times (-10) \times t^2 + 1.25$$

This makes $x_1 = 1.25$ when $t = 0$

$$x_1 = 1.25 - 5t^2 \qquad ①$$

x_1 decreases as t increases

For the second ball:

$$x_2 = 5 \times t + \tfrac{1}{2} \times (-10) \times t^2 + 0$$

$$x_2 = 5t - 5t^2 \qquad ②$$

Suppose the balls pass after a time t_2 s. This is when they are at the same height, so equate x_1 and x_2 from equations ① and ② using t_2 for t.

$$1.25 - 5{t_2}^2 = 5t_2 - 5{t_2}^2$$

$$1.25 = 5t_2$$

$$t_2 = 0.25$$

Then substituting $t_2 = 0.25$ in ① and ② gives

$$x_1 = 1.25 - 5 \times 0.25^2 = 0.9375$$

and

$$x_2 = 5 \times 0.25 - 5 \times 0.25^2 = 0.9375$$

These are the same, as expected

The balls pass after 0.25 seconds at a height of 1.2 + 0.94 m = 2.14 m above the ground (correct to the nearest centimetre).

Note The balls pass after half the time to reach the top, but *not* half-way up.

EXERCISE 3F

Use g = 9.8 ms^{-2} in this exercise unless otherwise specified.

1 A car is travelling along a straight road. It accelerates uniformly from rest to a speed of 15 ms^{-1} and maintains this speed for 10 minutes. It then decelerates uniformly to rest. If the acceleration and deceleration are 5 ms^{-2} and 8 ms^{-2} respectively, find the total journey time and the total distance travelled during the journey.

2 A skier pushes off at the top of a slope with an initial speed of $2\,\text{ms}^{-1}$. She gains speed at a constant rate throughout her run. After 10 s she is moving at $6\,\text{ms}^{-1}$.

(a) Find an expression for her speed t seconds after she pushes off.

(b) Find an expression for the distance she has travelled at time t seconds.

(c) The length of the ski slope is 400 m. What is her speed at the bottom of the slope?

3 Towards the end of a half-marathon Sabina is 100 m from the finish line and is running at a constant speed of $5\,\text{ms}^{-1}$. Daniel, who is 140 m from the finish and is running at $4\,\text{ms}^{-1}$, decides to accelerate to try to beat Sabina. If he accelerates uniformly at $0.25\,\text{ms}^{-2}$ does he succeed?

4 Rupal throws a ball upwards at $2\,\text{ms}^{-1}$ from a window which is 4 m above ground level.

(a) Write down an equation for the height h m of the ball above the ground after t s (while it is still in the air).

(b) Use your answer to part (a) to find the time the ball hits the ground.

(c) How fast is the ball moving just before it hits the ground?

(d) In what way would you expect your answers to parts (b) and (c) to change if you were able to take air resistance into account?

5 Nathan hits a tennis ball straight up into the air from a height of 1.25 m above the ground. The ball hits the ground after 2.5 seconds. Assuming $g = 10\,\text{ms}^{-2}$, find

(a) the speed Nathan hits the ball

(b) the greatest height above the ground reached by the ball

(c) the speed the ball hits the ground

(d) how high the ball bounces if it loses 0.2 of its speed on hitting the ground.

(e) Is your answer to part (a) likely to be an over- or under-estimate given that you have ignored air resistance?

6 A ball is dropped from a building of height 30 m and at the same instant a stone is thrown vertically upwards from the ground so that it hits the ball. In modelling the motion of the ball and stone it is assumed that each object moves in a straight line with a constant downward acceleration of magnitude $10\,\text{ms}^{-2}$. The stone is thrown with initial speed of $15\,\text{ms}^{-1}$ and is h_s metres above the ground t seconds later.

(a) Draw a diagram of the ball and stone before they collide, marking their positions.

(b) Write down an expression for h_s at time t.

(c) Write down an expression for the height h_b of the ball at time t.

(d) When do the ball and stone collide?

(e) How high above the ground do the ball and stone collide?

7 When Kim rows her boat, the two oars are both in the water for 3 s and then both out of the water for 2 s. This 5 s cycle is then repeated. When the oars are in the water the boat accelerates at a constant 1.8 ms^{-2} and when they are not in the water it decelerates at a constant 2.2 ms^{-2}.

(a) Find the change in speed that takes place in each 3 s period of acceleration.

(b) Find the change in speed that takes place in each 2 s period of deceleration.

(c) Calculate the change in the boat's speed for each 5 s cycle.

(d) A race takes Kim 45 s to complete. If she starts from rest what is her speed as she crosses the finishing line?

(e) Discuss whether this is a realistic speed for a rowing boat.

8 A ball is dropped from a tall building and falls with acceleration of magnitude 10 ms^{-2}. The distance between floors in the block is constant. The ball takes 0.5 s to fall from the 14th to the 13th floor and 0.3 s to fall from the 13th floor to the 12th. What is the distance between floors?

9 Two clay pigeons are launched vertically upwards from exactly the same spot at 1 s intervals. Each clay pigeon has initial speed 30 ms^{-1} and acceleration 10 ms^{-2} downwards. How high above the ground do they collide?

EXERCISE 3G Examination-style questions

1 To demonstrate the depth of a well, a guide drops a small stone down it. The splash is heard 2.5 s later.

(a) Estimate the depth of the well.

(b) What have you ignored in your model?

(c) What would be the effect of improving the model?

2 A narrow boat is travelling at a constant speed of 1.75 ms^{-1} along a straight canal when it comes to a lock. The boat is put into reverse and stops in a distance of 8 m. Find the deceleration, assumed constant.

3 A motorist passes a speed-limit sign on entering a built-up area at a speed of 15 ms^{-1}. The motorist maintains this steady speed for 10 s, and then halts for some traffic lights using a constant deceleration. The braking process takes 5 s.

(a) Draw a speed–time graph for this motion.

(b) How far from the speed-limit sign does the motorist come to rest?

4 A car is travelling at 35 ms^{-1} along a motorway when it comes to an area of road works. The car slows down to 25 ms^{-1} over a time of 5 s, using a constant deceleration. The car then travels at a constant speed for 500 m past the road works. It then speeds up using a constant acceleration for 3 s to its original speed. How much time has been lost due to the road works?

5 The diagram shows a velocity–time graph for a lift going up.

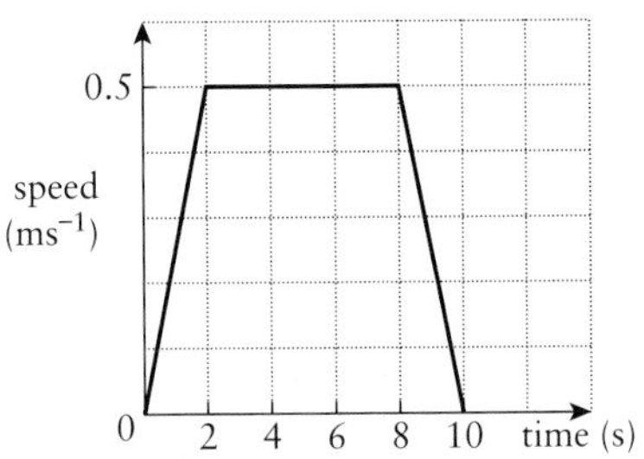

(a) How far has the lift risen?

(b) 5 s after the lift starts, an athletic person starts from the same floor and runs up the stairs with a constant vertical component of velocity of 1 ms^{-1}. Does the person beat the lift, and if so, by what time?

6 The diagram shows the speed of a sailing craft during a tack round a buoy.

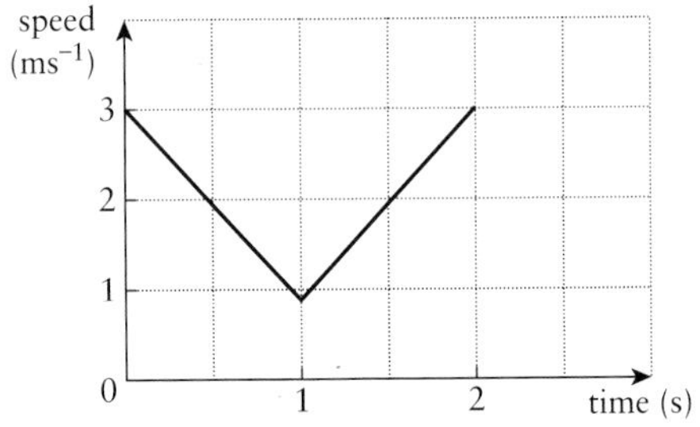

(a) Find the distance covered during the manoeuvre.

(b) Find the time lost compared to an accompanying motorboat which goes round the buoy at a constant speed of 3 ms^{-1} without slowing down.

7 A juggler throws a ball straight up at 4.4 ms^{-1}. After a pause of 0.3 s, the juggler throws a second ball straight up at the same speed. Where and when do the two balls cross?

8 A train leaving a station at which it was at rest passes a marker post 400 m from the station after 40 s.

(a) Find the acceleration, assumed constant.

(b) The train passes another marker post a further 400 m from the station after another 17 s. Does this information support the constant acceleration model?

9 An electron being accelerated in an electron gun passes three anodes while moving in a straight line. The first two anodes are separated by 0.75 cm, and the second two by 1 cm. The electron takes 3×10^{-10} s to move from anode 1 to anode 2, and 2×10^{-10} s to move from anode 2 to anode 3.

(a) Find the acceleration, assumed constant.

(b) Find the velocity at which it passes anode 1.

10 A cyclist starts from rest and accelerates with an acceleration of $3\,\text{ms}^{-2}$ for 6 s and then continues at constant speed. As the cyclist stops accelerating, a car starts from the same point with a constant acceleration of $2\,\text{ms}^{-2}$.

(a) Find the time when the car overtakes the cyclist.

(b) Find how far they both are from the start point at that moment.

11 A car moves with constant acceleration along a straight horizontal road. The car passes the point A with speed $5\,\text{ms}^{-1}$ and 4 s later it passes the point B, where AB = 50 m.

(a) Find the acceleration of the car.

When the car passes the point C, it has speed $30\,\text{ms}^{-1}$.

(b) Find the distance AC.

[Edexcel]

12 A competitor makes a dive from a high springboard into a diving pool. She leaves the springboard vertically with a speed of $4\,\text{ms}^{-1}$ upwards. When she leaves the springboard, she is 5 m above the surface of the pool. The diver is modelled as a particle moving vertically under gravity alone and it is assumed that she does not hit the springboard as she descends.

(a) Find her speed when she reaches the surface of the pool.

(b) Find the time taken to reach the surface of the pool.

(c) State two physical factors which have been ignored in the model.

[Edexcel]

13 Two trains A and B run on parallel straight tracks. Initially both are at rest in a station and level with each other. At time $t = 0$, A starts to move. It moves with constant acceleration for 12 s up to a speed of $30\,\text{ms}^{-1}$, and then moves at a constant speed of $30\,\text{ms}^{-1}$. Train B starts to move in the same direction as A when $t = 40$, where t is measured in seconds. It accelerates with the same initial acceleration as A, up to a speed of $60\,\text{ms}^{-1}$. It then moves at a constant speed of $60\,\text{ms}^{-1}$. Train B overtakes A after both trains have reached their maximum speed. Train B overtakes A when $t = T$.

(a) Sketch, on the same diagram, the speed-time graphs of both trains for $0 \leqslant t \leqslant T$.

(b) Find the value of T.

[Edexcel]

KEY POINTS

Vectors (with magnitude and direction)
Displacement
Position – displacement from a fixed origin
Velocity – rate of change of position
Acceleration – rate of change of velocity

Scalars (magnitude only)
Distance
Speed – magnitude of velocity
Time

Vertical is towards the centre of the earth; **horizontal** is perpendicular to vertical.

Diagrams

Motion along a line can be illustrated vertically (as shown) or horizontally.

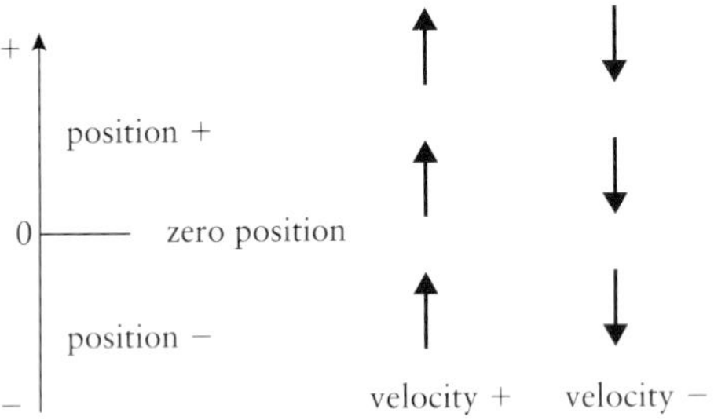

$$\textbf{Average speed} = \frac{\text{total distance travelled}}{\text{total time taken}}$$

$$\textbf{Average velocity} = \frac{\text{displacement}}{\text{time taken}}$$

Graphs

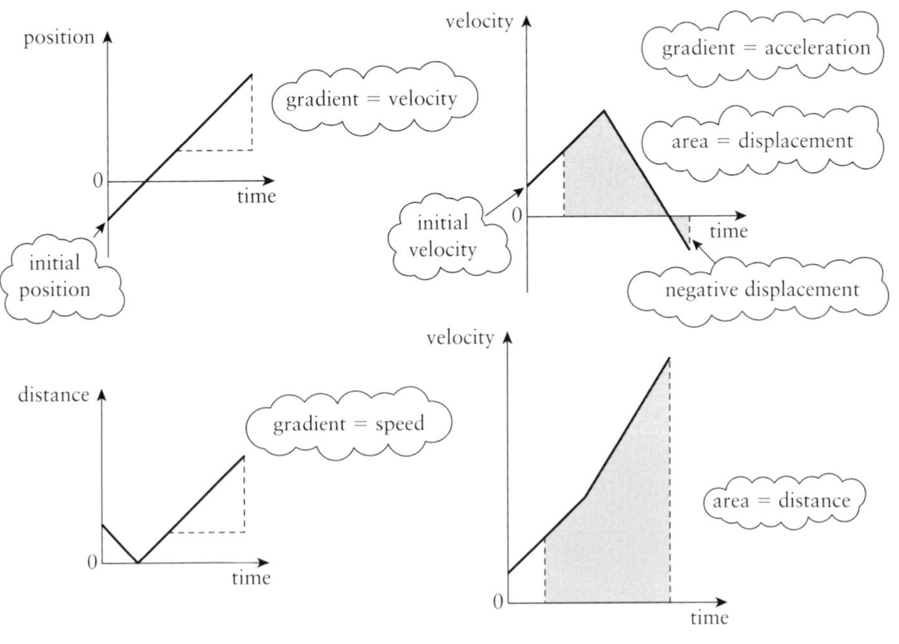

The equations for motion with constant acceleration are

1 $v = u + at$ **2** $s = \dfrac{(u + v)}{2} \times t$

3 $s = ut + \frac{1}{2}at^2$ **4** $v^2 = u^2 + 2as$

5 $s = vt - \frac{1}{2}at^2$

where a is the constant acceleration, s is the displacement from the starting position at time t, v is the velocity at time t, u is the velocity when $t = 0$.

If $s = s_0$ when $t = 0$, replace s in each question with $(s - s_0)$.

Vertical motion under gravity
The acceleration due to gravity (g) is $9.8\,\mathrm{m\,s^{-2}}$ vertically downwards.

Always draw a diagram and decide in advance where your origin is and which way is positive.

Make sure that your units are compatible.

Chapter four

Forces and Newton's laws of motion

Nature, and Nature's laws lay hid in night.
God said, *Let Newton be!* and all was light.

Alexander Pope

Force diagrams

The picture shows a crate of medical supplies being dropped into a remote area by parachute. What forces are acting on the crate of supplies and the parachute?

One force which acts on every object near the earth's surface is its own *weight*. This is the force of gravity pulling it towards the centre of the earth. The weight of the crate acts on the crate and the weight of the parachute acts on the parachute.

The parachute is designed to make use of *air resistance*. A resistance force is present whenever a solid object moves through a liquid or gas. It acts in the opposite direction to the motion and depends on the speed of the object. The crate also experiences air resistance, but to a lesser extent than the parachute.

Other forces are the *tensions* in the guy lines attaching the crate to the parachute. These pull upwards on the crate and downwards on the parachute.

All these forces can be shown most clearly if you draw *force diagrams* for the crate and the parachute.

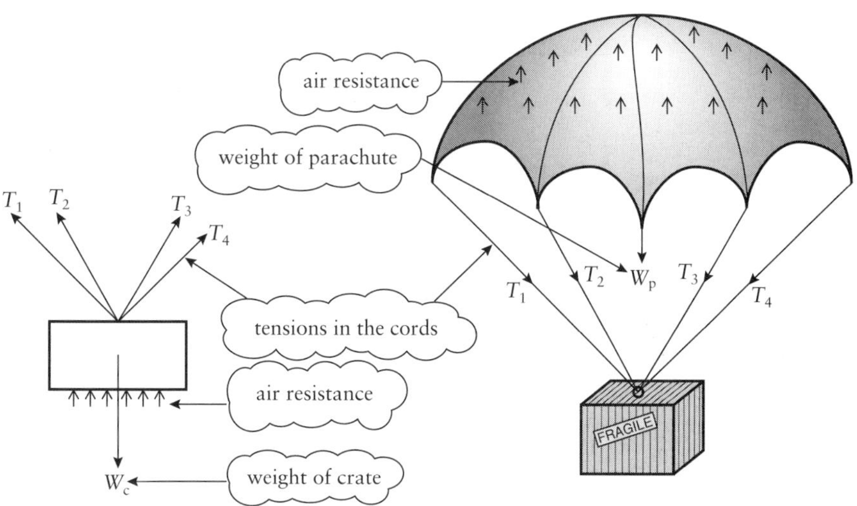

FIGURE 4.1 *Forces acting on the crate*

FIGURE 4.2 *Forces acting on the parachute*

Every part of an object has weight, but we consider the *resultant* of all these separate weights as one force acting at a point called the *centre of mass* or *centre of gravity* of the object. The weight can then be represented by an arrow through the centre of mass. Force diagrams are essential for the understanding of most mechanical situations. A force is a vector: it has a magnitude, or size, and a direction. It also has a *line of action*. This line often passes through a point of particular interest. Any force diagram should show clearly

- the direction of the force
- a label showing the magnitude
- the line of action.

In figures 4.1 and 4.2 each force is shown by an arrow along its line of action. The air resistance has been depicted by a lot of separate arrows but this is not very satisfactory. It is much better if the combined effect can be shown by one arrow. By using vectors, the tensions in the guy lines can also be combined into one force if you wish. The forces on the crate and parachute can then be simplified.

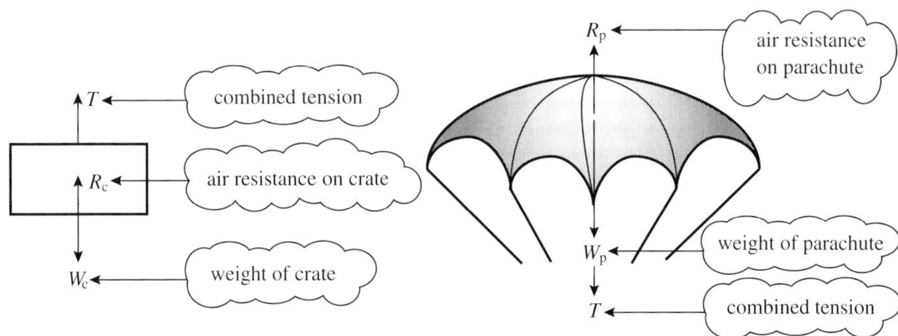

Figure 4.3 *Forces acting on the crate*

Figure 4.4 *Forces acting on the parachute*

Centre of mass and the particle model

Think about balancing a pen on your finger. The diagrams show the forces acting on the pen.

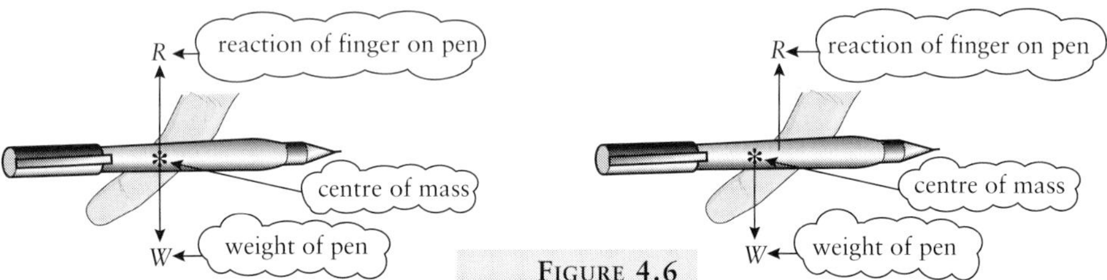

Figure 4.5

Figure 4.6

So long as you place your finger under the centre of mass of the pen, as in figure 4.5, it will balance. There is a force called a *reaction* between your finger and the pen which balances the weight of the pen. The forces on the pen are then said to be *in equilibrium*. If you place your finger under another point, as in figure 4.6, the pen will turn and fall. The pen can only be in equilibrium if the two forces have the same line of action.

If you balance the pen on two fingers, there is a reaction between each finger and the pen at the point where it touches the pen. These reactions can be combined into one resultant vertical reaction acting through the centre of mass.

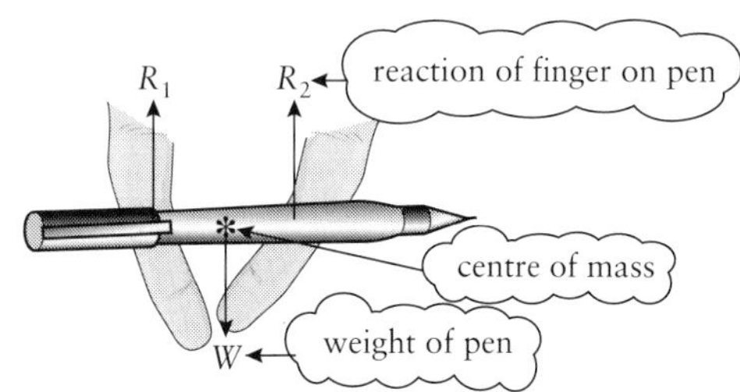

Figure 4.7

The behaviour of objects which are liable to rotate under the action of forces is covered in Chapter 9. This chapter deals with situations where the resultant of the forces does not cause rotation. An object can then be modelled as a particle, that is a point mass, situated at its centre of mass.

NEWTON'S THIRD LAW OF MOTION

Sir Isaac Newton (1642–1727) is famous for his work on gravity and the mechanics you learn in this course is often called Newtonian Mechanics because it is based entirely on Newton's three laws of motion. These laws provide us with an extremely powerful model of how objects, ranging in size from specks of dust to planets and stars, behave when they are influenced by forces.

We start with Newton's *third law* which states that:

> When one object exerts a force on another there is always a reaction of the same kind which is equal, and opposite in direction, to the acting force.

You might have noticed that the combined tensions acting on the parachute and the crate in figures 4.3 and 4.4 are both marked with the same letter, T. The crate applies a force on the parachute through the supporting guy lines and the parachute applies an equal and opposite force on the crate. When you apply a force to a chair by sitting on it, it responds with an equal and opposite force on you. Figure 4.8 shows the forces acting when someone sits on a chair.

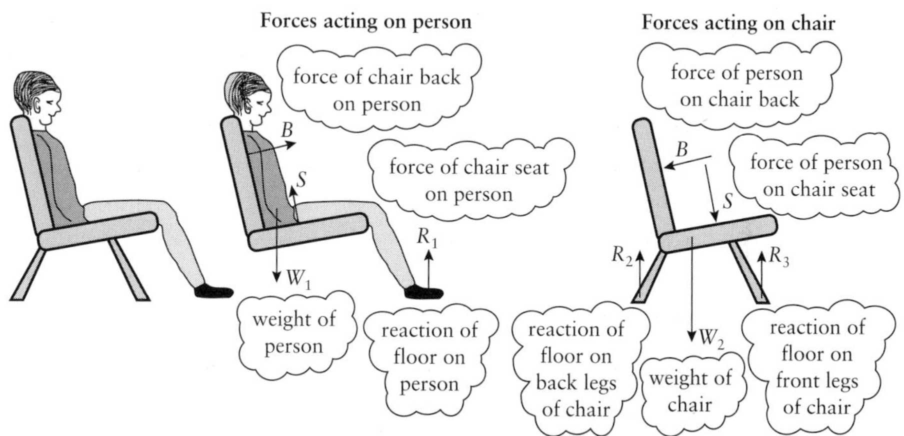

FIGURE 4.8

The reactions of the floor on the chair and on your feet act where there is contact with the floor. You can use R_1, R_2 and R_3 to show that they have different magnitudes. There are equal and opposite forces acting on the floor, but the forces on the floor are not being considered so do not appear here.

Gravitational forces obey Newton's third law just as other forces between bodies. According to Newton's universal law of gravitation, the earth pulls us towards its centre and we pull the earth in the opposite direction. However, in this book we are only concerned with the gravitational force on us and not the force we exert on the earth.

All the forces you meet in mechanics apart from the gravitational force are the result of physical contact. This might be between two solids or between a solid and a liquid or gas.

Friction and normal reaction

When you push your hand along a table, the table reacts in two ways.

- Firstly there are forces which stop your hand going through the table. Such forces are always present when there is any contact between your hand and the table. They are at right angles to the surface of the table and their resultant is called the *normal reaction* between your hand and the table.
- There is also another force which tends to prevent your hand from sliding. This is the *friction* and it acts in a direction which opposes the sliding.

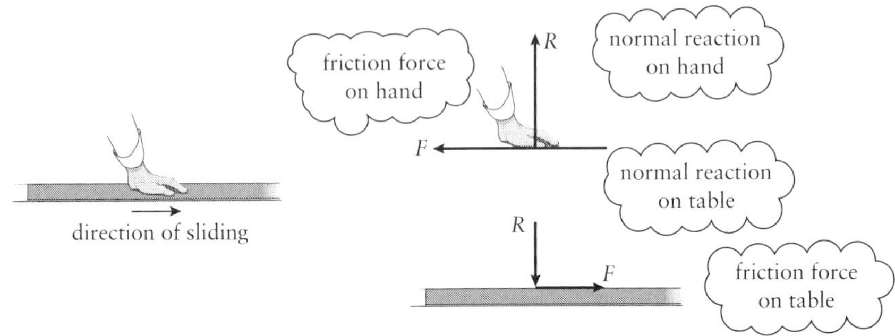

Figure 4.9

The diagram shows the reaction forces acting on your hand and on the table. By Newton's third law they are equal and opposite to each other. The frictional force is due to tiny bumps on the two surfaces (see the electronmicrograph below). When you hold your hands together you will feel the normal reaction between them. When you slide them against each other you will feel the friction.

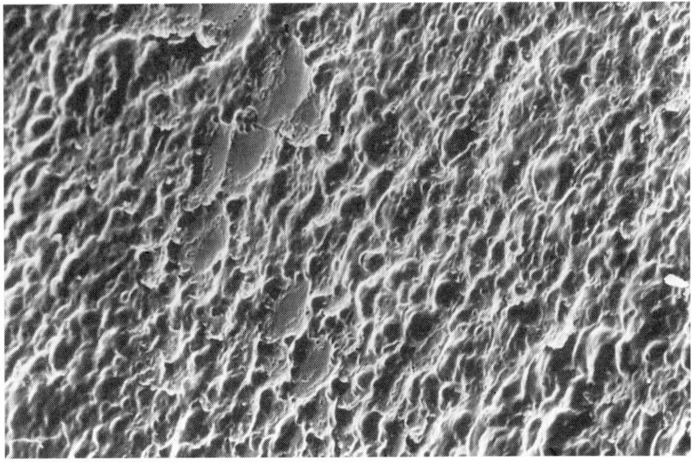

Etched glass magnified to high resolution, showing the tiny bumps.

When the friction between two surfaces is negligible, at least one of the surfaces is said to be *smooth*. This is a modelling assumption which you will meet frequently in this book. Oil can make surfaces smooth and ice is often modelled as a smooth surface.

> When the contact between two surfaces is smooth, the only force between them is at right angles to any possible sliding and is just the normal reaction.

What direction is the reaction between the sweeper's broom and the smooth ice?

EXAMPLE 4.1

A TV set is standing on a small table. Draw a diagram to show the forces acting on the TV and on the table as seen from the front.

Solution The diagram shows the forces acting on the TV and on the table. They are all vertical because the weights are vertical and there are no horizontal forces acting.

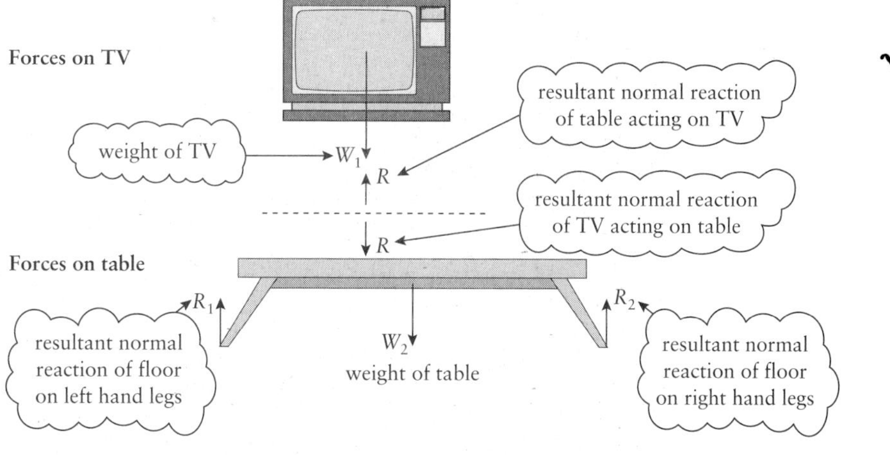

FIGURE 4.10

EXAMPLE 4.2

Draw diagrams to show the forces acting on a tennis ball which is hit downwards across the court:

(a) at the instant it is hit by the racket
(b) as it crosses the net
(c) at the instant it lands on the other side.

Solution

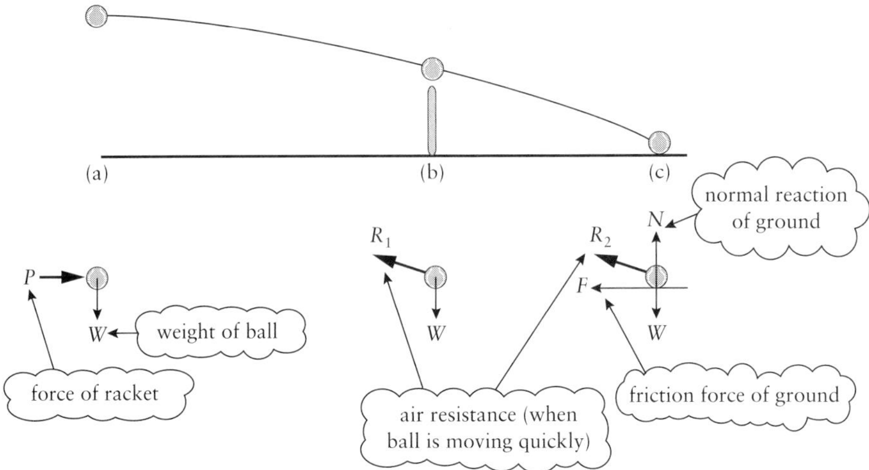

Figure 4.11

Exercise 4A

In this exercise draw clear diagrams to show the forces acting on the objects named in italics. Clarity is more important than realism when drawing these diagrams.

1 A *gymnast* hanging at rest on a bar.

2 A *light bulb* hanging from a ceiling.

3 A *book* lying at rest on a table.

4 A *book* at rest on a table but being pushed by a small horizontal force.

5 *Two books* lying on a table, one on top of the other.

6 A *horizontal plank* being used to bridge a stream.

7 A *snooker ball* on a table which can be assumed to be smooth
(a) as it lies at rest on the table
(b) at the instant it is hit by the cue.

8 An *ice hockey puck*
(a) at the instant it is hit when standing on smooth ice
(b) at the instant it is hit when standing on rough ice.

9 A *cricket ball* which follows the path shown here. Draw diagrams for each of the three positions A, B and C (include air resistance).

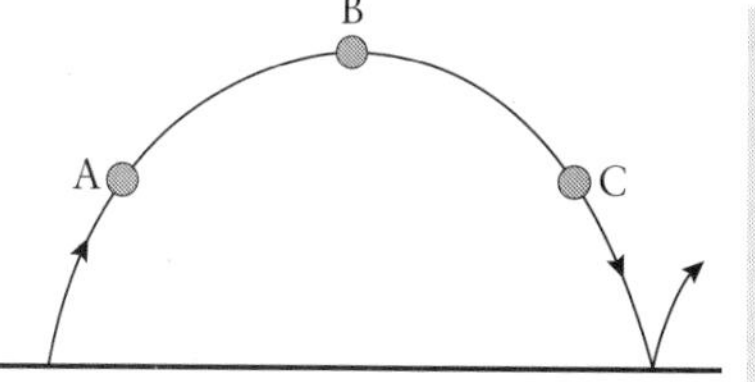

10 (a) *Two balls* colliding in mid-air. (b) *Two balls* colliding on a snooker table.

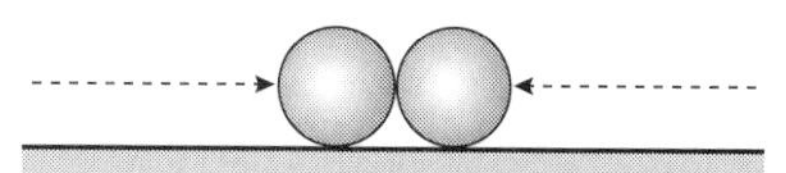

11 A *paving stone* leaning against a wall.

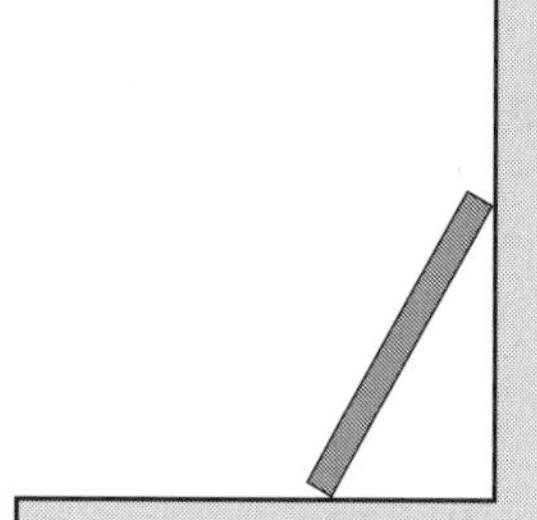

12 A *cylinder* at rest on smooth surfaces.

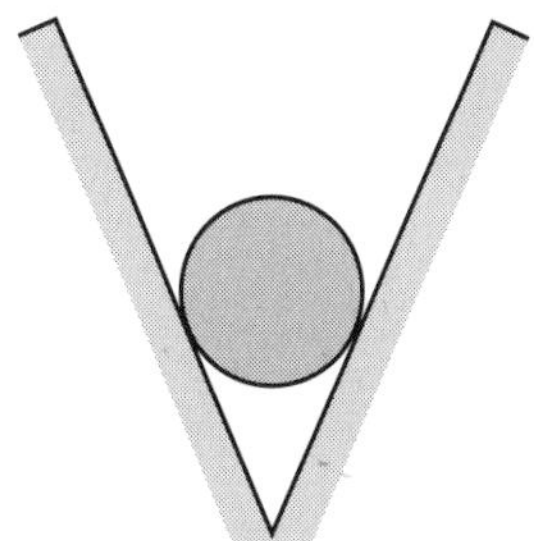

FORCE AND MOTION

How are the rails and handles provided in buses and trains used by standing passengers?

NEWTON'S FIRST LAW

Newton's *first law* can be stated as follows:

> Every particle continues in a state of rest or uniform motion in a straight line unless acted on by a resultant external force.

Newton's first law provides a reason for the handles on trains and buses. When you are on a train which is stationary or moving at constant speed in a straight line you can easily stand without support. But when the velocity of the train changes, a force is required to change your velocity to match. This happens when the train slows down or speeds up. It also happens when the train goes round a bend even if the speed does not change. The velocity changes because the direction changes.

Why is Josh's car in the pond?

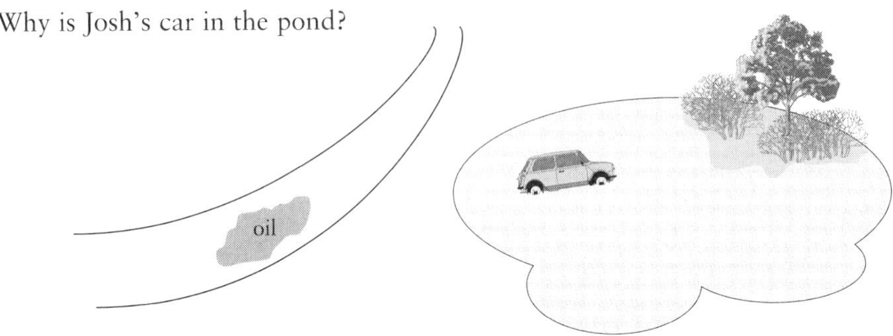

FIGURE 4.12

EXAMPLE 4.3

A 1p coin is balanced on your finger and then you move it upwards.

By considering Newton's first law, what can you say about W and R in these situations?

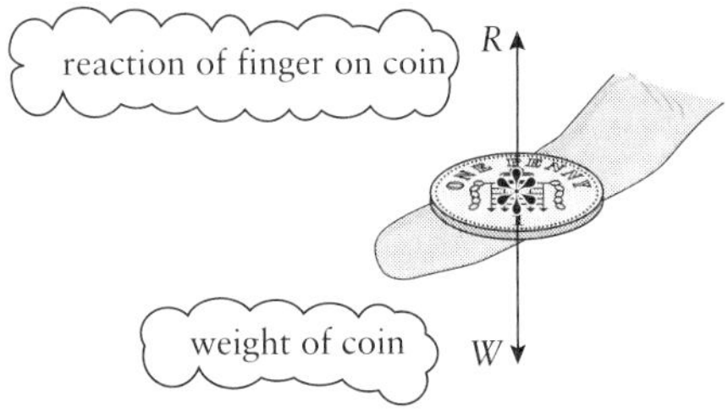

reaction of finger on coin

R

weight of coin

W

FIGURE 4.13

(a) The coin is stationary.
(b) The coin is moving upwards with a constant velocity.
(c) The speed of the coin is increasing as it moves upwards.
(d) The speed of the coin is decreasing as it moves upwards.

Solution

(a) When the coin is stationary the velocity does not change. The forces are in equilibrium and $R = W$.

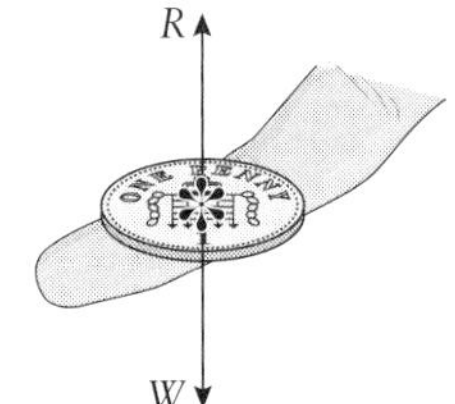

FIGURE 4.14

(b) When the coin is moving upwards with a constant velocity the velocity does not change. The forces are in equilibrium and $R = W$.

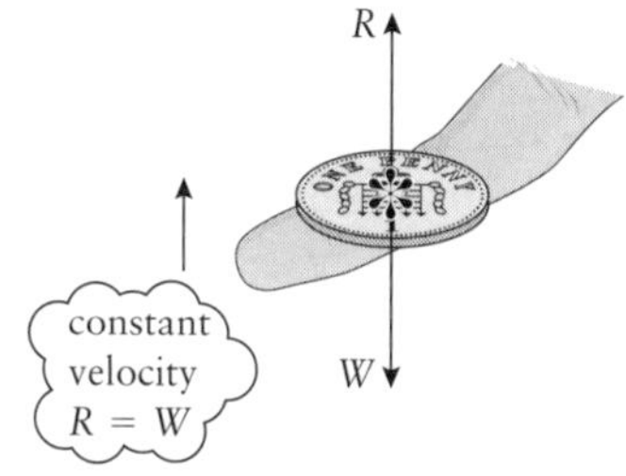

FIGURE 4.15

(c) When the speed of the coin is increasing as it moves upwards there must be a net upwards force to make the velocity increase in the upwards direction so $R > W$. The net force is $R - W$.

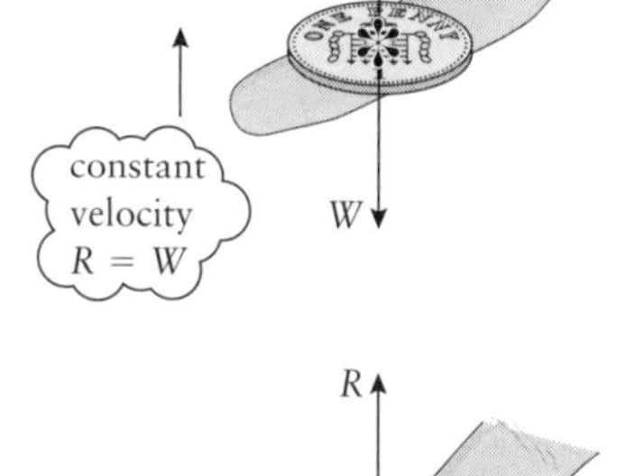

FIGURE 4.16

(d) When the speed of the coin is decreasing as it moves upwards there must be a net downwards force to make the velocity decrease and slow the coin down as it moves upwards. In this case $W > R$ and the net force is $W - R$.

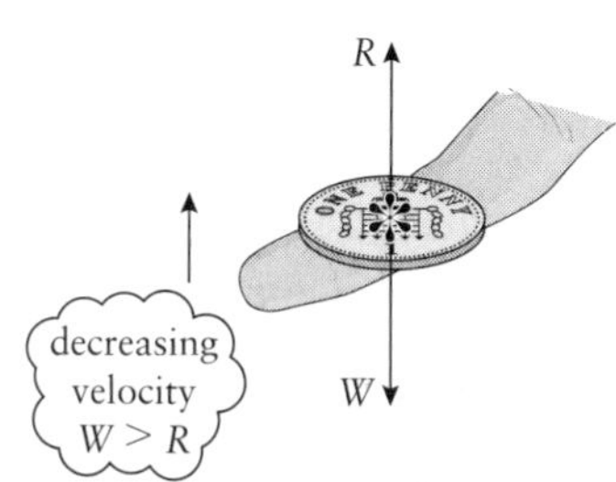

FIGURE 4.17

EXERCISE 4B

1 A book is resting on an otherwise empty table.

(a) Draw diagrams showing the forces acting on

(i) the book

(ii) the table as seen from the side.

(b) Write down equations connecting the forces acting on the book and on the table.

2 You balance a coin on your finger and move it up and down. The reaction of your finger on the coin is R and its weight is W. Decide in each case whether R is greater than, less than or equal to W and describe the net force.

(a) The coin is moving downwards with a constant velocity.

(b) The speed of the coin is increasing as it moves downwards.

(c) The speed of the coin is decreasing as it moves downwards.

3 In each of the following situations say whether the forces acting on the object are in equilibrium by deciding whether its motion is changing.

(a) A car that has been stationary, as it moves away from a set of traffic lights.

(b) A motorcycle as it travels at a steady 60 mph along a straight road.

(c) A parachutist descending at a constant rate.

(d) A box in the back of a lorry as the lorry picks up speed along a straight, level motorway.
(e) An ice hockey puck sliding across a smooth ice rink.
(f) A book resting on a table.
(g) An aircraft flying at a constant speed in a straight line, but losing height at a constant rate.
(h) A car going round a corner at constant speed.

4 Explain each of the following in terms of Newton's laws.
(a) Seat belts must be worn in cars.
(b) Head rests are necessary in a car to prevent neck injuries when there is a collision from the rear.

Driving forces and resistances to the motion of vehicles

In problems about such things as cycles, cars and trains, all the forces acting along the line of motion will usually be reduced to two or three: the *driving force* forwards, the *resistance* to motion (air resistance, etc.) and possibly a *braking force* backwards.

Resistances due to air or water always act in a direction opposite to the velocity of a vehicle or boat and are usually more significant for fast-moving objects.

Tension and thrust

The lines joining the crate of supplies to the parachute described at the beginning of this chapter are in tension. They pull upwards on the crate and downwards on the parachute. You are familiar with tensions in ropes and strings, but rigid objects can also be in tension.

When you hold the ends of a pencil, one with each hand, and pull your hands apart, you are pulling on the pencil. What is the pencil doing to each of your hands? Draw the forces acting on your hands and on the pencil.

Now draw the forces acting on your hands and on the pencil when you push the pencil inwards.

Your first diagram might look like figure 4.18. The pencil is in tension so there is an inward *tension* force on each hand.

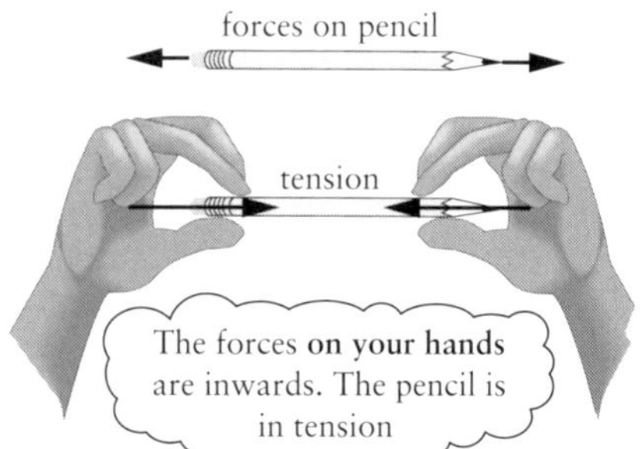
forces on pencil
tension
The forces **on your hands** are inwards. The pencil is in tension

Figure 4.18

When you push the pencil inwards the forces on your hands are outwards as in figure 4.19. The pencil is said to be *in compression* and the outward force on each hand is called a *thrust*.

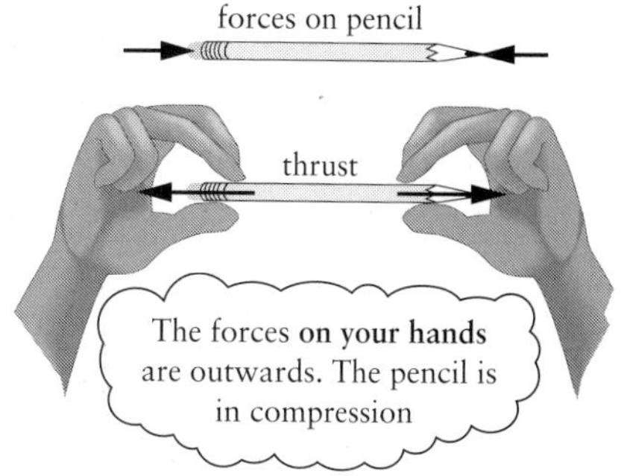
forces on pencil
thrust
The forces **on your hands** are outwards. The pencil is in compression

FIGURE 4.19

If each hand applies a force of 2 units on the pencil, the tension or thrust acting on each hand is also 2 units because each hand is in equilibrium.

A string or a rope can only be in tension; the forces acting on the objects attached to its ends are always away from the objects. A bar such as a tow bar for a car trailer can be in tension or compression.

RESULTANT FORCES AND EQUILIBRIUM

You have already met the idea that a single force can have the same effect as several forces acting together. Imagine that several people are pushing a car. A single rope pulled by another car can have the same effect. The force of the rope is equivalent to the resultant of the forces of the people pushing the car. When there is no resultant force, the forces are in equilibrium and there is no change in motion.

EXAMPLE 4.4

A car is using a tow bar to pull a trailer along a straight, level road. There are resisting forces R acting on the car and S acting on the trailer. The driving force of the car is D and its braking force is B.

Draw diagrams showing the horizontal forces acting on the car and the trailer

(a) when the car is moving at constant speed
(b) when the speed of the car is increasing
(c) when the car brakes and slows down rapidly.

In each case write down the resultant force acting on the car and on the trailer.

Solution

(a) When the car moves at constant speed, the forces are as shown in figure 4.20. The tow bar is in tension and the effect is a forward force on the trailer and an equal and opposite backward force on the car.

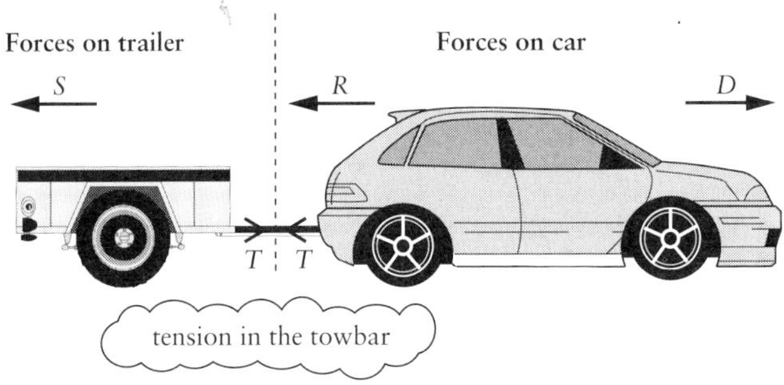

FIGURE 4.20 *Car travelling at constant speed*

There is no resultant force on either the car or the trailer when the speed is constant; the forces on each are in equilibrium.

For the trailer: $T - S = 0$

For the car: $D - R - T = 0$

(b) When the car speeds up, the same diagram will do, but now the magnitudes of the forces are different. There is a resultant *forward* force on both the car and the trailer.

For the trailer: resultant $= T - S$

For the car: resultant $= D - R - T$

(c) When the car brakes a resultant *backward* force is required to slow down the trailer. When the resistance S is not sufficiently large to do this, a thrust in the tow bar comes into play as shown in figure 4.21.

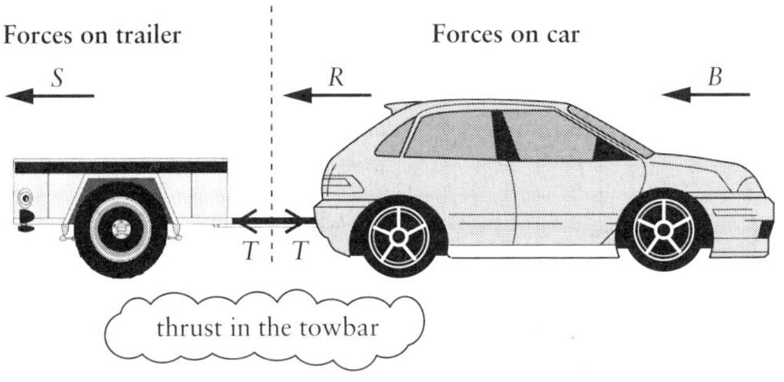

FIGURE 4.21 *Car braking*

For the trailer: resultant $= T + S$

For the car: resultant $= B + R - T$

NEWTON'S SECOND LAW

Newton's *second law* gives us more information about the relationship between the magnitude of the resultant force and the change in motion. Newton said that

The change in motion is proportional to the force.

For objects with constant mass, this can be interpreted as *the force is proportional to the acceleration.*

Resultant force = a constant × acceleration ①

The constant in this equation is proportional to the mass of the object: a more massive object needs a larger force to produce the same acceleration. For example, you and your friends would be able to give a car a greater acceleration than a lorry.

Newton's second law is so important that a special unit of force, the *newton (N)*, has been defined so that the constant in equation ① is actually equal to the mass. A force of 1 newton will give a mass of 1 kilogram an acceleration of $1\,\text{ms}^{-2}$. The equation then becomes:

Resultant force = mass × acceleration ②

This is written: $F = ma$

The resultant force and the acceleration are always in the same direction.

RELATING MASS AND WEIGHT

The *mass* of an object is related to the amount of matter in the object. It is a *scalar*. The *weight* of an object is a force. It has magnitude and direction and so is a *vector*.

The mass of an astronaut on the moon is the same as his mass on the earth but his weight is only about one-sixth of his weight on the earth. This is why he can bounce around more easily on the moon. The gravitational force on the moon is less because the mass of the moon is less than that of the earth.

When Buzz Aldrin made the first landing on the moon in 1969 with Neil Armstrong, one of the first things he did was to drop a feather and a hammer to demonstrate that they fell at the same rate. Their accelerations due to the gravitational force of the moon were equal, even though they had very different masses. The same is true on earth. If other forces were negligible all objects would fall with an acceleration g.

When the weight is the only force acting on an object, Newton's second law means that

$$\text{Weight in newtons} = \text{mass in kg} \times g \text{ in ms}^{-2}$$

Using standard letters: $W = mg$

Even when there are other forces acting, the weight can still be written as mg.

A good way to visualise a force of 1 N is to think of the weight of an apple. 1 kg of apples weighs (1×9.8) N, that is approximately 10 N. There are about 10 small to medium-sized apples in 1 kg, so each apple weighs about 1 N.

Note Anyone who says 1 kg of apples *weighs* 1 kg is not strictly correct. The terms weight and mass are often confused in everyday language but it is very important for your study of mechanics that you should understand the difference.

EXAMPLE 4.5

What is the weight of
(a) a baby of mass 3 kg?
(b) a golf ball, mass 46 g?

Solution
(a) The baby's weight is $3 \times 9.8 = 29.4$ N
(b) Mass of golf ball $= 46$ g
$= 0.046$ kg
Weight $= 0.046 \times 9.8$ N
$= 0.45$ N (to 2 sf)

EXERCISE 4C

Data for questions 1–6: On the earth $g = 9.8\,ms^{-2}$. On the moon $g = 1.6\,ms^{-2}$. 1000 newtons (N) = 1 kilonewton (kN).

1 Calculate the magnitude of the force of gravity on the following objects on the earth.
(a) A suitcase of mass 15 kg.
(b) A car of mass 1.2 tonnes. (1 tonne = 1000 kg)
(c) A letter of mass 50 g.

2 Find the mass of each of these objects on the earth.
  (a) A girl of weight 600 N.
  (b) A lorry of weight 11 kN.

3 A person has mass 65 kg. Calculate the force of gravity
  (a) of the earth on the person
  (b) of the person on the earth.

4 What reaction force would an astronaut of mass 70 kg experience while standing on the moon?

5 Two balls of the same shape and size but with masses 1 kg and 3 kg are dropped from the same height.
  (a) Which hits the ground first?
  (b) If they were dropped on the moon what difference would there be?

6 (a) Estimate your mass in kilograms.
  (b) Calculate your weight when you are on the earth's surface.
  (c) What would your weight be if you were on the moon?
  (d) When people say that a baby weighs 4 kg, what do they mean?

In this exercise you are asked to draw force diagrams using the various types of force you have met in this chapter. Remember that all the forces you need, other than weight, occur when objects are in contact or joined together in some way. Where motion is involved, indicate its direction clearly.

7 Draw labelled diagrams showing the forces acting on the objects in *italics*.
  (a) *A car* towing a caravan.
  (b) *A caravan* being towed by a car.
  (c) *A person* pushing a supermarket trolley.
  (d) *A suitcase* on a horizontal moving pavement (as at an airport)
    (i) immediately after it has been put down
    (ii) when it is moving at the same speed as the pavement.
  (e) *A sledge* being pulled uphill.

8 Ten boxes each of mass 5 kg are stacked on top of each other on the floor.
  (a) What forces act on the top box?
  (b) What forces act on the bottom box?

9 The diagrams show a box of mass m under different systems of forces.
  (a) In the first case the box is at rest. State the value of F_1.
  (b) In the second case the box is slipping. Write down the resultant horizontal force acting on it.

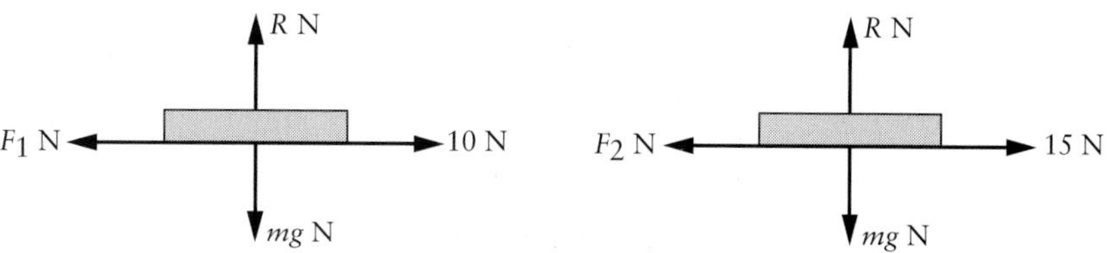

10 In this diagram the pulleys are smooth and light, the strings are light, and the table is rough.

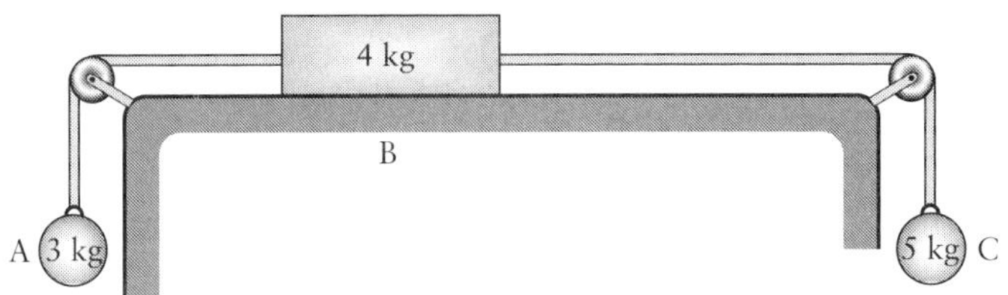

(a) What is the direction of the friction force on the block B?

(b) Draw clear diagrams to show the forces on each of A, B and C.

(c) By considering the equilibrium of A and C, calculate the tensions in the strings when there is no slipping.

(d) Calculate the magnitude of the friction when there is no slipping.

Now suppose that there is insufficient friction to stop the block from slipping.

(e) Write down the resultant force acting on each of A, B and C.

11 A man who weighs 720 N is doing some repairs to a shed. In each of these situations draw diagrams showing

(i) the forces the man exerts on the shed

(ii) all the forces acting on the man (ignore any tools he might be using).

In each case, compare the reaction between the man and the floor with his weight of 720 N.

720 N

(a) He is pushing upwards on the ceiling with force U N.

(b) He is pulling downwards on the ceiling with force D N.

(c) He is pulling upwards on a nail in the floor with force F N.

(d) He is pushing downwards on the floor with force T N.

12 The diagram shows a train, consisting of an engine of mass 50 000 kg pulling two trucks, A and B, each of mass 10 000 kg. The force of resistance on the engine is 2000 N and that on each of the trucks 200 N. The train is travelling at constant speed.

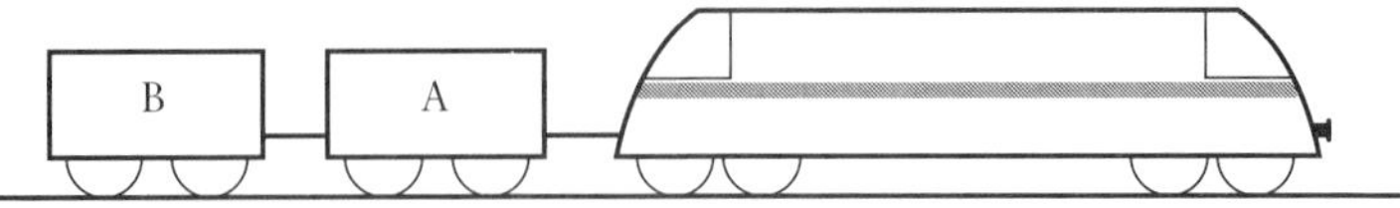

(a) Draw a diagram showing the horizontal forces on the train as a whole. Hence, by considering the equilibrium of the train as a whole, find the driving force provided by the engine.

The coupling connecting truck A to the engine exerts a force T_1 N on the engine and the coupling connecting truck B to truck A exerts a force T_2 N on truck B.

(b) Draw diagrams showing the horizontal forces on the engine and on truck B.

(c) By considering the equilibrium of the engine alone, find T_1.

(d) By considering the equilibrium of truck B alone, find T_2.

(e) Show that the forces on truck A are also in equilibrium.

Historical Note

Isaac Newton was born in Lincolnshire in 1642. He was not an outstanding scholar either as a schoolboy or as a university student, yet later in life he made remarkable contributions in dynamics, optics, astronomy, chemistry, music theory and theology. He became Member of Parliament for Cambridge University and later Warden of the Royal Mint. His tomb in Westminster Abbey reads 'Let mortals rejoice That there existed such and so great an Ornament to the Human Race'.

APPLYING NEWTON'S SECOND LAW

Attach a weight to a spring balance and move it up and down. What happens to the pointer on the balance?

What would you observe if you stood on some bathroom scales in a moving lift?

Hold a heavy book on your hand and move it up and down. What force do you feel on your hand?

Equation of motion

Suppose you make the book accelerate upwards at $a\,\text{ms}^{-2}$. Figure 4.22 shows the forces acting on the book and the acceleration.

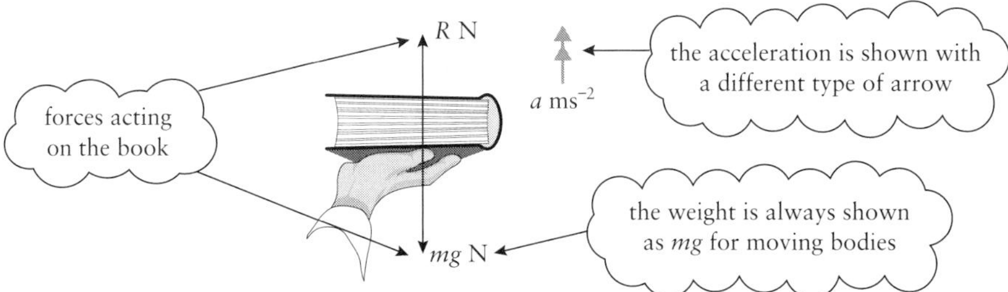

Figure 4.22

By Newton's first law, a resultant force is required to produce an acceleration. In this case the resultant upwards force is $R - mg$ newtons.

You were introduced to Newton's second law earlier in this chapter. When the forces are in newtons, the mass in kilograms and the acceleration in metres per second squared, this law is:

$$\text{Resultant force} = \text{mass} \times a$$

(Where force and acceleration are in the same direction)

So for the book:

$$R - mg = ma \qquad ①$$

When Newton's second law is applied, the resulting equation is called *the equation of motion*.

When you give a book of mass 0.8 kg an acceleration of $0.5\,\text{ms}^{-2}$ equation ① becomes

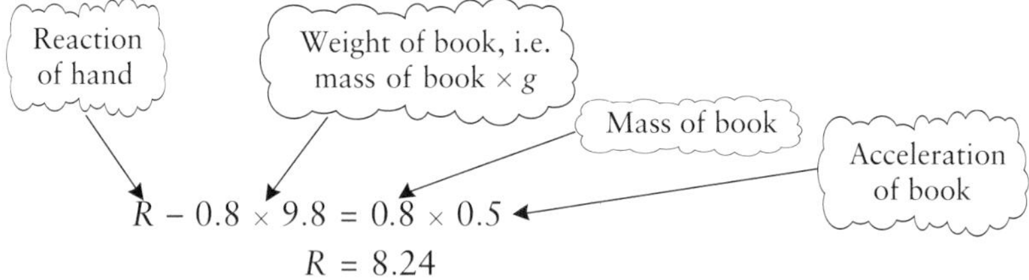

$$R - 0.8 \times 9.8 = 0.8 \times 0.5$$
$$R = 8.24$$

When the book is accelerating upwards the reaction force of your hand on the book is 8.24 N. This is equal and opposite to the force experienced by you so the book feels heavier than its actual weight, mg, which is $0.8 \times 9.8 = 7.84$ N.

Exercise 4D

1 Calculate the resultant force in newtons required to produce the following accelerations.

(a) A car of mass 800 kg has acceleration $2\,\text{ms}^{-2}$.

(b) A blue whale of mass 177 tonnes has acceleration $\frac{1}{2}\,\text{ms}^{-2}$.

(c) A pygmy mouse of mass 7.5 g has acceleration $3\,\text{ms}^{-2}$.

(d) A freight train of mass 4200 tonnes brakes with deceleration of $0.02\,\text{ms}^{-2}$.

(e) A bacterium of mass 2×10^{-16} g has acceleration $0.4\,\text{ms}^{-2}$.

(f) A woman of mass 56 kg falling off a high building has acceleration $9.8\ \text{ms}^{-2}$.
(g) A jumping flea of mass 0.05 mg accelerates at $1750\ \text{ms}^{-2}$ during take-off.
(h) A galaxy of mass 10^{42} kg has acceleration $10^{-12}\ \text{ms}^{-2}$.

2 A resultant force of 100 N is applied to a body. Calculate the mass of the body when its acceleration is

(a) $0.5\ \text{ms}^{-2}$
(b) $2\ \text{ms}^{-2}$
(c) $0.01\ \text{ms}^{-2}$
(d) $10g$.

3 What is the reaction between a book of mass 0.8 kg and your hand when it is

(a) accelerating downwards at $0.3\ \text{ms}^{-2}$?
(b) moving upwards at constant speed?

EXAMPLE 4.6

A lift and its passengers have a total mass of 400 kg. Find the tension in the cable supporting the lift when

(a) the lift is at rest
(b) the lift is moving at constant speed
(c) the lift is accelerating upwards at $0.8\ \text{ms}^{-2}$
(d) the lift is accelerating downwards at $0.6\ \text{ms}^{-2}$.

Solution Before starting the calculations you must define a direction as positive. In this example the upward direction is chosen to be positive.

(a) **At rest**

As the lift is at rest the forces must be in equilibrium. The equation of motion is

$$T - mg = 0$$
$$T - 400 \times 9.8 = 0$$
$$T = 3920$$

The tension in the cable is 3920 N.

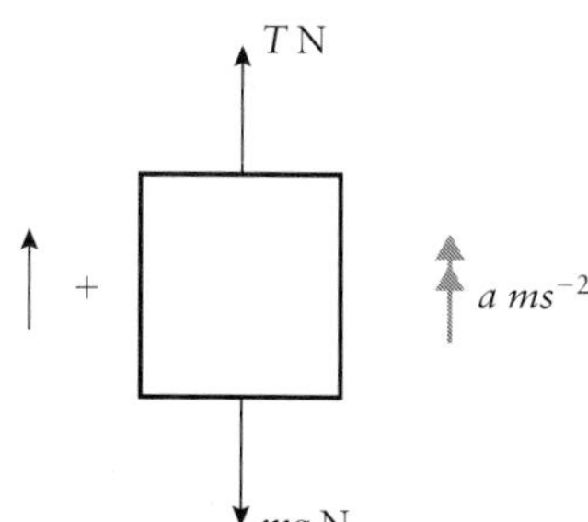

FIGURE 4.23

(b) **Moving at constant speed**

Again, the forces on the lift must be in equilibrium because it is moving at a constant speed, so the tension is 3920 N.

(c) **Accelerating upwards**

The resultant upward force on the lift is $T - mg$ so the equation of motion is

$$T - mg = ma$$

which in this case gives

$$T - 400 \times 9.8 = 400 \times 0.8$$
$$T - 3920 = 320$$
$$T = 4240$$

The tension in the cable is 4240 N.

(d) Accelerating downwards

The equation of motion is

$$T - mg = ma$$

In this case, a is negative so

$$T - 400 \times 9.8 = 400 \times (-0.6)$$
$$T - 3920 = -240$$
$$T = 3680$$

A downward acceleration of $0.6\,\text{ms}^{-2}$ is an upward acceleration of $-0.6\,\text{ms}^{-2}$

EXAMPLE 4.7

This example shows how the *uvast* equations for motion with constant acceleration, which you met in Chapter 3, can be used with Newton's second law.

A supertanker of mass 500 000 tonnes is travelling at a speed of $10\,\text{ms}^{-1}$ when its engines fail. It then takes half an hour for the supertanker to stop.

(a) Find the force of resistance, assuming it to be constant, acting on the supertanker.

When the engines have been repaired it takes the supertanker 10 minutes to return to its full speed of $10\,\text{ms}^{-1}$.

(b) Find the driving force produced by the engines, assuming this also to be constant.

Solution

Use the direction of motion as positive.

(a) First find the acceleration of the supertanker, which is constant for constant forces. Figure 4.24 shows the velocities and acceleration.

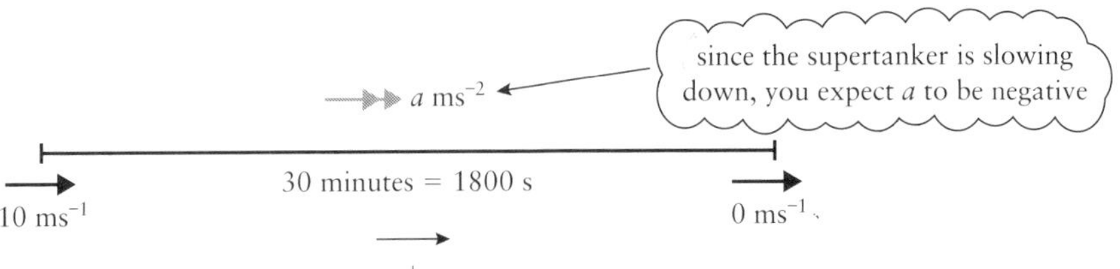
a ms⁻²
since the supertanker is slowing down, you expect a to be negative
30 minutes = 1800 s
10 ms⁻¹
0 ms⁻¹
+

FIGURE 4.24

You know $u = 10$, $v = 0$, $t = 1800$ and you want a, so use $v = u + at$.

$$0 = 10 + 1800a$$

$$a = -\frac{1}{180}$$

The acceleration is negative because the supertanker is slowing down

Now we can use Newton's second law (Newton II) to write down the equation of motion. Figure 4.25 shows the horizontal forces and the acceleration.

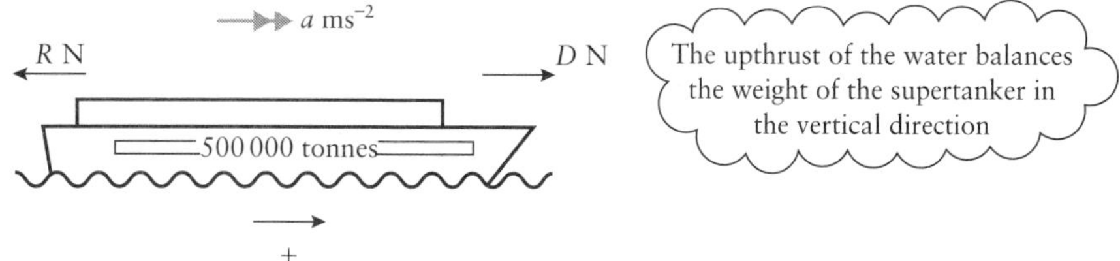
a ms⁻²
R N
D N
500 000 tonnes
+
The upthrust of the water balances the weight of the supertanker in the vertical direction

FIGURE 4.25

The resultant forwards force is $D - R$ newtons. When there is no driving force $D = 0$ so Newton II gives

The mass must be in kg

$$0 - R = 500\,000\,000 \times a$$

so when $a = -\frac{1}{180}$, $\quad -R = 500\,000\,000 \times \left(-\frac{1}{180}\right)$

The resistance to motion is 2.78×10^6 N or 2780 kN (correct to 3 sf).

You have to be very careful with signs here: the resultant force and acceleration are both positive towards the right.

(b) Now $u = 0$, $v = 10$ and $t = 600$, and we want a, so use $v = u + at$ again.

$$10 = 0 + a \times 600$$

$$a = \frac{1}{60}$$

Using Newton's second law again

$$D - R = 500\,000\,000 \times a$$

$$D - 2.78 \times 10^6 = 500\,000\,000 \times \frac{1}{60}$$

$$D = 2.78 \times 10^6 + 8.33 \times 10^6$$

The driving force is 11.11×10^6 N or 11 100 kN (correct to 3 sf).

TACKLING MECHANICS PROBLEMS

When you tackle mechanics problems such as these you will find them easier if you:

- always draw a clear diagram
- clearly indicate the positive direction
- label each object (A, B, etc. or whatever is appropriate)
- show all the forces acting on each object
- make it clear which object you are referring to when writing an equation of motion.

EXERCISE 4E

1 A man pushes a car of mass 400 kg on level ground with a force of 200 N. The car is initially at rest and the man maintains this force until the car reaches a speed of $5\,\mathrm{ms}^{-1}$. Ignoring any resistance forces, find

(a) the acceleration of the car

(b) the distance the car travels while the man is pushing.

2 The engine of a car of mass 1.2 tonnes can produce a driving force of 2000 N. Ignoring any resistance forces, find

(a) the car's resulting acceleration

(b) the time taken for the car to go from rest to $27\,\mathrm{ms}^{-1}$ (about 60 mph).

3 A top sprinter of mass 65 kg starting from rest reaches a speed of $10\,\mathrm{ms}^{-1}$ in 2 s.

(a) Calculate the force required to produce this acceleration, assuming it is uniform.

(b) Compare this to the force exerted by a weight lifter holding a mass of 180 kg above the ground.

4 An ice skater of mass 65 kg is initially moving with speed $2\,\mathrm{ms}^{-1}$ and glides to a halt over a distance of 10 m. Assuming that the force of resistance is constant, find

(a) the size of the resistance force

(b) the distance he would travel gliding to rest from an initial speed of $6\,\mathrm{ms}^{-1}$

(c) the force he would need to apply to maintain a steady speed of $10\,\mathrm{ms}^{-1}$.

5 A helicopter of mass 1000 kg is taking off vertically.

(a) Draw a labelled diagram showing the forces on the helicopter as it lifts off and the direction of its acceleration.

(b) Its initial upward acceleration is $1.5\,\mathrm{ms}^{-2}$. Calculate the upward force its rotors exert. Ignore the effects of air resistance.

6 Pat and Nicholas are controlling the movement of a canal narrow boat by means of long ropes attached to each end. The tension in the ropes may be assumed to be horizontal and parallel to the line and direction of motion of the boat, as shown in the diagrams.

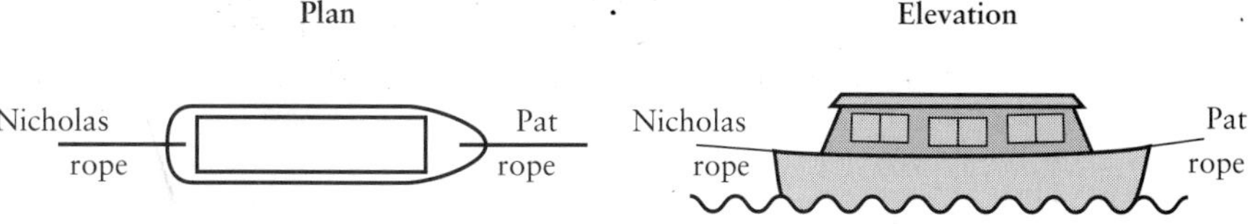

The mass of the boat is 12 tonnes and the total resistance to forward motion may be taken to be 250 N at all times. Initially Pat pulls the boat forwards from rest with a force of 400 N and Nicholas leaves his rope slack.

(a) Write down the equation of motion for the boat and hence calculate its acceleration.

Pat continues to pull with the same force until the boat has moved 10 m.

(b) What is the speed of the boat at this time and for what length of time did Pat pull?

Pat now lets her rope go slack and Nicholas brings the boat to rest by pulling with a constant force of 150 N.

(c) Calculate

(i) how long it takes the boat to come to rest

(ii) the total distance travelled by the boat from when it first moved

(iii) the total time taken for the motion.

[MEI, adapted]

7 A spaceship of mass 5000 kg is stationary in deep space. It fires its engines, producing a forward thrust of 2000 N for 2.5 minutes, and then turns them off.

(a) What is the speed of the spaceship at the end of the 2.5 minute period?

(b) Describe the subsequent motion of the spaceship.

The spaceship then enters a cloud of interstellar dust which brings it to a halt after a further distance of 7200 km.

(c) What is the force of resistance (assumed constant) on the spaceship from the interstellar dust cloud?

The spaceship is travelling in convoy with another spaceship which is the same in all respects except that it is carrying an extra 500 kg of equipment. The second spaceship carries out exactly the same procedure as the first one.

(d) Which spaceship travels further into the dust cloud?

8 A crane is used to lift a hopper full of cement to a height of 20 m on a building site. The hopper has mass 200 kg and the cement 500 kg. Initially the hopper accelerates upwards at 0.05 $\mathrm{ms^{-2}}$, then it travels at constant speed for some time before decelerating at 0.1 $\mathrm{ms^{-2}}$ until it is at rest. The hopper is then emptied.

(a) Find the tension in the crane's cable during each of the three phases of the motion and after emptying.

The cable's maximum safe load is 10 000 N.

(b) What is the greatest mass of cement that can safely be transported in the same manner?

The cable is in fact faulty and on a later occasion breaks without the hopper leaving the ground. On that occasion the hopper is loaded with 720 kg of cement.

(c) What can you say about the strength of the cable?

9 The police estimate that for good road conditions the frictional force, F, on a skidding vehicle of mass m is given by $F = 0.8\,mg$. A car of mass 450 kg skids to a halt, narrowly missing a child. The police measure the skid marks and find they are 12.0 m long.

(a) Calculate the deceleration of the car when it was skidding to a halt.

The child's mother says the car was travelling well over the speed limit but the driver of the car says she was travelling at 30 mph and the child ran out in front of her. (There are about 1600 m in a mile.)

(b) Calculate the speed of the car when it started to skid.

(c) Who was telling the truth?

NEWTON'S SECOND LAW IN TWO DIMENSIONS

When the forces acting on an object are not in equilibrium it will have an acceleration and you can use Newton's second law to solve problems about its motion.

The equation $\mathbf{F} = m\,\mathbf{a}$ is a vector equation. The resultant force acting on a particle is equal in both magnitude and direction to the mass × acceleration. It can be written in components as

$$F_1\,\mathbf{i} + F_2\,\mathbf{j} = m\,(a_1\,\mathbf{i} + a_2\,\mathbf{j})$$

so that $F_1 = ma_1$ and $F_2 = ma_2$.

EXAMPLE 4.8

A car of mass 1000 kg, including its driver, is being pushed along a horizontal road by three people as indicated in the diagram. The car is moving in the direction PQ.

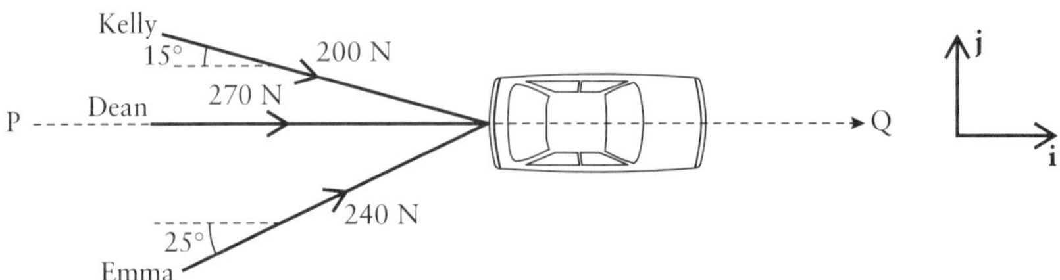

FIGURE 4.26

Take unit vectors **i** and **j** as shown in the diagram.

(a) Calculate the total force exerted by the three people.
(b) Explain briefly why the car does not move in the **j** direction.

Initially the car is stationary and 5 s later it has a speed of $2\,\text{ms}^{-1}$ in the **i** direction.

(c) Calculate the force of resistance to the car's movement in the direction PQ assuming the three people continue to push as described above.

[MEI, part]

Solution

(a) The forces in component form in newtons are:

Kelly	$200\cos 15°\mathbf{i} - 200\sin 15°\mathbf{j}$
	$= 193\mathbf{i} - 51.8\mathbf{j}$
Dean	$270\mathbf{i}$
Emma	$240\cos 25°\mathbf{i} + 240\sin 25°\mathbf{j}$
	$= 218\mathbf{i} + 101.4\mathbf{j}$

Total force $= 681\mathbf{i} + 49.6\mathbf{j}$ N

Total force in the direction perpendicular to PQ = 49.6 N.

(b) The car does not move in the **j** direction because the force in this direction is balanced by a sideways (lateral) friction force between the tyres and the road.

(c) Given $u = 0$, $v = 2$ and $t = 5$ use $v = u + at$ to find the acceleration, $a\,\text{ms}^{-2}$, of the car.

$$2 = 0 + 5a$$
$$a = 0.4$$

Suppose the resistance to motion is R N.
The diagram shows all the horizontal forces acting on the car and its acceleration.

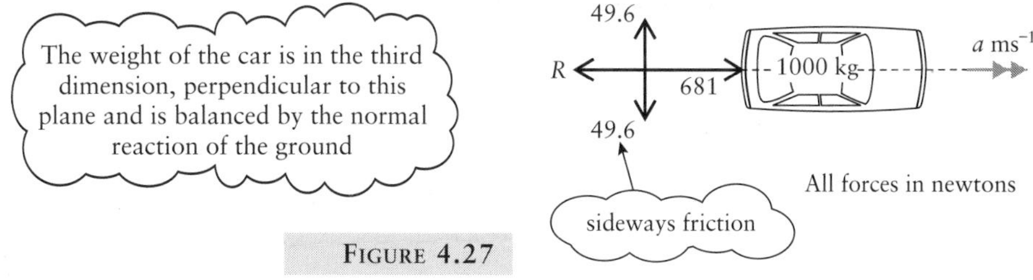
The weight of the car is in the third dimension, perpendicular to this plane and is balanced by the normal reaction of the ground
49.6
R
681
49.6
1000 kg
a ms⁻¹
sideways friction
All forces in newtons

FIGURE 4.27

The resultant force in the **i** direction is $(681 - R)$ N. So by Newton II

$$681 - R = 1000a$$
$$R = 681 - 400$$

The resistance to motion is $-281\mathbf{i}$ N.

EXERCISE 4F

1 The forces $\mathbf{F}_1 = 4\mathbf{i} - 5\mathbf{j}$ and $\mathbf{F}_2 = 2\mathbf{i} + \mathbf{j}$, in newtons, act on a particle of mass 4 kg.

(a) Find the acceleration of the particle in component form.

(b) Find the magnitude of the particle's acceleration.

2 Two forces $\mathbf{P}_1$ and $\mathbf{P}_2$ act on a particle of mass 2 kg giving it an acceleration of $5\mathbf{i} + 5\mathbf{j}$ (in ms^{-2}).

(a) If $\mathbf{P}_1 = 6\mathbf{i} - \mathbf{j}$ (in newtons), find $\mathbf{P}_2$.

(b) If instead $\mathbf{P}_1$ and $\mathbf{P}_2$ both act in the same direction but $\mathbf{P}_1$ is four times as big as $\mathbf{P}_2$, find both forces.

3 The diagram shows a girl pulling a sledge at steady speed across level snow-covered ground using a rope which makes an angle of 30° to the horizontal. The mass of the sledge is 8 kg and there is a resistance force of 10 N.

(a) Draw a diagram showing the forces acting on the sledge.

(b) Find the magnitude of the tension in the rope.

The girl comes to an area of ice where the resistance force on the sledge is only 2 N. She continues to pull the sledge with the same force as before and with the rope still taut at 30°.

(c) What acceleration must the girl have in order to do this?

(d) How long will it take to double her initial speed of $0.4\,\mathrm{ms}^{-1}$?

4 The picture shows a situation which has arisen between two anglers, Davies and Jones, standing at the ends of adjacent jetties. Their lines have become entangled under the water with the result that they have both hooked the same fish, which has mass 1.9 kg. Both are reeling in their lines as hard as they can in order to claim the fish.

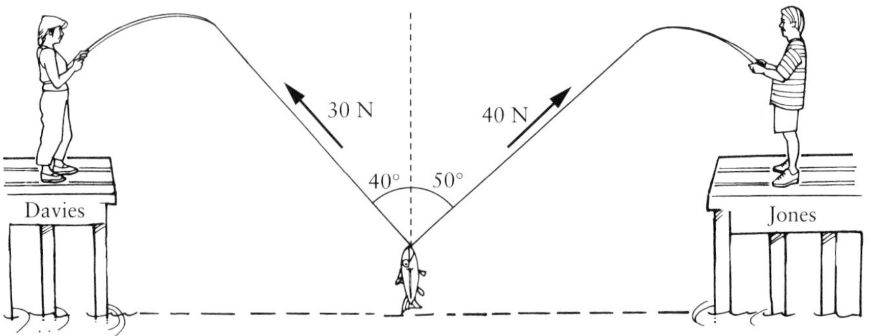

(a) Draw a diagram showing the forces acting on the fish.
(b) Resolve the tensions in both anglers' lines into horizontal and vertical components and so find the total force acting on the fish.
(c) Find the magnitude and direction of the acceleration of the fish.
(d) At this point Davies' line breaks. What happens to the fish?

5 A crate of mass 30 kg is being pulled up a smooth slope inclined at 30° to the horizontal by a rope which is parallel to the slope. The crate has acceleration $0.75\,\text{ms}^{-2}$.
(a) Draw a diagram showing the forces acting on the crate and the direction of its acceleration.
(b) Resolve the forces in directions parallel and perpendicular to the slope.
(c) Find the tension in the rope.
(d) The rope suddenly snaps. What happens to the crate?

6 Railway trucks in coal mines were sometimes pulled by men. One such truck is standing on a straight, horizontal section of track. The man pulls on a light inextensible rope AB. The rope is horizontal and at an angle θ to the direction of the track. The man walks parallel to the track.

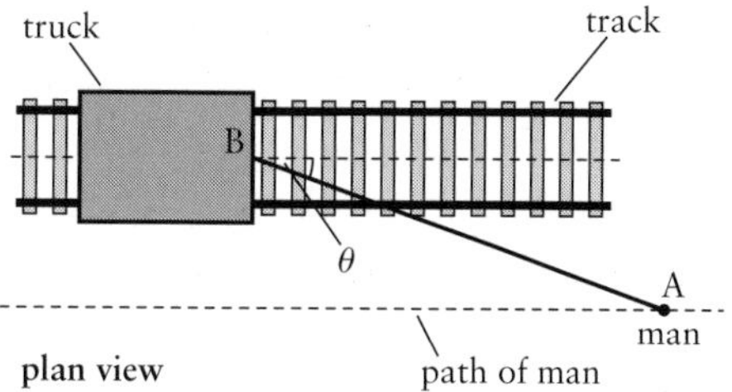

Initially the magnitude of the tension in the rope is 100 N and $\theta = 10°$. This tension in the rope is not enough to move the truck from rest.
(c) Calculate the components of the tension in the rope parallel and perpendicular to the track.
(b) What force prevents the truck from moving perpendicular to the track?
(c) What is the magnitude of the resistance to the forward motion of the truck?

The man now pulls harder to move the truck. The truck moves from rest against a resistance to its forward motion of $(100 + 44\sin\theta)$ N at all times. There is a constant tension in the rope and θ has the constant value of 10°. It takes the man 15 s to reach his normal walking speed of $1.5\,\text{ms}^{-1}$.

(d) Explain briefly why the acceleration of the truck is constant.
With what force must the man pull on the rope to maintain the speed of $1.5\,\text{ms}^{-1}$? How far does the man walk before he reaches his normal walking speed?
(e) In order to avoid an obstacle, the man follows a path in which θ is increased. Assuming that the force in the rope does not change, what effect does this have on the motion of the truck?

[MEI]

EXERCISE 4G

Examination-style questions

1 Find the force needed to accelerate a 400 tonne train from rest to $20\,\text{ms}^{-1}$ in a time of 45 s.

2 A man of mass 65 kg is in a lift. His weight appears to be 75 kg. Find the acceleration of the lift. Can you say whether the lift is ascending or descending?

3 **(a)** At a particular moment of his descent, a freefaller of mass 65 kg is experiencing an air resistance of 500 N. Find his acceleration.

(b) On opening the parachute, he experiences a further upward force of 800 N. Find his new acceleration.

4 In this question, take all motion to be vertical. At take-off, a Saturn V rocket develops a thrust equal to the weight of a mass of 3400 tonnes. It contains 2545 tonnes of propellant. An observer estimates the initial acceleration as $\frac{1}{3}g$.

(a) Find the mass of the rocket (including propellant) at take-off.

Another observer estimates that the initial acceleration is $\frac{1}{4}g$.

(b) Assuming that the second observer is correct, find the mass of the empty first stage plus second and subsequent stages.

(c) Just before the propellant is exhausted, the thrust is unaltered but the rocket has an upward acceleration of $10g$. Find a new estimate for the initial acceleration.

5 A particle of mass 4 kg starts from rest and is acted upon by a force of $8\mathbf{i} - 2\mathbf{j}$ N.

(a) Find its acceleration.

(b) Find its velocity 3 s after the start.

6 An ice skater of mass 60 kg is moving with velocity $4\mathbf{i} + 3\mathbf{j}\,\text{ms}^{-1}$. 2 s later the skater's velocity is $-2\mathbf{i} + 7\mathbf{j}\,\text{ms}^{-1}$. Find the force acting on the skater, assuming it to be constant.

7 During a gust of wind, a sailing dinghy of mass 200 kg (including the occupants) experiences a driving force of $800\mathbf{i} - 1000\mathbf{j}$ N. Its resistance to motion is $-200\mathbf{i} + 900\mathbf{j}$ N.

(a) Find the acceleration of the dinghy.

Before the gust, the dinghy had a velocity of $2\mathbf{i}\,\text{ms}^{-1}$. The gust lasts for 3 s.

(b) Find the velocity of the dinghy at the end of the gust.

8 Two children are pulling a toboggan of mass 25 kg with forces of $15\mathbf{i} + 10\mathbf{j}$ N and $10\mathbf{i} - 5\mathbf{j}$ N.

(a) Find the initial acceleration of the toboggan.

When the toboggan has started to move, it experiences a resistance force of $-10\mathbf{i} - 5\mathbf{j}$ N.

(b) Find the new acceleration of the toboggan.

9 In this question, take unit vectors **i** horizontally and **j** vertically. During a trampoline session, Laura, of mass 30 kg, experiences a force of 12**i** + 600**j** N, exerted by the trampoline, in addition to her weight for a time of 2 s.

(a) Find her acceleration during this time, giving your answer in vector form.

As she approaches the trampoline her velocity is –**i** – 9**j** ms^{-1}.

(b) Find the velocity with which she leaves the trampoline.

10 A particle of mass 10 kg is being dragged up a rough plane which is at an angle of 20° to the horizontal by a light string which is at an angle of 30° to the plane. The friction force has value 20 N, and the particle has an acceleration of 2 ms^{-2}. Find the tension in the string.

11 A particle P of mass 1.5 kg is moving under the action of a constant force (3**i** – 7.5**j**) N. Initially P has velocity (2**i** + 3**j**) ms^{-1}. Find

(a) the magnitude of the acceleration of P

(b) the velocity of P, in terms of **i** and **j**, when P has been moving for 4 seconds.

[Edexcel]

12 A particle P of mass 2 kg moves in a plane under the action of a single constant force **F** newtons. At time t seconds, the velocity of P is **v** ms^{-1}. When t = 0, **v** = (– 5**i** + 7**j**) and when t = 3, **v** = (**i** – 2**j**).

(a) Find in degrees the angle between the direction of motion of P when t = 3 and the vector **j**.

(b) Find the acceleration of P.

(c) Find the magnitude of **F**.

(d) Find in terms of t the velocity of P.

(e) Find the time at which P is moving parallel to the vector **i** + **j**.

[Edexcel]

KEY POINTS

Newton's laws of motion

1 Every object remains stationary or in uniform motion in a straight line unless it is made to change that state by a resultant external force.

2 Resultant force = mass × acceleration or **F** = m**a**

3 When one object exerts a force on another there is always a reaction which is equal to and opposite in direction to the acting force.

Force is a vector, **mass** is a scalar.

The **weight** of an object is the force of gravity pulling it towards the centre of the earth. Weight = mg vertically downwards.

Types of force include gravity, normal contact force, friction, tension and thrust, air resistance and buoyancy.

Chapter five

CONNECTED PARTICLES

Then the Elephant's Child sat back on his little haunches, and pulled, and pulled, and pulled, and his nose began to stretch.

Rudyard Kipling, The Elephant's Child

This chapter is about using Newton's second law for more than one object. It is important to be very clear which forces act on which object in these cases.

A stationary helicopter is raising two people of masses 90 kg and 70 kg as shown in figure 5.1.

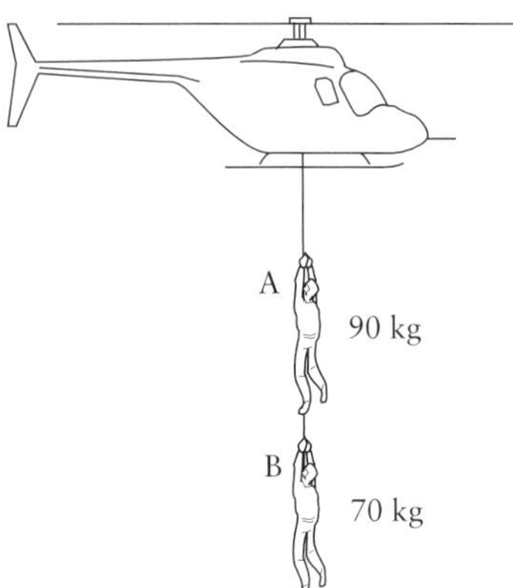

FIGURE 5.1

Imagine that you are each person in turn. Your eyes are shut so you cannot see the helicopter or the other person. What forces act on you?

Remember that all the forces acting, apart from your weight, are due to contact between you and something else.

Which forces acting on A and B are equal in magnitude? What can you say about their accelerations?

EXAMPLE 5.1

(a) Draw a diagram to show the forces acting on the two people being raised by the helicopter in figure 5.1 and their acceleration.

(b) Write down the equation of motion for each person.

(c) When the force applied to the first person, A, by the helicopter is $180g$ N, calculate

(i) the acceleration of the two people being raised

(ii) the tension in the ropes.

Use $10\,\text{ms}^{-2}$ for g.

Solution

(a) Figure 5.2 shows the acceleration and forces acting on the two people.

(b) When the helicopter applies a force T_1 N to A, the resultant upward forces are

A $\quad T_1 - 90g - T_2$

B $\quad T_2 - 70g$

Their equations of motion are

A (↑) $\quad T_1 - 90g - T_2 = 90a \quad$ ①

B (↑) $\quad T_2 - 70g = 70a \quad$ ②

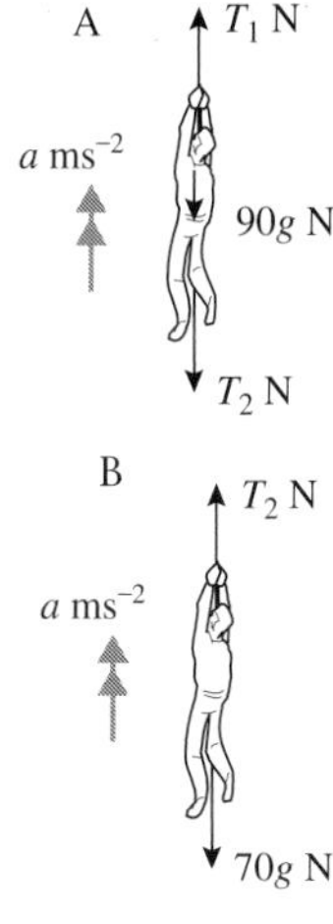

FIGURE 5.2

(c) You can eliminate T_2 from equations ① and ② by adding:

$$T_1 - 90g - T_2 + T_2 - 70g = 160a$$

$$T_1 - 160g = 160a \quad ③$$

When the force applied by the helicopter is $T_1 = 180g$

$$20g = 160a$$

$$a = 1.25$$

Substituting for a in equation ② gives $\quad T_2 = 70 \times 1.25 + 70g$

$$= 787.5$$

The acceleration is 1.25 ms^{-2} and the tensions in the ropes are 1800 N and 787.5 N.

A NOTE ON MATHEMATICAL MODELLING

Several modelling assumptions have been made in the solution to Example 5.1. It is assumed that:

- The only forces acting on the people are their weights and the tensions in the ropes. Forces due to the wind or air turbulence are ignored.
- The motion is vertical and nobody swings from side to side.
- The ropes do not stretch (i.e. they are inextensible) so the accelerations of the two people are equal.
- The people are rigid bodies which do not change shape and can be treated as particles.

All these modelling assumptions make the problem simpler. In reality, if you were trying to solve such a problem you might work through it first using these assumptions. You would then go back and decide which ones needed to be modified to produce a more realistic solution.

In the next example one person is moving vertically and the other horizontally. You might find it easier to decide on which forces are acting if you imagine you are Alvin or Bernard and you can't see the other person.

EXAMPLE 5.2

Alvin is using a snowmobile to pull Bernard out of a crevasse. His rope passes over a smooth block of ice at the top of the crevasse as shown in figure 5.3 and Bernard hangs freely away from the side. Alvin and his snowmobile together have a mass of 300 kg and Bernard's mass is 75 kg. Ignore any resistance to motion.

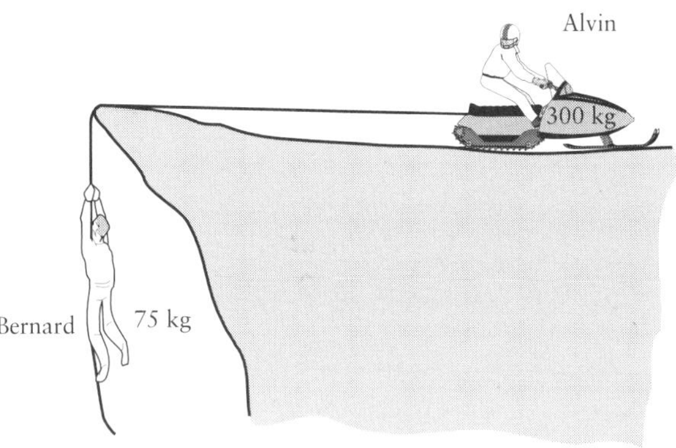

FIGURE 5.3

(a) Draw diagrams showing the forces on the snowmobile (including Alvin) and on Bernard.

(b) Calculate the driving force required for the snowmobile to give Bernard an upward acceleration of $0.5\,\mathrm{ms}^{-2}$ and the tension in the rope for this acceleration.

(c) How long will it take for Bernard's speed to reach $5\,\mathrm{ms}^{-1}$ starting from rest and how far will he have been raised in this time?

Solution

(a) Figure 5.4 shows the essential features of the problem.

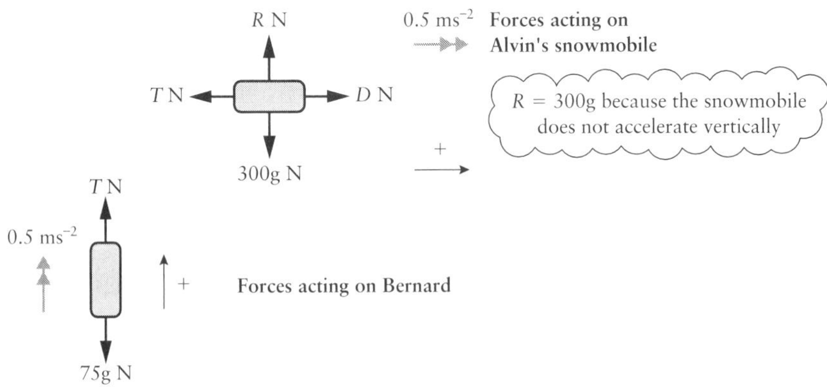

FIGURE 5.4

(b) Alvin and Bernard have the same acceleration providing the rope does not stretch. The tension in the rope is T newtons and Alvin's driving force is D newtons.

The equations of motion are:

Alvin (→) $\quad D - T = 300 \times 0.5$

$D - T = 150 \quad ①$

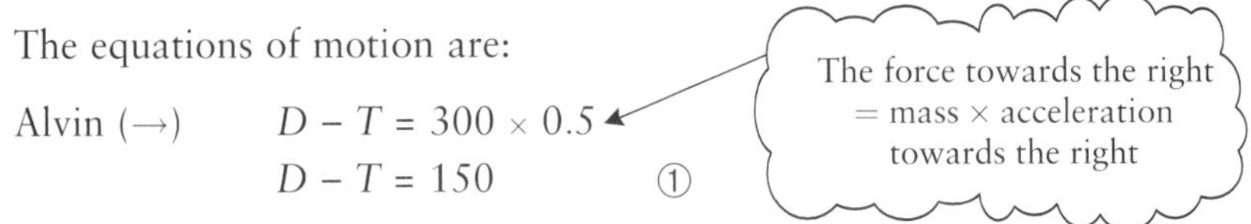

Bernard (↑) $T - 75g = 75 \times 0.5$

$T - 75g = 37.5$ ②

$T = 37.5 + 75g$

$T = 772.5$

The upwards force = mass × upwards acceleration

Substituting in equation ①

$$D - 772.5 = 150$$
$$D = 922.5$$

The driving force required is 922.5 N and the tension in the rope is 772.5 N.

(c) When $u = 0$, $v = 5$, $a = 0.5$ and t is required.

$$v = u + at$$
$$5 = 0 + 0.5 \times t$$
$$t = 10$$

The time taken is 10 seconds.

Then using $s = ut + \frac{1}{2}at^2$ to find s gives

$$s = 0 + \tfrac{1}{2}at^2$$
$$s = \tfrac{1}{2} \times 0.5 \times 100$$
$$s = 25$$

$v^2 = u^2 + 2as$ would also give s

EXAMPLE 5.3

A woman of mass 60 kg is standing in a lift.

(a) Draw a diagram showing the forces acting on the woman.

Find the normal reaction of the floor of the lift on the woman in the following cases.

(b) The lift is moving upwards at a constant speed of $3\,\text{ms}^{-1}$.
(c) The lift is moving upwards with an acceleration of $2\,\text{ms}^{-2}$ upwards.
(d) The lift is moving downwards with an acceleration of $2\,\text{ms}^{-2}$ downwards.
(e) The lift is moving downwards and slowing down with a deceleration of $2\,\text{ms}^{-2}$.

In order to calculate the maximum number of occupants that can safely be carried in the lift, the following assumptions are made:

The lift has mass 300 kg, all resistances to motion may be neglected, the mass of each occupant is 75 kg and the tension in the supporting cable should not exceed 12 000 N.

(f) What is the greatest number of occupants that can be carried safely if the magnitude of the acceleration does not exceed $3\,\text{ms}^{-2}$?

[MEI]

Solution **(a)** The diagram shows the forces acting on the woman and her acceleration.

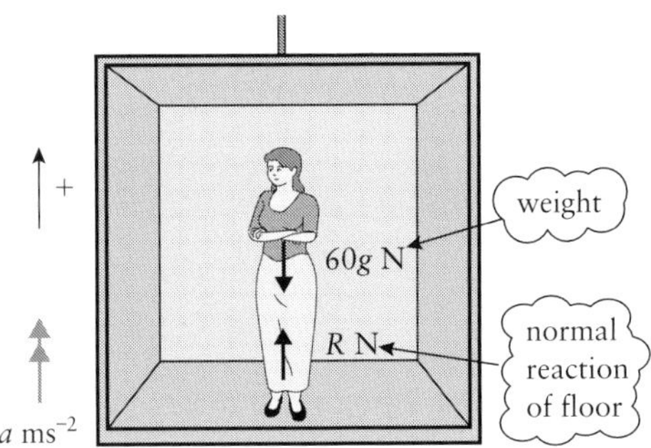

FIGURE 5.5

In general, when positive is upwards, her equation of motion is

(↑) $R - 60g = 60a$

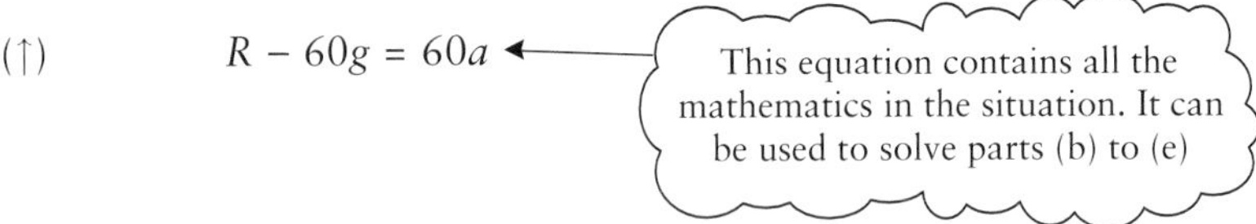

(b) When the speed is constant $a = 0$ so $R = 60g = 588$. ← $g = 9.8\ \text{ms}^{-2}$
The normal reaction is 588 N.

(c) When $a = 2$

$$R - 60g = 60 \times 2$$
$$R = 120 + 588$$
$$= 708$$

The normal reaction is 708 N.

(d) When the acceleration is downwards, $a = -2$ so

$$R - 60g = 60 \times (-2)$$
$$R = 468$$

The normal reaction is 468 N.

(e) When the lift is moving downwards and slowing down, the acceleration is negative downwards, so it is positive upwards, and $a = +2$. Then $R = 708$ as in part (c).

(f) When there are n passengers in the lift, the combined mass of these and the lift is $(300 + 75n)$ kg and their weight is $(300 + 75n)g$ N.

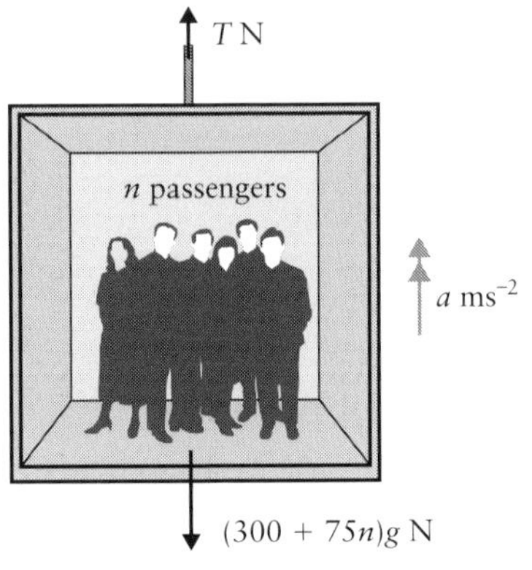

FIGURE 5.6

The equation of motion for the lift and passengers together is

$$T - (300 + 75n)g = (300 + 75n)\,a$$

So when $a = 3$ and $g = 9.8$, $T = (300 + 75n) \times 3 + (300 + 75n) \times 9.8$

$$= 12.8\,(300 + 75n)$$

For a maximum tension of 12 000 N,

$$12\,000 = 12.8\,(300 + 75n)$$
$$937.5 = 300 + 75n$$
$$637.5 = 75n$$
$$n = 8.5$$

The lift cannot carry more than 8 passengers.

PULLEYS

A pulley can be used to change the direction of a force; for example it is much easier to pull down on a rope than to lift a heavy weight. When a pulley is well designed it takes a relatively small force to make it turn and such a pulley is modelled as being *smooth and light*. Whatever the direction of the string passing over this pulley, its tension is the same on both sides.

Figure 5.7 shows the forces acting when a pulley is used to lift a heavy parcel.

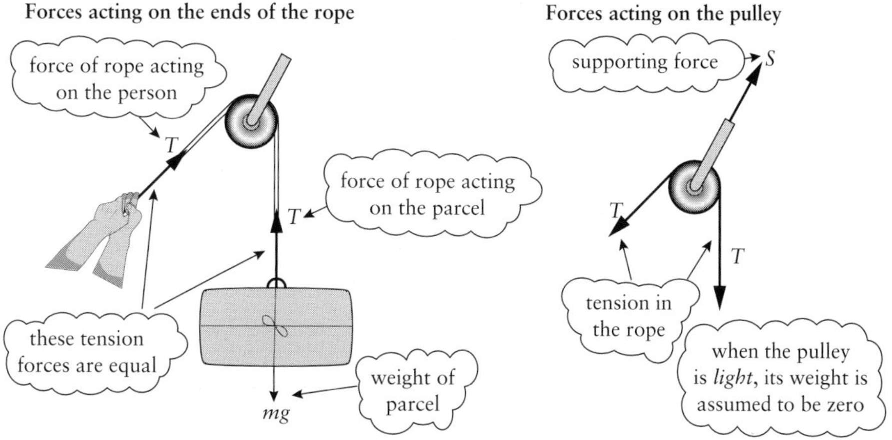

FIGURE 5.7

Note that the rope is in tension. It is not possible for a rope to exert a thrust force.

EXAMPLE 5.4

In this diagram the pulley is smooth and light and the 2 kg block, A, is on a rough surface.

(a) Draw diagrams to show the forces acting on each of A and B.

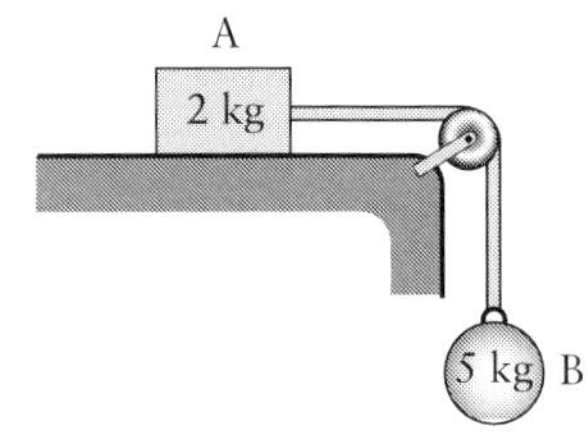

FIGURE 5.8

(b) If the block A does not slip, find the tension in the string and calculate the magnitude of the friction force on the block.

(c) Write down the resultant force acting on each of A and B if the block slips and accelerates.

Solution **(a)**

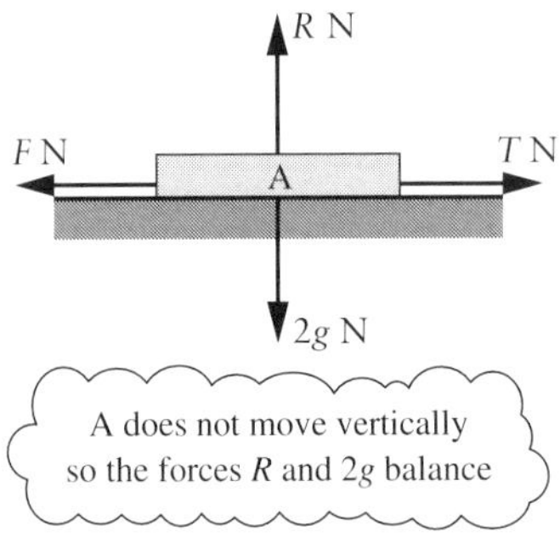

Forces on A

R N

F N

A

T N

$2g$ N

A does not move vertically so the forces R and $2g$ balance

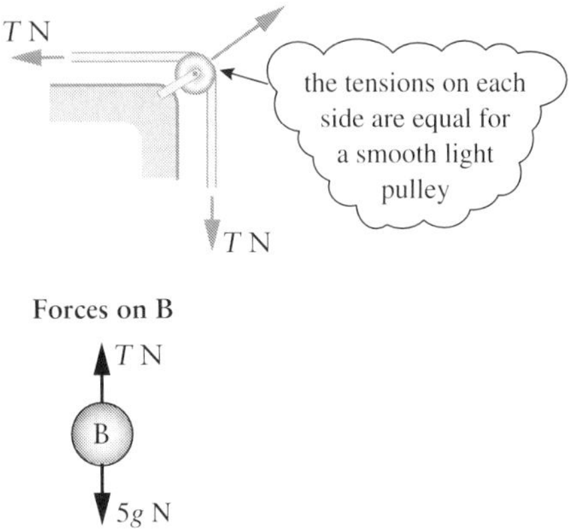

Forces on pulley

T N

the tensions on each side are equal for a smooth light pulley

T N

Forces on B

T N

B

$5g$ N

FIGURE 5.9

Note that the masses of 2 kg and 5 kg are not shown in the force diagram. The weights 2g N and 5g N are more appropriate.

(b) When the block does not slip, the forces on B are in equilibrium so

$$5g - T = 0$$
$$T = 5g$$

The tension throughout the string is $5g$ N.

For A, the resultant horizontal force is zero so

$$T - F = 0$$
$$F = T = 5g$$

The friction force is $5g$ N towards the left.

(c) When the block slips, the forces are not in equilibrium and T and F have different magnitudes.

The resultant horizontal force on A is $(T - F)$ N towards the right.
The resultant force on B is $(5g - T)$ N vertically downwards.

EXERCISE 5A

Remember: Always make it clear which object each equation of motion refers to.

1 Masses A of 100 g and B of 200 g are attached to the ends of a light, inextensible string which hangs over a smooth pulley as shown in the diagram.

Initially B is held at rest 2 m above the ground and A rests on the ground with the string taut. Then B is let go.

(a) Draw a diagram for each mass showing the forces acting on it and the direction of its acceleration at a later time when A and B are moving with an acceleration of $a\,\text{ms}^{-2}$ and before B hits the ground.

(b) Write down the equation of motion of each mass in the direction it moves using Newton's second law.

(c) Use your equations to find a and the tension in the string.

(d) Find the time taken for B to hit the ground.

2 In this question you should take g to be $10\,\text{ms}^{-2}$. The diagram shows a block of mass 5 kg lying on a smooth table. It is attached to a block of mass 3 kg by a string which passes over a smooth pulley. The tension in the string is T, as shown, and the block has acceleration $a\,\text{ms}^{-2}$.

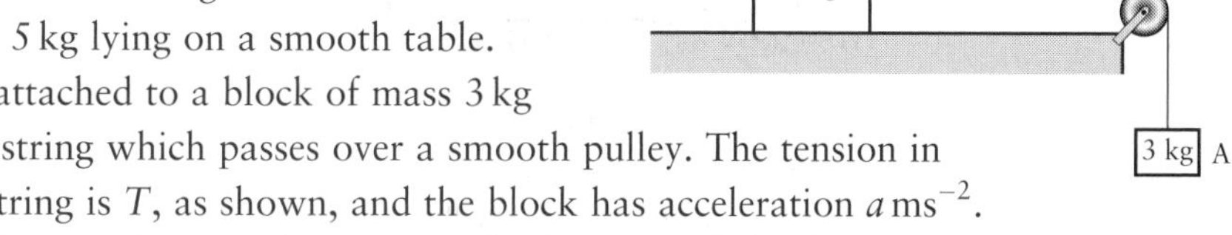

(a) Draw a diagram for each block, showing all the forces acting on it and its acceleration.

(b) Write down the equation of motion for each of the blocks.

(c) Use your equations to find the values of a and T.

In practice, the table is not truly smooth and a is found to be $2.5\,\text{ms}^{-2}$.

(d) Repeat parts (a) and (b) including a frictional force on the 5 kg block and use your new equations to find the frictional force that would produce this result.

3 A car of mass 800 kg is pulling a caravan of mass 1000 kg along a straight, horizontal road. The caravan is connected to the car by means of a light, rigid tow bar. The car is exerting a driving force of 1270 N. The resistances to the forward motion of the car and caravan are 400 N and 600 N respectively; you may assume that these resistances remain constant.

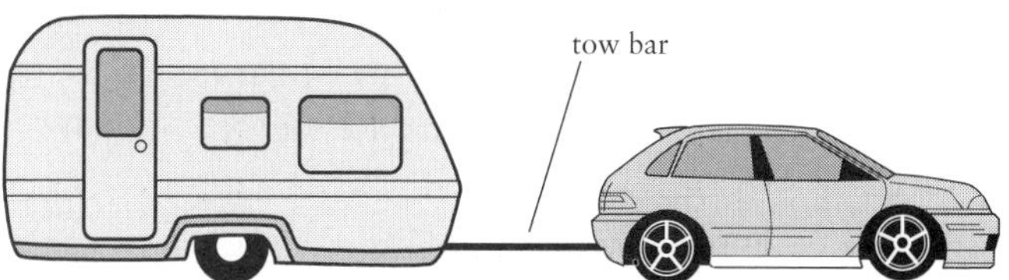

(a) Show that the acceleration of the car and caravan is $0.15\,\text{ms}^{-2}$.

(b) Draw a diagram showing all the forces acting on the caravan along the line of its motion. Calculate the tension in the tow bar.

The driving force is removed but the car's brakes are not applied.

(c) Determine whether the tow bar is now in tension or compression.

The car's brakes are then applied gradually. The brakes of the caravan come on automatically when the tow bar is subjected to a compression force of at least 50 N.

(d) Show that the acceleration of the caravan just before its brakes come on automatically is $-0.65\,\text{ms}^{-2}$ in the direction of its motion. Hence, calculate the braking force on the car necessary to make the caravan brakes come on.

[MEI]

4 The diagram shows a block A of mass 4 kg resting on a rough table, connected by a light string passing over a smooth pulley to a particle B of mass 2 kg which hangs vertically. The friction force between A and the table has value 15 N.

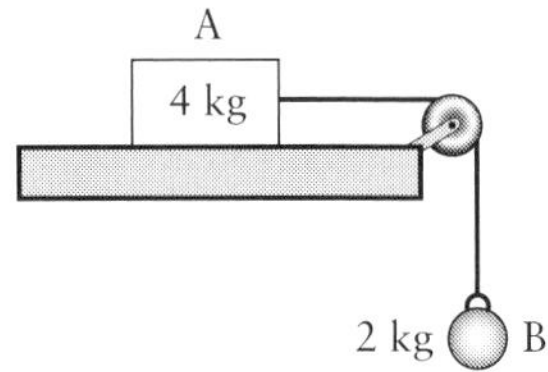

(a) Find the magnitude of the acceleration of the particles.

(b) Find the tension in the string.

5 The diagram shows two particles A, of mass 4 kg, and B, of mass 3 kg, connected by a light inextensible string which passes over a smooth pulley. A lies on a smooth horizontal plane, and B lies on a smooth plane inclined at 30° to the horizontal. The particles are released from rest with the string taut. Calculate

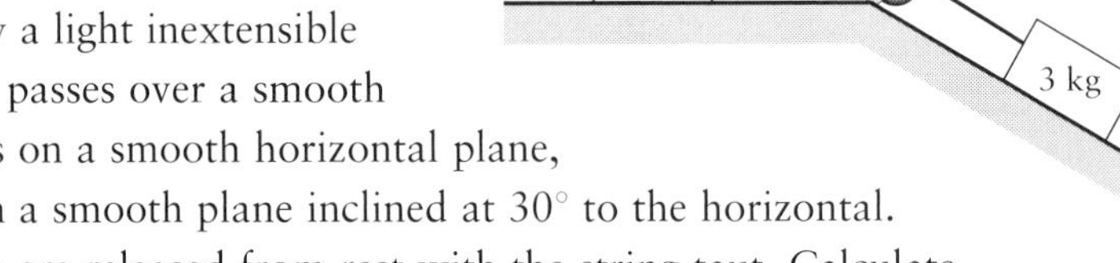

(a) the magnitude of their accelerations

(b) the tension in the string.

(c) State where in your calculation you have used the modelling assumption that the string is inextensible.

6 The diagram shows a lift containing a single passenger.

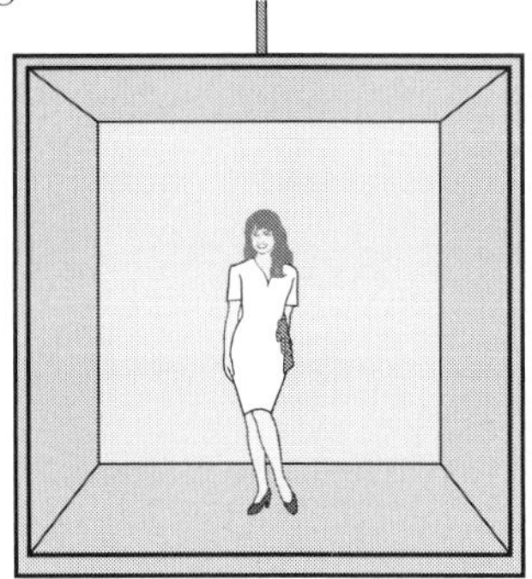

(a) Make clear diagrams to show the forces acting on the passenger and the forces acting on the lift using the following letters:

the tension in the cable, T N
the reaction of the lift on the passenger, R_P N
the reaction of the passenger on the lift, R_L N
the weight of the passenger, mg N
the weight of the lift, Mg N.

The masses of the lift and the passenger are 450 kg and 50 kg respectively.

(b) Calculate T, R_P and R_L when the lift is stationary.

The lift then accelerates upwards at $0.8\,\text{ms}^{-2}$.

(c) Find the new values of T, R_P and R_L.

EXERCISE 5B Examination-style questions

Many examination questions on connected particles also require knowledge of the coefficient of friction. Examples of these will be found in Chapter 8.

1 The diagram shows two particles A and B, connected by a light inextensible string passing over a smooth fixed pulley. A is of mass 3 kg and B is of mass 5 kg. The system is held with the string taut and released from rest. Find

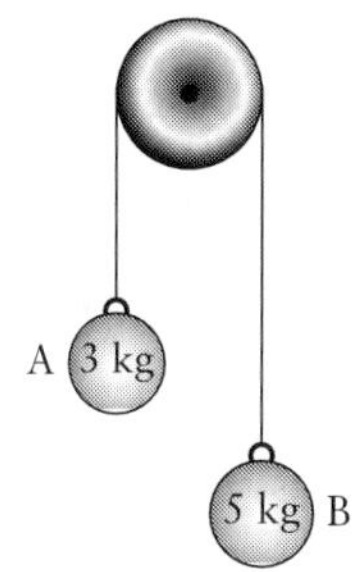

(a) the acceleration of the system

(b) the tension in the string

(c) the force exerted by the string on the pulley.

2 The diagram shows two particles A and B, connected by a light inextensible string passing over a smooth fixed pulley. A is of mass m kg, where $m > 6$, and B is of mass 6 kg. The system is held with the string taut and released from rest. The acceleration is $1.4\,\text{ms}^{-2}$. Find

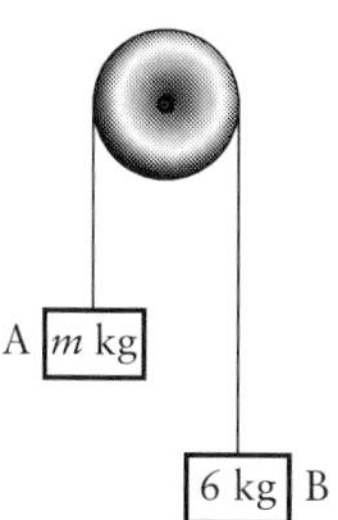

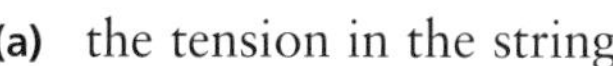

(a) the tension in the string

(b) the value of m

(c) the force exerted by the string on the pulley.

(d) State where in your model you have used the fact that the pulley is smooth.

3 The diagram shows two particles connected by a light inextensible string which passes over a smooth pulley. A is of mass m kg and lies on a smooth plane which is inclined at an angle α to the horizontal, where $\tan\alpha = \frac{5}{12}$. B is of mass $2m$ kg and hangs freely. The system is released from rest with the string taut and B 0.5 m above the floor.

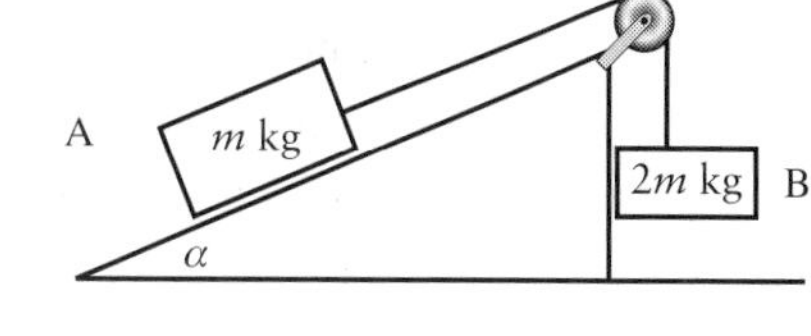

(a) Find the initial acceleration of the system in terms of g.

(b) Find the distance travelled by A after B hits the floor and the string goes slack.

(c) State where you have used the modelling assumption that the string is inextensible.

4 A particle A of mass 3 kg lies on a rough horizontal plane. The force of friction between the particle and the plane has a maximum value of 10 N. A is connected to another particle B by a light inextensible string which passes over a smooth pulley. Particle B is of mass 8 kg and lies on a smooth plane which is inclined at an angle of 30° to the horizontal. The system is released from rest with the string taut, and the string remains taut throughout the motion which follows.

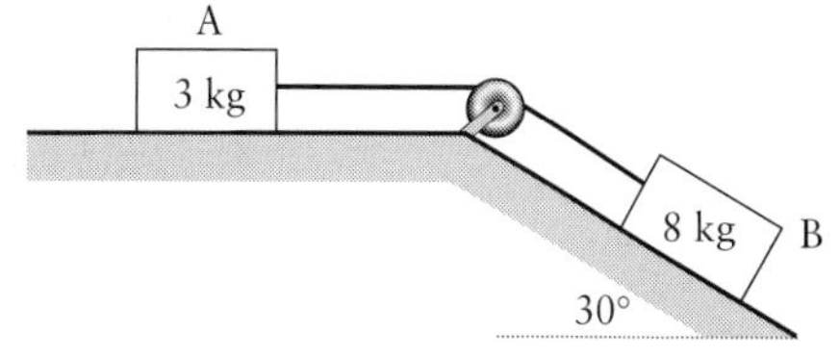

(a) Write down the equations of motion for each particle.

(b) Hence find the acceleration of the system and the tension in the string.

(c) State where you have used the modelling assumption that the pulley is smooth.

5 The diagram shows two particles joined by a light inextensible string which passes over a smooth pulley. A is of mass 2 kg and rests on a smooth plane inclined at arctan $\frac{3}{4}$ to the horizontal. B is of mass m kg and rests on a smooth plane inclined at arctan $\frac{5}{12}$ to the horizontal. The system is in equilibrium with the string taut.

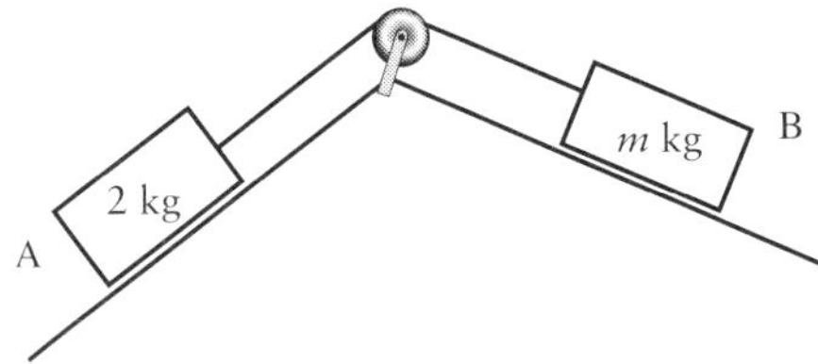

(a) Find m.

B is now replaced by a mass of $2m$ kg, and the system is released from rest.

(b) Find the acceleration of the system.

6 A car A of mass 1200 kg is towing another car B of mass 800 kg along a level road by means of a light inextensible tow bar. Each car experiences a resistance force of magnitude 1000 N, which may be assumed to remain constant throughout the motion. Initially the acceleration of the two cars is $2\,\text{ms}^{-2}$.

(a) Find the driving force being produced by car A.

(b) Find the tension in the tow bar.

Car A now removes the driving force.

(c) Find the new force in the tow bar, stating whether it is tension or thrust.

7 Two particles A and B have masses $3m$ and km respectively, where $k > 3$. They are connected by a light inextensible string which passes over a smooth fixed pulley. The system is released from rest with the string taut and the hanging parts of the string vertical, as shown in the diagram. While the particles are moving freely, A has an acceleration of magnitude $\frac{2}{5}g$.

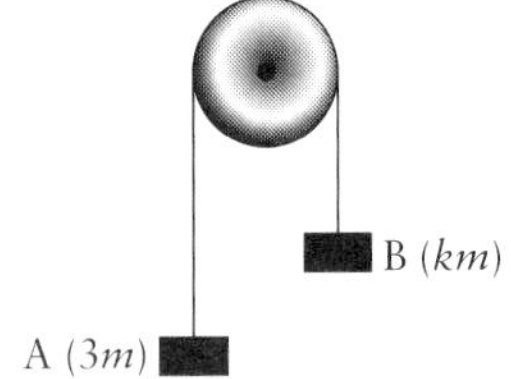

(a) Find, in terms of m and g, the tension in the string.

(b) State why B also has an acceleration of magnitude $\frac{2}{5}g$.

(c) Find the value of k.

(d) State how you have used the fact that the string is light.

[Edexcel]

8 A breakdown van of mass 2000 kg is towing a car of mass 1200 kg along a straight horizontal road. The two vehicles are joined by a tow bar which remains parallel to the road. The van and the car experience constant resistances to motion of magnitudes 800 N and 240 N respectively. There is a constant driving force acting on the van of 2900 N. Find

(a) the magnitude of the acceleration of the van and the car

(b) the tension in the tow bar.

The two vehicles come to a hill inclined at an angle of α to the horizontal, where $\sin \alpha = \frac{1}{20}$. The driving force and the resistances to motion are unchanged.

(c) Find the magnitude of the acceleration of the van and the car as they move up the hill and state whether their speed increases or decreases.

[Edexcel]

9 A car which has run out of petrol is being towed by a breakdown truck along a straight horizontal road. The truck has mass 1200 kg and the car has mass 800 kg. The truck is connected to the car by a horizontal rope which is modelled as light and inextensible. The truck's engine provides a constant driving force of 2400 N. The resistances to motion of the truck and the car are modelled as constant and of magnitude 600 N and 400 N respectively. Find

(a) the acceleration of the truck and the car

(b) the tension in the rope.

When the truck and car are moving at $20\ \text{ms}^{-1}$, the rope breaks. The engine of the truck provides the same driving force as before. The magnitude of the resistance to the motion of the truck remains 600 N.

(c) Show that the truck reaches a speed of $28\ \text{ms}^{-1}$ approximately 6 s earlier than it would have done if the rope had not broken.

[Edexcel]

KEY POINTS

The tension in a string is the same at both ends.

The particles at the ends of the string have the same acceleration along the string.

Newton's second law applies to each particle separately.

Chapter six

IMPULSE AND MOMENTUM

I collided with a stationary truck coming the other way.

Statement on an insurance form, reported in the Toronto News.

The karate expert in the picture has just broken a pile of roof-tiles with a single blow from his head. Forces in excess of 3000 N have been measured during karate chops. How is this possible?

IMPULSE

Although the karate expert produces a very large force, it acts for only a short time. This is often the case in situations where impacts occur, as in the following example involving a tennis player.

EXAMPLE 6.1

A tennis player hits the ball as it is travelling towards her at $10\,\mathrm{ms}^{-1}$ horizontally. Immediately after she hits it, the ball is travelling away from her at $20\,\mathrm{ms}^{-1}$ horizontally. The mass of the ball is 0.06 kg. What force does the tennis player apply to the ball?

Solution You cannot tell unless you know how long the impact lasts, and that will vary from one shot to another.

While you cannot calculate the force unless you know the time for which it acts, you can work out the product force × time. This is called the *impulse*.

When a constant force acts for a time t the impulse of the force is defined as

$$\text{impulse} = \text{force} \times \text{time}$$

The impulse is a vector in the direction of the force. When the force and time cannot be known separately, as in the case of the tennis ball, an impulse is often denoted by **J** and its magnitude by J. The S.I. unit for impulse is the newton second (Ns).

IMPULSE AND MOMENTUM

When the motion is in one dimension and the velocity of an object of mass m is changed from u to v by a constant force F you can use Newton's second law and the equations for motion with constant acceleration.

$$F = ma$$

and $$v = u + at$$

give $$mv = mu + mat$$

Substituting F for ma gives $$mv = mu + Ft$$

so $$Ft = mv - mu \qquad (1)$$

The quantity 'mass × velocity' is defined as the *momentum* of the moving object.

Equation (1) can then be written as

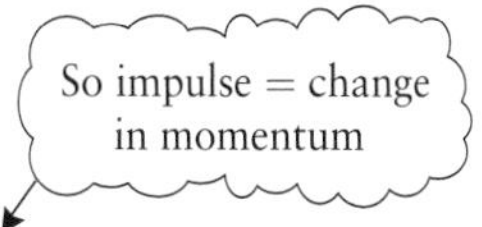
So impulse = change in momentum

$$\text{impulse of force} = \text{final momentum} - \text{initial momentum}$$

This equation also holds for any large force acting for a short time even when it cannot be assumed to be constant. The force on the tennis ball will increase as it embeds itself into the strings and then decrease as it is catapulted away, but you can calculate the impulse of the tennis racket on the ball as

$0.06 \times 20 - 0.06 \times (-10) = 1.8\,\text{Ns}$ (the -10 takes account of the change in direction)

EXAMPLE 6.2

A ball of mass 50 g hits the ground with a speed of $4\,\text{ms}^{-1}$ and rebounds with an initial speed of $3\,\text{ms}^{-1}$. If the ball is in contact with the ground for 0.01 s, find the average force exerted on the ball.

Solution The impulse is given by:

$$\begin{aligned} J &= mv - mu \\ &= 0.05 \times 3 - 0.05 \times (-4) \\ &= 0.35 \end{aligned}$$

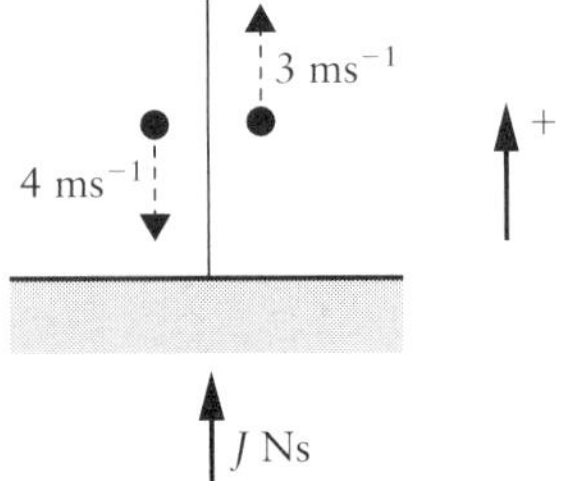

FIGURE 6.1

The impulse J is also given by

$$J = Ft$$

where F is the average force, i.e. the constant force which, acting for the same time interval, would have the same effect as the variable force which actually acted.

$$\Rightarrow \quad 0.35 = F \times 0.01$$
$$F = 35$$

So the ground exerts an average upward force of 35 N.

Although the force of gravity acts during the impact, its impulse is negligible over such a short time.

EXAMPLE 6.3

A car of mass 800 kg is pushed with a constant force of magnitude 200 N for 10 s. If the car starts from rest, find its speed at the end of the ten-second interval.

Solution The force of 200 N acts for 10 s, so the impulse on the car is

$$J = 200 \times 10 = 2000 \text{ (in Ns).}$$

(The impulse is in the direction of the force.)

Hence the change in momentum (in Ns) is

$$mv = 2000$$

$$\Rightarrow \quad v = \frac{2000}{800} = 2.5$$

The speed at the end of the time interval is $2.5\,\text{ms}^{-1}$.

EXERCISE 6A

1 Find the momentum of the following objects, assuming each of them to be travelling in a straight line.

(a) An ice skater of mass 50 kg travelling with speed 10 ms^{-1}.

(b) An elephant of mass 5 tonnes moving at 4 ms^{-1}.

(c) A train of mass 7000 tonnes travelling at 40 ms^{-1}.

(d) A bacterium of mass 2×10^{-16} g moving with speed 1 mm s^{-1}.

2 Calculate the impulse required in each of these situations:

(a) to stop a car of mass 1.3 tonnes travelling at 14 ms^{-1}

(b) to putt a golf ball of mass 1.5 g with speed 1.5 ms^{-1}

(c) to stop a cricket ball of mass 0.15 kg travelling at 20 ms^{-1}

(d) to fire a bullet of mass 25 g with speed 400 ms^{-1}.

3 A stone of mass 1.5 kg is dropped from rest. After a time interval t s, it has fallen a distance s m and has velocity v ms^{-1}.

Take g to be 10 ms^{-2} and neglect air resistance.

(a) Write down the force F (in N) acting on the stone.

(b) Find the distance, s, that the stone has fallen when $t = 2$.

(c) Find the velocity, v (in ms^{-1}), of the stone when $t = 2$.

(d) Write down the value, units and meaning of Ft and explain why this has the same value as $1.5v$.

4 A girl throws a ball of mass 0.06 kg vertically upwards with initial speed 20 ms^{-1}. Take g to be 10 ms^{-2} and neglect air resistance.

(a) What is the initial momentum of the ball?

(b) How long does it take for the ball to reach the top of its flight?

(c) What is the momentum of the ball when it is at the top of its flight?

(d) What impulse acted on the ball over the period between its being thrown and its reaching maximum height?

5 A netball of mass 425 g is moving horizontally with speed 5 ms^{-1} when it is caught.

(a) Find the impulse needed to stop the ball.

(b) Find the average force needed to stop the ball if it takes

(i) 0.1 s (ii) 0.05 s.

(c) Why does the action of taking a ball into your body make it easier to catch?

6 A car of mass 0.9 tonnes is travelling at 13.2 ms^{-1} when it crashes head-on into a wall. The car is brought to rest in a time of 0.12 s. Find

(a) the impulse acting on the car

(b) the average force acting on the car

(c) the average deceleration of the car in terms of g (taken to be 10 ms^{-2}).

(d) Explain why many cars are designed with crumple zones rather than with completely rigid construction.

7 Boris is sleeping on a bunk-bed at a height of 1.5 m when he rolls over and falls out. His mass is 20 kg.

(a) Find the speed with which he hits the floor.

(b) Find the impulse that the floor has exerted on him when he has come to rest.

(c) Find the impulse he has exerted on the floor.

It takes Boris 0.2 s to come to rest.

(d) Find the average force acting on him during this time.

8 A railway truck of mass 10 tonnes is travelling at $3\,\text{ms}^{-1}$ along a siding when it hits some buffers. After the impact it is travelling at $1.5\,\text{ms}^{-1}$ in the opposite direction.

(a) Find the initial momentum of the truck, remembering to specify its direction.

(b) Find the momentum of the truck after it has left the buffers.

(c) Find the impulse that has acted on the truck.

During the impact the force F N that the buffers exert on the truck varies as shown in this graph.

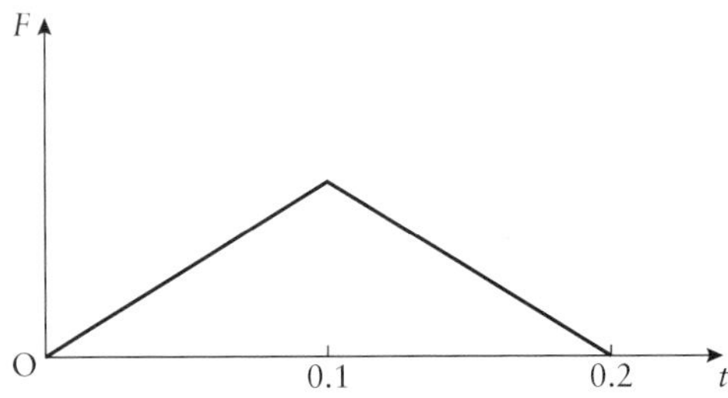

(d) State what information is given by the area under the graph.

(e) What is the greatest value of the force F?

Conservation of momentum

Collisions

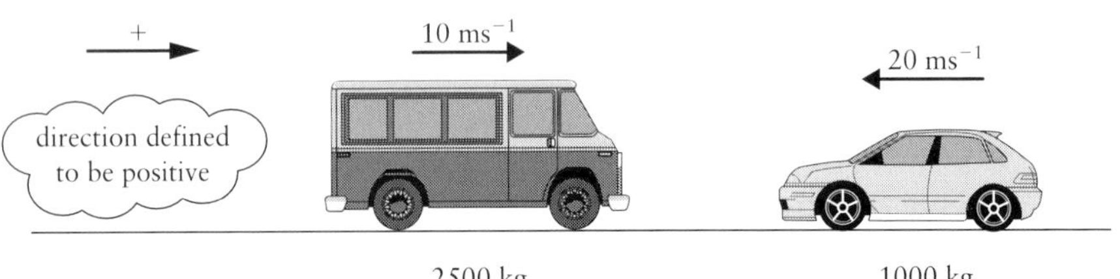

Figure 6.2

In an experiment to investigate car design two vehicles were made to collide head-on. How would you investigate this situation? Can you find a relationship between the change in momentum of the van and that of the car?

The first thing to remember is Newton's third law. The force that body A exerts on body B is equal to the force that B exerts on A, but in the opposite direction.

Suppose that once the van is in contact with the car, it exerts a force F on the car for a time t. Newton's third law tells us that the car also exerts a force F on the van for a time t. (This applies whether F is constant or variable.) So both vehicles receive equal impulses, but in opposite directions. Consequently the increase in momentum of the car in the positive direction is exactly equal to the increase in momentum of the van in the negative direction. For the two vehicles together, the total change in momentum is zero.

This example illustrates the *law of conservation of momentum.*

> The law of conservation of momentum states that when there are no external influences on a system, the total momentum of the system is constant.

For a collision, you can say

> total momentum before collision = total momentum after collision

---

EXAMPLE 6.4

The two vehicles in the previous discussion collide head-on, and as a result the van comes to rest.

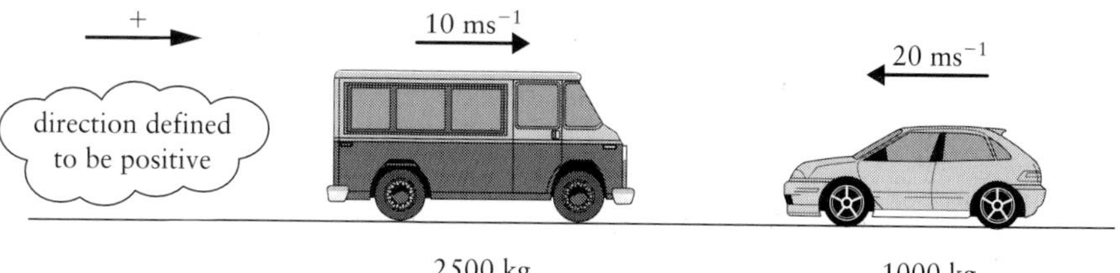

FIGURE 6.3

Find

(a) the final velocity of the car, $v\,\text{ms}^{-1}$

(b) the impulse on each vehicle.

(c) If it is assumed that the impact lasts for one-twentieth of a second, find the force on each vehicle and its acceleration.

Solution **(a)**

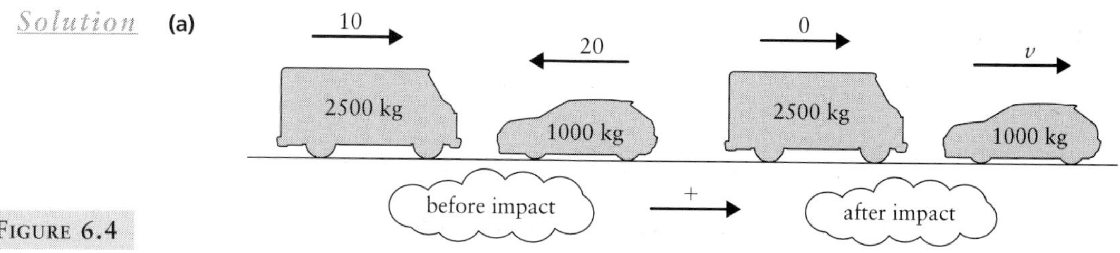

FIGURE 6.4

Using conservation of momentum, and taking the positive direction as being to the right:

$$2500 \times 10 + 1000 \times (-20) = 2500 \times 0 + 1000 \times v$$
$$5000 = 1000v$$
$$v = 5$$

The final velocity of the car is $5\,\text{ms}^{-1}$ in the positive direction (i.e. the car travels backwards).

(b) Impulse = final momentum − initial momentum

For the van, impulse $= 2500 \times 0 - 2500 \times 10$
$= -25\,000\,\text{Ns}$

For the car, impulse $= 1000 \times 5 - 1000 \times (-20)$
$= +25\,000\,\text{Ns}$

The van experiences an impulse of 25 000 Ns in the negative direction, the car an equal and opposite impulse.

(c) Impulse = average force × time

$$25\,000 = F \times \tfrac{1}{20}$$
$F = 500\,000\,\text{N}$ (acting to the right on the car and to the left on the van)

Using $F = ma$ on each vehicle gives an average acceleration of $500\,\text{ms}^{-2}$ for the car and $-200\,\text{ms}^{-2}$ for the van.

EXPERIMENT

Set up the apparatus as shown in figure 6.5. Truck A can be released from the top of the slope so that it always hits truck B at the same speed.

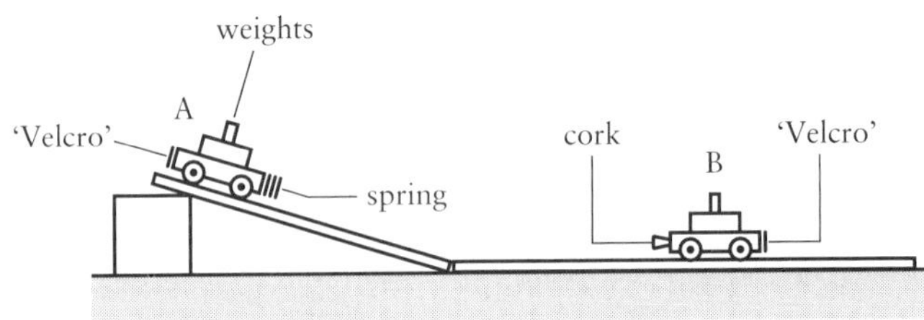

FIGURE 6.5

For each situation below describe what you think will happen and then test your prediction.

1 Arrange the trucks so that the spring on truck A hits the cork on truck B.
  - **(a)** Load both trucks with the same mass, then release A so that it rolls down and hits B.
  - **(b)** Now load B so that it is very much heavier than A.
  - **(c)** Now load A so that it is very much heavier than B.

2 Arrange the trucks so that the Velcro tabs hit each other during the collision. Now repeat experiments (a) to (c) above.

3 Rearrange the track as shown below.

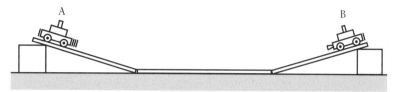

FIGURE 6.6

(a) Release trucks that are loaded equally from both ends of the track, so that the spring and cork come into contact.

(b) Repeat (a), but with one truck loaded so that it is much heavier than the other.

(c) Release equally loaded trucks from each end so that the Velcro ends come into contact.

(d) Repeat (c), but with one truck loaded so that it is much heavier than the other.

EXAMPLE 6.5

In an experiment on lorry bumper design, the Transport Research Laboratory arranged for a car and a lorry, of masses 1 and 3.5 tonnes, to travel towards each other, both with speed $9\,\text{ms}^{-1}$. After colliding both vehicles moved together and the total momentum had been conserved.

What was their combined velocity after the collision?

Solution The situation before the collision is illustrated below.

FIGURE 6.7

Taking the positive direction to be to the right, before the collision

momentum of the car in Ns: $1000 \times 9 = 9000$

momentum of the lorry in Ns: $3500 \times (-9) = -31\,500$

total momentum in Ns: $9000 - 31\,500 = -22\,500$

After the collision, assume they move as a single object of mass 4.5 tonnes with velocity $v\,\text{ms}^{-1}$ in the positive direction so the total momentum is now $4500v$ Ns.

Momentum is conserved so $\quad 4500v = -22\,500$

$$v = -5$$

The car and lorry move at $5\,\text{ms}^{-1}$ in the direction the lorry was moving.

When two particles combine to form a single mass, they are said to **coalesce**. ***You may meet this term in exam questions.***

EXAMPLE 6.6

A child of mass 30 kg running through a supermarket at $4\,\text{ms}^{-1}$ leaps on to a stationary shopping trolley of mass 15 kg. Find the speed of the child and trolley together, assuming that the trolley is free to move easily.

Solution The diagram shows the situation before the child hits the trolley.

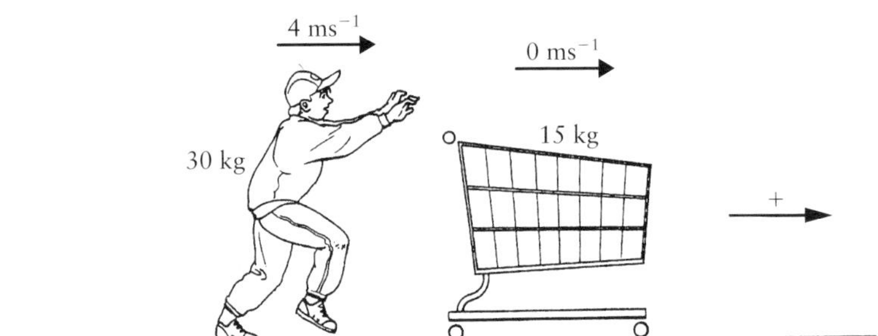

FIGURE 6.8

Taking the direction of the child's velocity as positive, total momentum (in Ns) before impact is

$$4 \times 30 + 0 \times 15 = 120$$

The situation after impact is shown below.

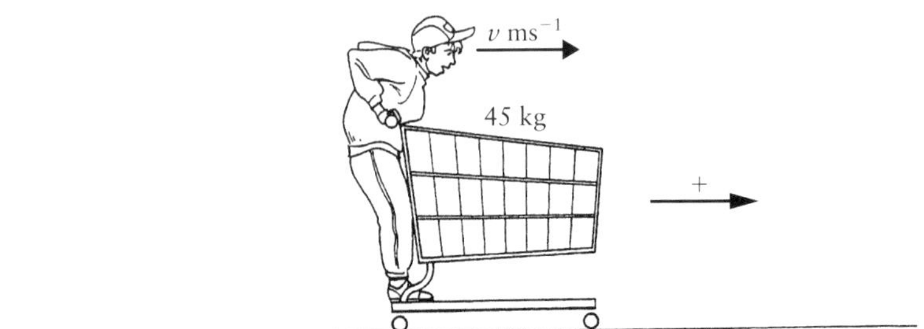

FIGURE 6.9

The total mass of child and trolley is 45 kg, so the total momentum after is $45v$ Ns. Conservation of momentum gives

$$45v = 120$$
$$v = 2\tfrac{2}{3}.$$

The child and the trolley together move at $2\frac{2}{3}\,\text{ms}^{-1}$.

EXPLOSIONS

Conservation of momentum also applies when explosions take place provided there are no external forces, for example when a bullet is fired from a rifle, or a rocket is launched.

EXAMPLE 6.7

A rifle of mass 8 kg is used to fire a bullet of mass 80 g at a speed of $200\,\text{ms}^{-1}$. Calculate the initial recoil speed of the rifle.

Solution Before the bullet is fired the total momentum of the system is zero.

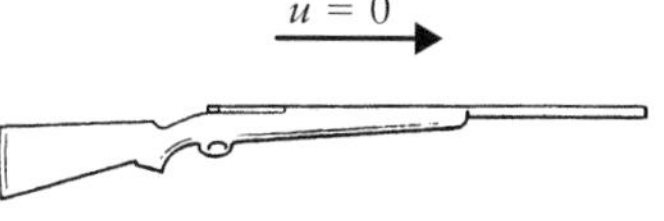

FIGURE 6.10

After the firing the situation is as illustrated below.

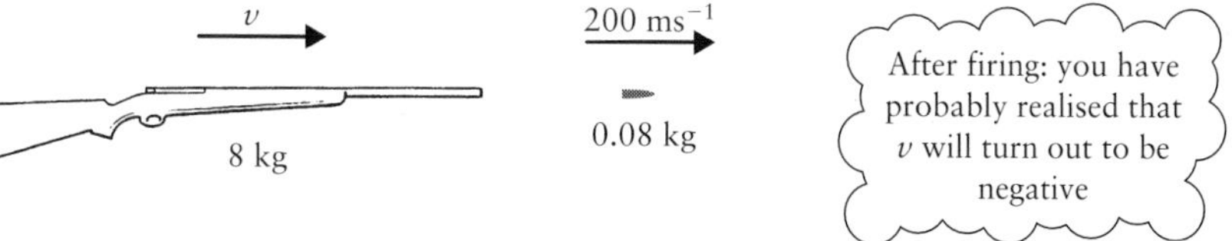

FIGURE 6.11

The total momentum in the positive direction after the firing is $8v + 0.08 \times 200$.

For momentum to be conserved,

$$8v + 0.08 \times 200 = 0$$

so that

$$8v = -200 \times 0.08$$
$$v = -2$$

The recoil speed of the rifle is $2\,\text{ms}^{-1}$.

EXERCISE 6B

1 A spaceship of mass 50 000 kg travelling with speed 200 ms^{-1} docks with a space station of mass 500 000 kg travelling in the same direction with speed 195 ms^{-1}. What is their speed after the docking is completed?

2 A railway truck of mass 20 tonnes is shunted with speed 3 ms^{-1} towards a stationary truck of mass 10 tonnes. After impact the trucks remain in contact. What is their speed?

3 The driver of a car of mass 1000 kg falls asleep while it is travelling at 30 ms^{-1}. The car runs into the back of the car in front, which has mass 800 kg and is travelling in the same direction at 20 ms^{-1}. The bumpers of the two cars become locked together and they continue as one vehicle.

(a) What is the final speed of the cars?

(b) What impulse does the larger car give to the smaller one?

(c) What impulse does the smaller car give to the larger one?

4 A lorry of mass 5 tonnes is towing a car of mass 1 tonne. Initially the tow rope is slack and the car stationary. As the rope becomes taut the lorry is travelling at 2 ms^{-1}.

(a) Find the speed of the car once it is being towed.

(b) Find the magnitude of the impulse transmitted by the tow rope and state the direction of the impulse on each vehicle.

5 A bullet of mass 50 g is moving horizontally at 200 ms^{-1} when it becomes embedded in a stationary block of mass 16 kg which is free to slide on a smooth horizontal table.

(a) Calculate the speed of the bullet and the block after the impact.

(b) Find the impulse from the bullet on the block.

The bullet takes 0.01 s to come to rest relative to the block.

(c) What is the average force acting on the bullet while it is decelerating?

6 A spaceship of mass 50 000 kg is travelling through space with speed 5000 ms^{-1} when a crew member throws a box of mass 5 kg out of the back with speed 10 ms^{-1} relative to the spaceship.

(a) What is the absolute speed of the box?

(b) What is the speed of the spaceship after the box has been thrown out?

7 A gun of mass 500 kg fires a shell of mass 5 kg horizontally with muzzle speed 300 ms^{-1}.

(a) Calculate the recoil speed of the gun.

An army commander would like soldiers to be able to fire such a shell from a rifle held against their shoulders (so they can attack armoured vehicles).

(b) Explain why such an idea has no hope of success.

8 Manoj (mass 70 kg) and Alka (mass 50 kg) are standing stationary facing each other on a smooth ice rink. They then push against each other with a force of 35 N for 1.5 s. The direction in which Manoj faces is taken as positive.

(a) What is their total momentum before they start pushing?

(b) Find the velocity of each of them after they have finished pushing.

(c) Find the momentum of each of them after they have finished pushing.

(d) What is their total momentum after they have finished pushing?

9 A pile-driver has a block of mass 2 tonnes which is dropped from a height of 5 m on to a pile of mass 600 kg which it is driving vertically into the ground. The block rebounds with a speed of $2\,\text{ms}^{-1}$ immediately after the impact. Taking g to be $10\,\text{ms}^{-2}$ find

(a) the speed of the block immediately before the impact

(b) the impulse acting on the block

(c) the impulse acting on the pile.

From the moment of impact the pile takes 0.025 s to come to rest.

(d) Calculate the force of resistance on the pile, assuming it to be constant.

(e) How far does the pile move?

10 The diagram shows Nicholas, whose mass is 80 kg, standing at the front of a sleigh of length 5 m and mass 40 kg. The sleigh is initially stationary and on smooth ice. Nicholas then walks towards the back of the sleigh with speed $1\,\text{ms}^{-1}$ relative to the sleigh.

(a) Find the velocity of the sleigh while Nicholas is walking towards the back of it.

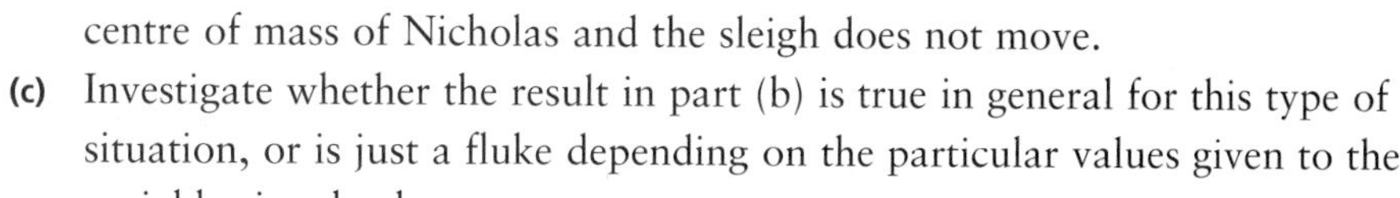

(b) Show that, throughout his walk, the combined centre of mass of Nicholas and the sleigh does not move.

(c) Investigate whether the result in part (b) is true in general for this type of situation, or is just a fluke depending on the particular values given to the variables involved.

EXERCISE 6C

Examination-style questions

1 A particle A of mass m is moving towards another particle B with velocity $3u$. Particle B has mass km and velocity u towards A. They collide and combine to form one particle, which moves with velocity $2u$ in the same direction as A was moving originally. Find k.

2 A firework of mass 1.5 kg is moving directly upwards with a velocity of $30\,\text{ms}^{-1}$ when it explodes into two parts. Immediately after the explosion the front part, of mass 1 kg, is moving vertically up with a velocity of $40\,\text{ms}^{-1}$. The rear part is of mass 0.5 kg. Find the velocity of the rear part.

3 A spacecraft of mass 8 tonnes is moving freely in orbit at a speed of $7500\,\text{ms}^{-1}$. The spacecraft fires a small rocket to adjust its position. The rocket produces a force of 500 N for 30 s along the line of motion of the spacecraft. Ignoring the loss of mass in firing the rocket, find the new velocity of the spacecraft.

4 A particle A of mass m is moving towards another particle B with velocity $3u$. Particle B has mass km and velocity u towards A. They collide and coalesce to form one particle, which moves with velocity $0.5u$ in the same direction as B was moving originally.

(a) Find k.

(b) Show that, whatever the value of k, the velocity v of the combined particle obeys the inequality $-u \leqslant v \leqslant 3u$.

5 A stationary rifle of mass 4 kg fires a bullet of mass 30 g with a velocity of $400\,\text{ms}^{-1}$. The rifle recoils and is stopped in a time of 0.025 s.

(a) Find the recoil velocity of the rifle.

(b) Find the impulse exerted by the rifle on the bullet.

(c) Find the force (assumed constant) exerted on the rifle by the firer during the recoil period.

6 A rugby wing three-quarter of mass 85 kg is running straight towards the try line with velocity $8\,\text{ms}^{-1}$. He is tackled by a stationary full back of mass 95 kg. The two continue as one particle, whose motion is resisted by a force of 600 N. Calculate

(a) their common velocity

(b) the distance they slide before coming to rest.

7 In a game of shove-ha'penny, two discs A and B of mass 6 g each collide directly. Before the collision, A is stationary and B is moving with velocity $0.9\,\text{ms}^{-1}$ towards A. After the collision, A is moving with twice the velocity of B, and the motion of each disc is resisted by a force of 0.02 N. Calculate

(a) the velocity of each disc after the collision

(b) the magnitude of the impulse exerted on A by B in the collision

(c) the distance travelled by A after the collision before coming to rest.

8 A tractor unit is backing on to a trailer to connect up. The trailer has mass 7.5 tonnes and is initially at rest with the brakes on. The brakes can produce a force of up to 44 000 N. The tractor is of mass 2.5 tonnes and is initially moving at $1\,\text{ms}^{-1}$. They connect automatically when contact occurs and carry on as one vehicle.

(a) Find their common velocity immediately after the collision.

(b) Find the impulse exerted by the tractor on the trailer during the collision.

(c) The driving force is removed just before the collision. Calculate the time it takes for the combination to stop.

(d) Find the distance the combination moves before stopping.

9 A particle A of mass m kg is moving with velocity $7\,\text{ms}^{-1}$ directly towards a stationary particle B of mass 3 kg. They collide, and after the collision A has velocity $3\,\text{ms}^{-1}$ and B has velocity $5\,\text{ms}^{-1}$, both in the direction of A's original motion.

(a) Find m.

(b) Find the impulse exerted by particle A on particle B.

After the collision, A is resisted by a force of 12 N.

(c) Find the time it takes for particle A to come to rest.

(d) How far does particle A travel in that time?

10 A sledgehammer of mass 7 kg is allowed to fall freely from rest under gravity for 0.5 s. It then strikes a peg of mass 2 kg, and they continue together vertically downwards, resisted by a force of 650 N.
Calculate

(a) the velocity with which the hammer hits the peg

(b) the common velocity after the collision

(c) the impulse given to the hammer by the peg

(d) the time that elapses before the peg comes to rest

(e) the distance that the peg moves in that time.

11 Two particles A and B have mass 0.12 kg and 0.08 kg respectively. They are initially at rest on a smooth horizontal table. Particle A is then given an impulse in the direction AB so that it moves with speed $3\,\text{ms}^{-1}$ directly towards B.

(a) Find the magnitude of this impulse, stating clearly the units in which your answer is given.

Immediately after the particles collide, the speed of A is $1.2\,\text{ms}^{-1}$, its direction of motion being unchanged.

(b) Find the speed of B immediately after the collision.

(c) Find the magnitude of the impulse exerted on A in the collision.

[Edexcel]

12 The masses of two particles A and B are 0.5 kg and m kg respectively. The particles are moving on a smooth horizontal table in opposite directions and collide directly. Immediately before the collision the speed of A is $5\,\text{ms}^{-1}$ and the speed of B is 3ms^{-1}. In the collision, the magnitude of the impulse exerted by B on A is 3.6 Ns. As a result of the collision the direction of motion of A is reversed.

(a) Find the speed of A immediately after the collision.

The speed of B immediately after the collision is $1\,\text{ms}^{-1}$.

(b) Find the two possible values of m.

[Edexcel]

13 A railway truck P of mass 1500 kg is moving on a straight horizontal track. The truck P collides with a truck Q of mass 2500 kg at a point A. Immediately before the collision, P and Q are moving in the same direction with speeds $10\,\mathrm{m\,s^{-1}}$ and $5\,\mathrm{m\,s^{-1}}$ respectively. Immediately after the collision, the direction of motion of P is unchanged and its speed is $4\,\mathrm{m\,s^{-1}}$. By modelling the trucks as particles

(a) show that the speed of Q immediately after the collision is $8.6\,\mathrm{m\,s^{-1}}$.

After the collision at A, the truck P is acted upon by a constant braking force of magnitude 500 N. The truck P comes to rest at the point B.

(b) Find the distance AB.

After the collision Q continues to move with constant speed $8.6\,\mathrm{m\,s^{-1}}$.

(c) Find the distance between P and Q at the instant when P comes to rest.

[Edexcel]

14 A railway truck A of mass 1800 kg is moving along a straight horizontal track with speed $4\,\mathrm{m\,s^{-1}}$. It collides directly with a stationary truck B of mass 1200 kg on the same track. In the collision, A and B are coupled and move off together.

(a) Find the speed of the trucks immediately after the collision.

After the collision, the trucks experience a constant resistive force of magnitude R newtons. They come to rest 8 s after the collision.

(b) Find R.

[Edexcel]

KEY POINTS

The **impulse** from a force F is given by Ft where t is the time for which the force acts. Impulse is a vector quantity.

The **momentum** of a body of mass m travelling with velocity v is given by mv. Momentum is a vector quantity.

The **impulse–momentum equation** is

$$\text{Impulse} = \text{change in momentum}$$

The **law of conservation of momentum** states that when no external forces are acting on a system, the total momentum of the system is constant.

Chapter seven

STATICS OF A PARTICLE

Everything was at rest, free and immortal.

Thomas Traherne

FINDING RESULTANT FORCES

A child on a sledge is being pulled up a smooth slope of 20° by a rope which makes an angle of 40° with the slope. The mass of the child and sledge together is 20 kg and the tension in the rope is 170 N. Draw a diagram to show the forces acting on the child and sledge together. In what direction is the resultant of these forces?

When the child and sledge are modelled as a particle, all the forces can be assumed to be acting at a point. There is no friction force because the slope is smooth. Here is the force diagram.

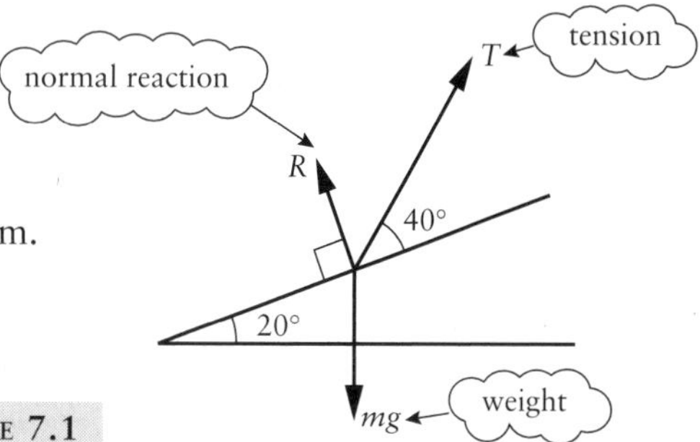

FIGURE 7.1

The resultant of these forces can be found by the vector methods covered in Chapter 2. You could draw a scale diagram with the forces represented by the sides of a polygon taken in order (with the arrows following each other) as shown in figure 7.2. Then the resultant is represented by the fourth side AD. This must be parallel to the slope.

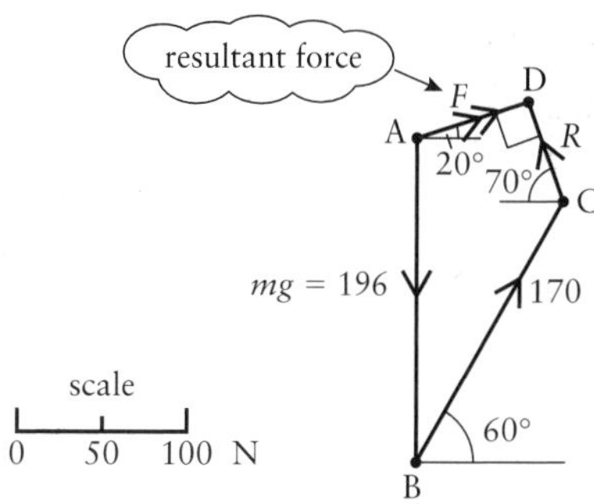

FIGURE 7.2

From the diagram you can estimate the normal reaction to be about 80 N and the resultant 60 N.

EXERCISE 7A

For each of the situations below, carry out the following steps. All forces are in newtons.

(a) Draw a scale diagram to show the polygon of the forces and the resultant.

(b) State whether you think the forces are in equilibrium and, if not, estimate the magnitude and direction of the resultant.

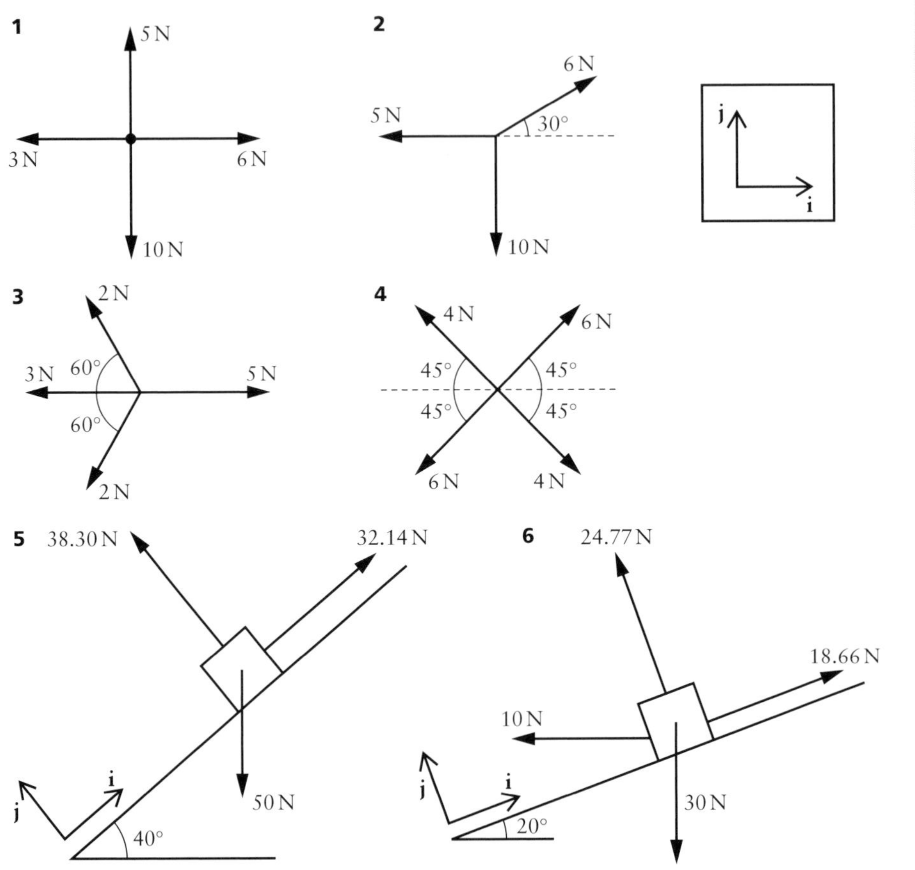

USING COMPONENTS

It is easiest to use components of the forces parallel and perpendicular to the slope. In the original diagram choose unit vectors **i** and **j** as shown.

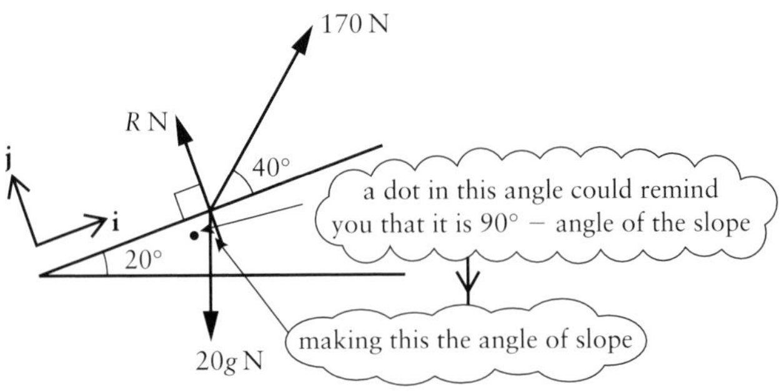

FIGURE 7.3

You can treat the components in the **i** and **j** directions separately as follows. Remember that a force perpendicular to a direction has no component in that direction.

Resolve parallel to the slope (↗)

The resultant $F = 170\cos 40° - 20g\sin 20°$
$= 63.2$

$\cos(90° - 20°) = \sin 20°$

Resolve perpendicular to the slope (↖)

$R + 170\sin 40° - 20g\cos 20° = 0$

$R = 20g\cos 20° - 170\sin 40°$
$= 74.9$

The resultant has no component in this direction

The normal reaction is 75 N and the resultant 63 N up the slope.

Note Try resolving horizontally and vertically. You will obtain two equations in the two unknowns R and F. It is perfectly possible to solve these equations, but quite a lot of work. It is much easier to choose to resolve in directions which ensure that one component of at least one of the unknown forces is zero.

EXERCISE 7B

For each example in Exercise 7A, do the following.

(a) Write the forces in component form, using the directions indicated. Perform the vector addition in this form and so obtain the components of the resultant. Hence find the magnitude and direction of the resultant.

(b) Compare your answers with those you obtained in Exercise 7A.

FORCES IN EQUILIBRIUM

When forces are in equilibrium their vector sum is zero and the sum of their resolved parts in *any* direction is zero.

EXAMPLE 7.1

A brick of mass 3 kg is at rest on a rough plane inclined at an angle of 30° to the horizontal. Find the friction force F N, and the normal reaction R N of the plane on the brick.

Solution The diagram shows the forces acting on the brick.

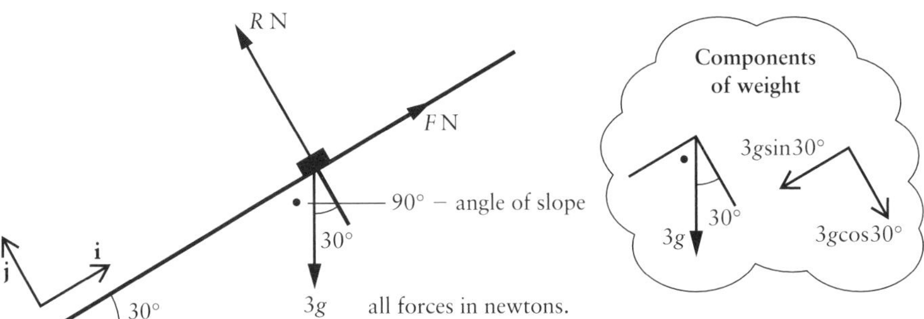

FIGURE 7.4

Take unit vectors **i** and **j** parallel and perpendicular to the plane as shown. Since the brick is in equilibrium the resultant of the three forces acting on it is zero.

Resolving in the **i** direction (↗): $F - 29.4\sin 30^\circ = 0$ ← $3g = 29.4$ ①

Resolving in the **j** direction (↖): $R - 29.4\cos 30^\circ = 0$ ②

$\Rightarrow \quad F = 14.7 \quad \text{and} \quad R = 25.5$

THE TRIANGLE OF FORCES

When there are only three (non-parallel) forces acting and they are in equilibrium, the polygon of forces becomes a closed triangle as shown for the brick on the plane.

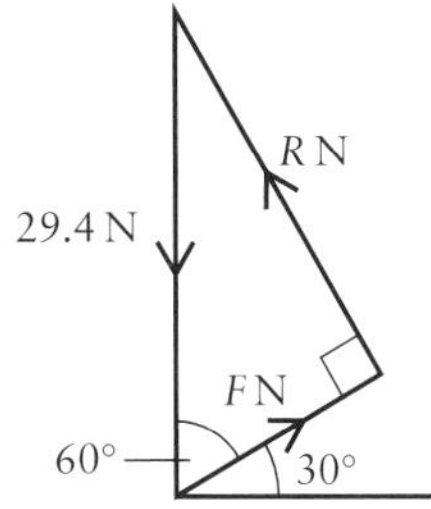

FIGURE 7.5

Then $\dfrac{F}{29.4} = \cos 60^\circ$

$F = 29.4\cos 60^\circ$

and similarly $R = 29.4\sin 60^\circ$

This is an example of the theorem known as the *triangle of forces*.

> When a body is in equilibrium under the action of three non-parallel forces, then
> - the forces can be represented in magnitude and direction by the sides of a triangle
> - the lines of action of the forces pass through the same point.

When more than three forces are in equilibrium the first statement still holds but the triangle is then a polygon. The second is not necessarily true.

EXAMPLE 7.2

This example illustrates two methods for solving problems involving forces in equilibrium. With experience, you will find it easier to judge which method is best for a particular problem.

A sign of mass 10 kg is to be suspended by two strings arranged as shown in the diagram below. Find the tension in each string.

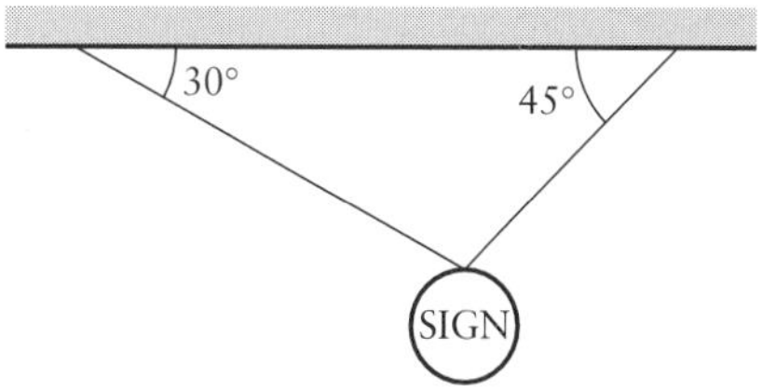

FIGURE 7.6

Solution The force diagram for this situation is given below.

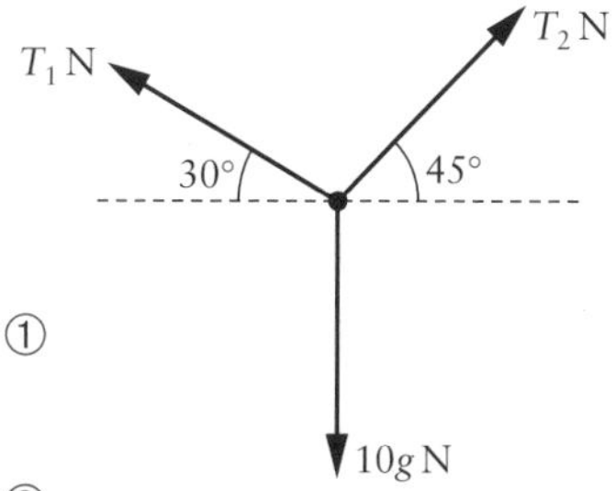

FIGURE 7.7

Method 1: Resolving forces

Vertically (↑): $T_1 \sin 30° + T_2 \sin 45° - 10g = 0$

$$0.5T_1 + 0.707T_2 = 98 \quad ①$$

Horizontally (→): $-T_1 \cos 30° + T_2 \cos 45° = 0$

$$-0.866T_1 + 0.707T_2 = 0 \quad ②$$

Subtracting ② from ① $\quad 1.366T_1 = 98$

This gives $\quad T_1 = 71.74$

Back substitution gives $\quad T_2 = 87.87$

The tensions are 71.7 N and 87.9 N.

Method 2: Triangle of forces

Since the three forces are in equilibrium they can be represented by the sides of a triangle taken in order.

You can estimate the tensions by measurement, or calculate them by using the sine and cosine rules if you are familiar with them. This will tell you that $T_1 = 72$ and $T_2 = 88$ in newtons.

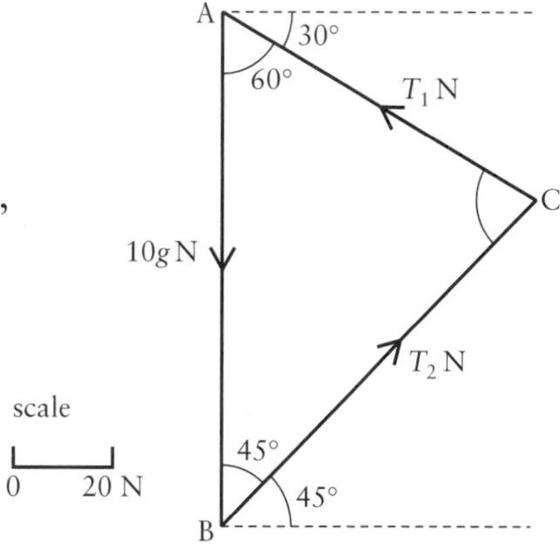
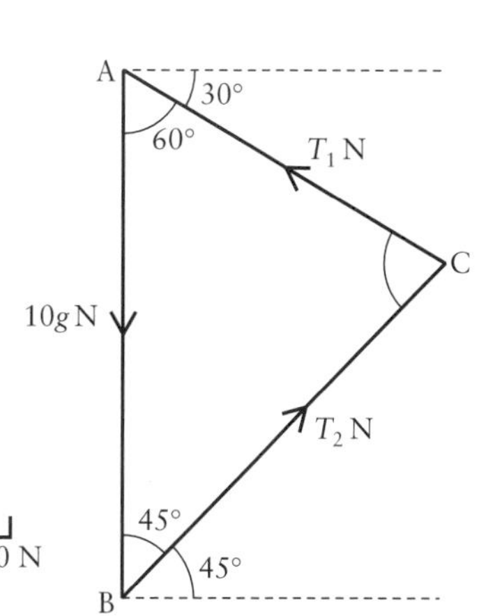

FIGURE 7.8

EXERCISE 7C

1 The picture shows a boy, Halley, holding onto a post while his two older sisters, Sheuli and Veronica, try to pull him away.

Taking **i** and **j** to be unit vectors in perpendicular horizontal directions the forces, in newtons, exerted by the two girls are:

Sheuli	24**i** + 18**j**
Veronica	25**i** + 60**j**

(a) Calculate the magnitude and direction of the force of each of the girls.

(b) Use a scale drawing to estimate the magnitude and direction of the resultant of the forces exerted by the two girls.

(c) Write the resultant in terms of **i** and **j** and so calculate (to 3 significant figures) its magnitude and direction.

Check that your answers agree with those obtained by scale drawing in part (b).

2 The diagram shows a girder CD of mass 20 tonnes being held stationary by a crane (which is not shown). The rope from the crane (AB) is attached to a ring at B. Two ropes, BC and BD, of equal length attach the girder to B; the tension in each of these ropes is T N.

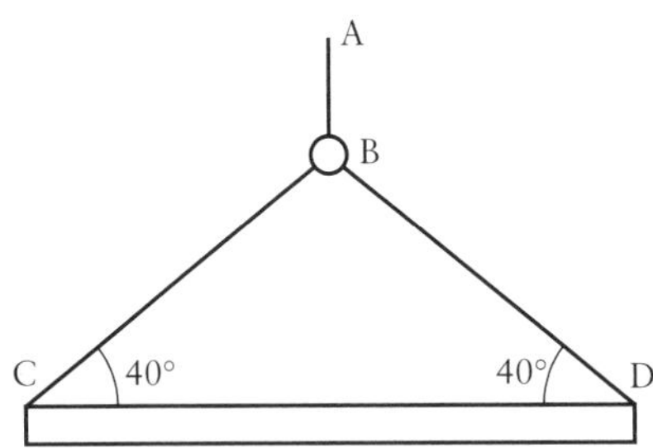

(a) Draw a diagram showing the forces acting on the girder.

(b) Write down, in terms of T, the horizontal and vertical components of the tensions in the ropes acting at C and D.

(c) Hence show that the tension in the rope BC is 152.5 kN (to 1 dp).

(d) Draw a diagram to show the three forces acting on the ring at B.

(e) Hence calculate the tension in the rope AB.

(f) How could you have known the answer to part (e) without any calculations?

3 The diagram shows a simple model of a crane. The structure is at rest in a vertical plane. The rod and cables are of negligible mass and the load suspended from the joint at A is 30 N.

(a) Draw a diagram showing the forces acting on
(i) the load (ii) the joint at A.

(b) Calculate the forces in the rod and cable 1 and state whether they are in compression or in tension.

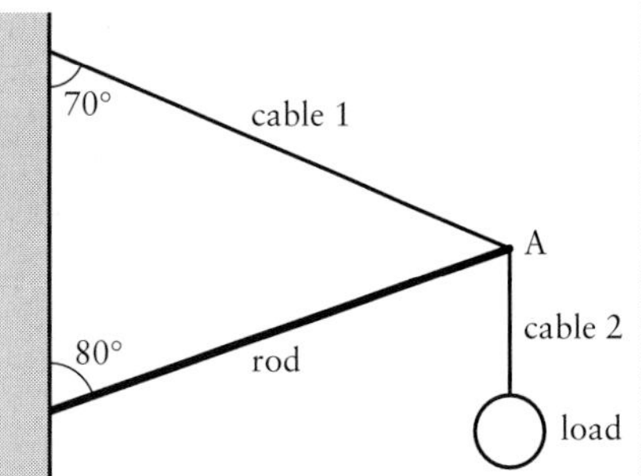

4 An angler catches a very large fish. When he tries to weigh it he finds that it is more than the 10 kg limit of his spring balance. He borrows another spring balance of exactly the same design and uses the two to weigh the fish, as shown in diagram A. Both balances read 8 kg.

(a) What is the mass of the fish?

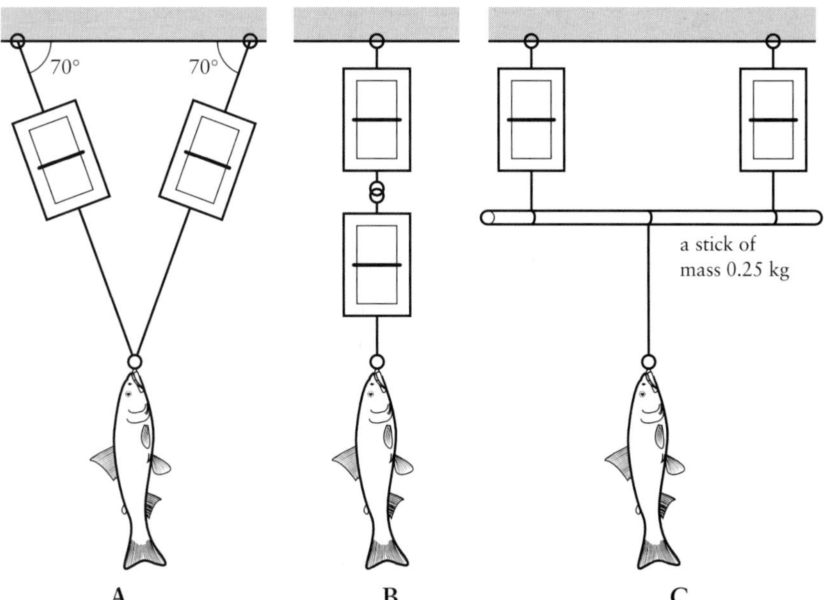

The angler believes the mass of the fish is a record and asks a witness to confirm it. The witness agrees with the measurements but cannot follow the calculations. He asks the angler to weigh the fish in two different positions, still using both balances. These are shown in diagrams B and C.

Assuming the spring balances themselves to have negligible mass, state the readings of the balances as set up in

(b) diagram B

(c) diagram C.

(d) Which of the three methods do you think is the best?

5 The diagram shows a device for crushing scrap cars. The light rod AB is hinged at A and raised by a cable which runs from B round a pulley at D and down to a winch at E. The vertical strut EAD is rigid and strong and AD = AB.

A weight of mass 1 tonne is suspended from B by the cable BC. When the weight is correctly situated above the car it is released and falls on to the car.

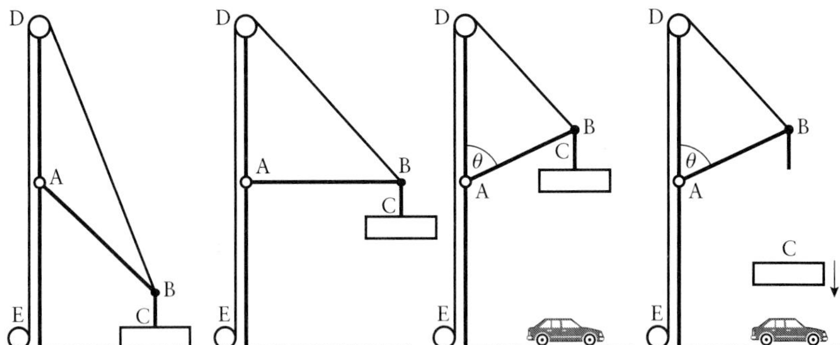

Just before the weight is released the rod AB makes angle θ with the upward vertical AD and the weight is at rest.

(a) Draw a diagram showing the forces acting at point B in this position.

(b) Explain why the rod AB must be in thrust and not in tension.

(c) Draw a diagram showing the vector sum of the forces at B (i.e. the polygon of forces).

(d) Calculate each of the three forces acting at B when

(i) $\theta = 90^\circ$ **(ii)** $\theta = 60^\circ$.

6 A ship is being towed by two tugs. Each tug exerts forces on the ship as indicated. There is also a drag force on the ship.

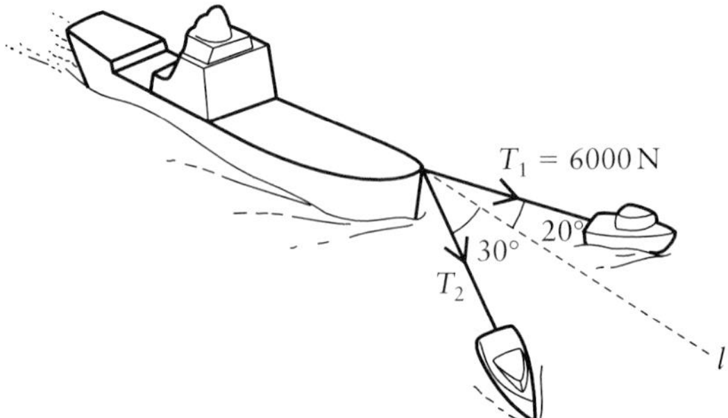

(a) Write down the components of the tensions in the towing cables along and perpendicular to the line of motion, l, of the ship.

(b) There is no resultant force perpendicular to the line l. Find T_2.

(c) The ship is travelling with constant velocity along the line l. Find the magnitude of the drag force acting on it.

7 A boat of mass 500 kg is being winched up a beach which slopes at 10° to the horizontal. The maximum friction between the boat and the beach is 3500 N and the rope from the boat to the winch is parallel to the slope of the beach. The boat is on the point of moving up the beach.

(a) Draw a diagram showing all the forces acting on the boat.

(b) Write all these forces in components parallel and perpendicular to the slope.

(c) Find the tension in the rope.

A little later the boat is moving at a constant speed of $1\,\mathrm{cm\,s^{-1}}$.

(d) What is the tension in the rope now?

The rope breaks.

(e) Will the boat ever start to slide back down the slope?

8 A skier of mass 50 kg is skiing straight down a 15° slope.

(a) Draw a diagram showing the forces acting on the skier.

(b) Resolve these forces into components parallel and perpendicular to the slope.

The skier is travelling at constant speed.

(c) Find the normal reaction of the slope on the skier and the resistance force on her.

The skier later returns to the top of the slope by being pulled up it at constant speed by a rope parallel to the slope.

(d) Assuming the resistance on the skier is the same as before, calculate the tension in the rope.

9 The diagram shows a block of mass 5 kg on a rough inclined plane. The block is attached to a 3 kg weight by a light string which passes over a smooth pulley and is on the point of sliding up the slope.

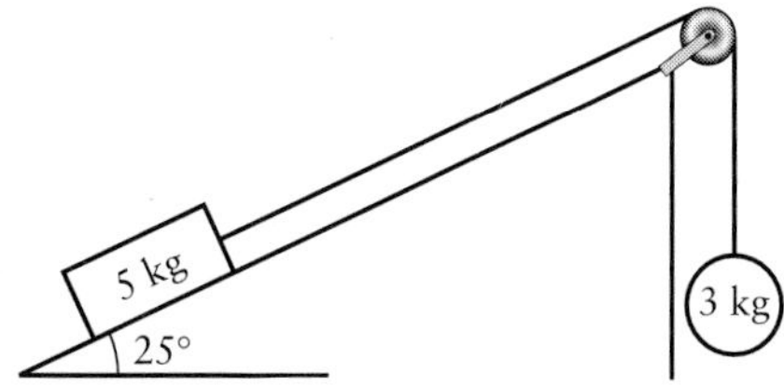

(a) Draw a diagram showing the forces acting on the block.

(b) Resolve these forces into components parallel and perpendicular to the slope.

(c) Find the force of resistance to the block's motion.

The 3 kg weight is replaced by one of mass m kg.

(d) Find the value of m for which the block is on the point of sliding down the slope, assuming the resistance to motion is the same as before.

10 Two husky dogs are pulling a sledge. They both exert forces of 60 N but at different angles to the line of the sledge, as shown in the diagram. The sledge is moving straight forwards.

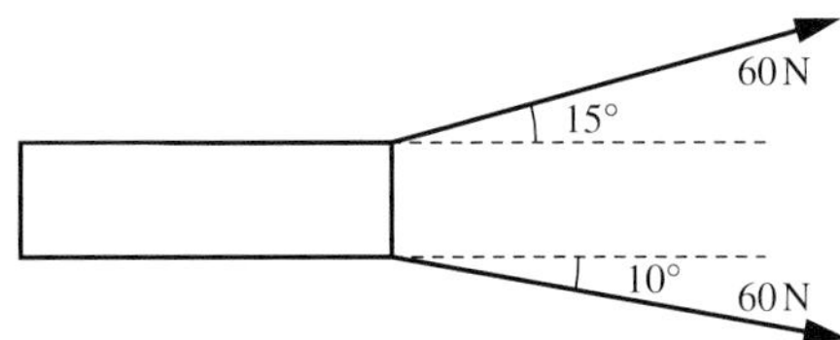

(a) Resolve the two forces into components parallel and perpendicular to the line of the sledge.

(b) Hence find

(i) the overall forward force from the dogs

(ii) the sideways force.

The resistance to motion is 20 N along the line of the sledge but up to 400 N perpendicular to it.

(c) Find the magnitude and direction of the overall horizontal force on the sledge.

(d) How much force is lost due to the dogs not pulling straight forwards?

11 One end of a string of length 1 m is fixed to a mass of 1 kg and the other end is fixed to a point A. Another string is fixed to the mass and passes over a frictionless pulley at B which is 1 m horizontally from A but 2 m above it. The tension in the second string is such that the mass is held at the same horizontal level as the point A.

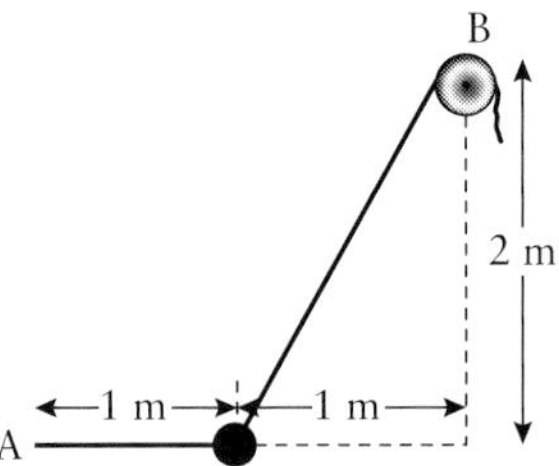

(a) Show that the tension in the horizontal string fixed to the mass and to A is 4.9 N and find the tension in the string which passes over the pulley at B. Find also the angle that this second string makes with the horizontal.

(b) If the tension in this second string is slowly increased by drawing more of it over the pulley at B describe the path followed by the mass. Will the point A, the mass and the point B ever lie in a straight line? Give reasons for your answer.

[MEI]

EXERCISE 7D **Examination-style questions**

1 The diagram shows two water-skiers being towed by a speedboat. The rope to skier A makes an angle of 20° with the wake of the boat and has a tension of 100 N. The rope to skier B makes an angle of 30° with the wake and has a tension of P N. The speedboat exerts a force of T N in the direction of motion. The system is moving at constant velocity. Find P and T.

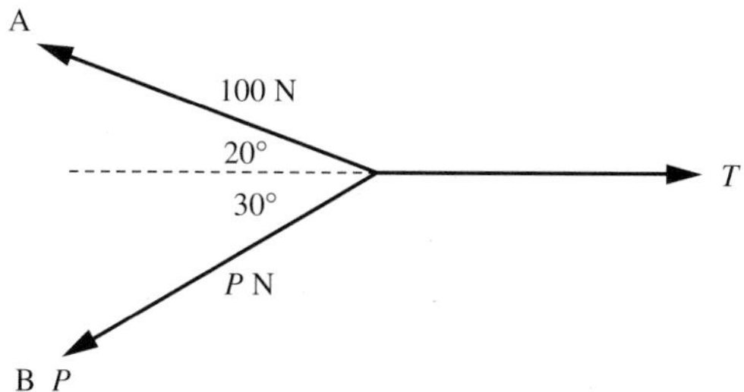

2 A decoration of mass 0.3 kg is suspended by two light strings, which are at 25° and 35° to the horizontal.

(a) Find the tension in the two strings.

(b) Comment on the assumption that the strings are light.

3 A parcel of mass 8 kg rests on a smooth slope, and is connected by a light string which passes over a smooth pulley to a mass of 2 kg, which hangs freely. The system is in equilibrium. Find the angle of the slope.

4 A block of mass 5 kg, which may be modelled as a particle, is on a smooth slope which is at an angle of 30° to the horizontal. It is held in equilibrium by a force P N which is at 20° to the horizontal.

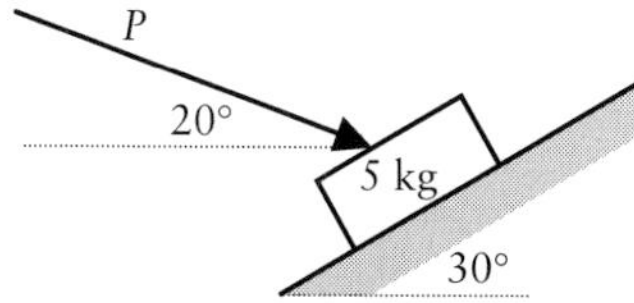

(a) Find P.

(b) Find the normal reaction between the mass and the slope.

5 The diagram shows a parcel of mass 6 kg being carried by means of the string around it. The string section AB is at 40° to the horizontal, while the section AC is at 20°.

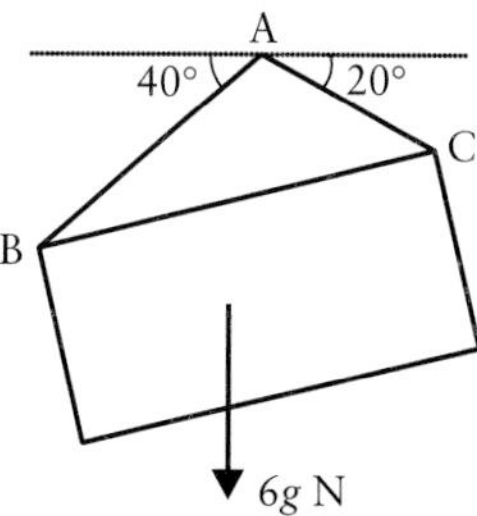

Find, to 3 significant figures, the tensions in string section

(a) AB **(b)** AC.

6 The diagram shows a particle of mass 8 kg resting on a smooth slope which is at an angle α to the horizontal, where $\tan\alpha = \frac{5}{12}$. The particle is held in equilibrium by a horizontal force P N.

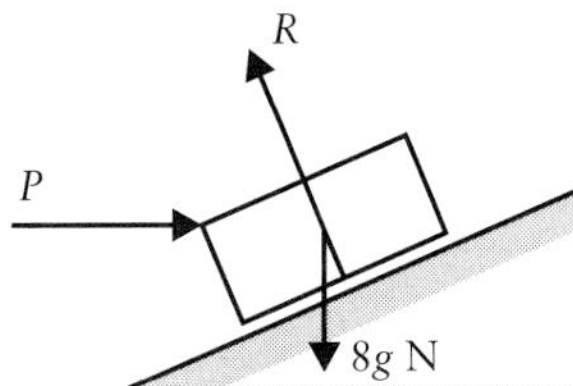

Find, to 3 significant figures

(a) the magnitude of the normal reaction between the particle and the plane

(b) the magnitude of P.

7 At a steam rally, a tug-of-war has been arranged between a traction engine and two teams of people. Team A is pulling at an angle of 20° to the centre line of the traction engine with a force of 10 kN. Team B is pulling at an angle of α on the other side of the centre line with a force of 7 kN. The traction engine is pulling with force P kN along its centre line, and the whole system is in equilibrium.

(a) Find α. **(b)** Find P.

8 The diagram shows a game of conkers in which the two strings have become entangled. Conker A has mass 20 g, and conker B has mass 15 g.

(a) Suggest a suitable model for each conker.

(b) Find the tension in string section AB.

(c) Find the tensions in string sections BC and BD.

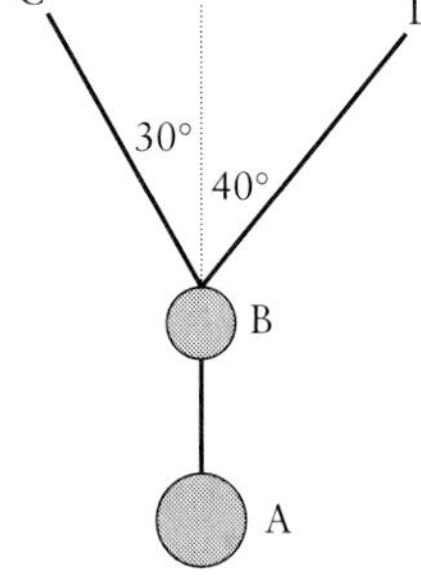

9 The diagram shows a light washing line ABCD with two heavy garments hanging on it. The string section AB is at 15° to the horizontal, BC is horizontal, while the section CD is at an angle of α to the horizontal.

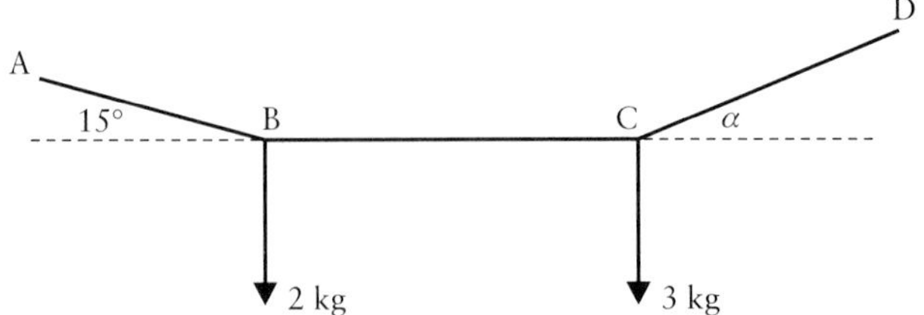

(a) Suggest suitable models for the garments and the washing line.

(b) Find the tension in AB.

(c) Find the tension in BC.

(d) Find the tension in CD and the angle α.

10 The diagram shows a portion of the rigging of a schooner. The mast BD is vertical and may be modelled as a light rod. The stay section AB is at 15° to the vertical and has a tension of 2 kN. The stay section BC is at 70° to the vertical. Both stays may be modelled as light strings. The system is in equilibrium.

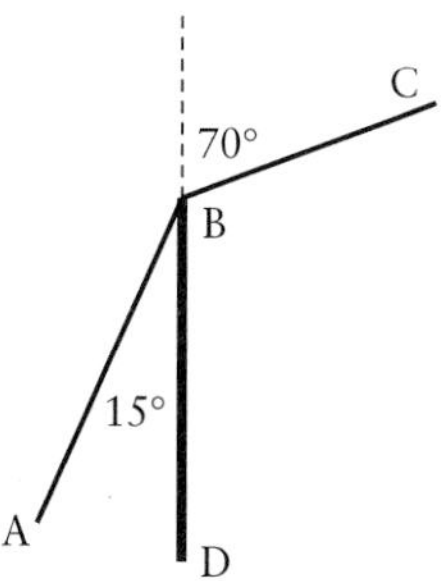

(a) Find the tension in stay BC.

(b) Find the thrust in the mast.

11

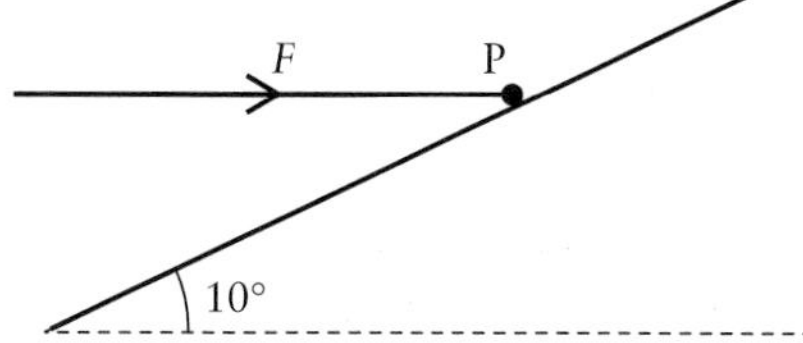

A smooth plane is inclined at an angle 10° to the horizontal. A particle P of mass 2 kg is held in equilibrium on the plane by a horizontal force of magnitude F newtons, as shown in the diagram. Find, to 3 significant figures

(a) the normal reaction exerted by the plane on P

(b) the value of F.

[Edexcel]

12

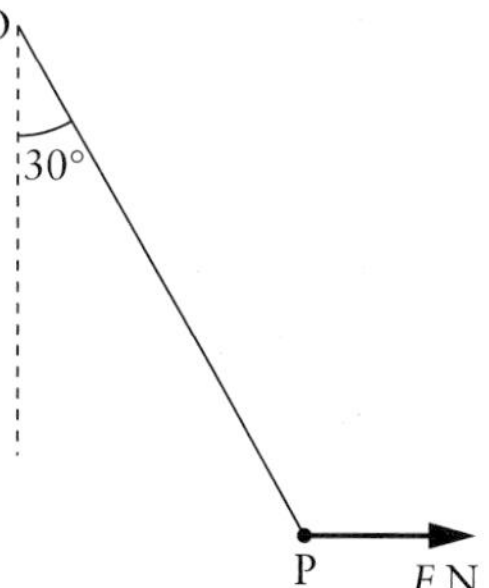

A particle P of weight 6 N is attached to one end of a light inextensible string. The other end of the string is attached to a fixed point O. A horizontal force of magnitude F newtons is applied to P. The particle P is in equilibrium under gravity with the string making an angle of 30° with the vertical, as shown in the diagram. Find, to 3 significant figures

(a) the tension in the string

(b) the value of F.

[Edexcel]

13 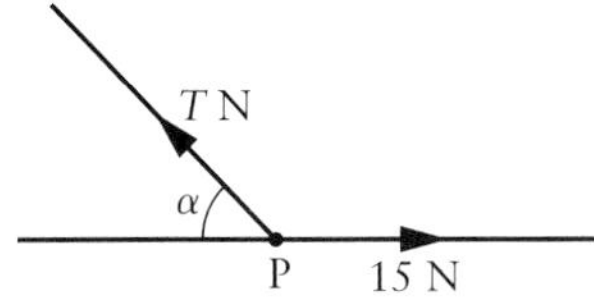

A particle P of mass 2 kg is held in equilibrium under gravity by two light inextensible strings. One string is horizontal and the other is inclined at an angle α to the horizontal, as shown in the diagram. The tension in the horizontal string is 15 N. The tension in the other string is T newtons.

(a) Find the size of the angle α.

(b) Find the value of T.

[Edexcel]

KEY POINTS

1 The forces acting on a particle can be combined to form a *resultant force* using scale drawing (trigonometry) or components.

Scale drawing

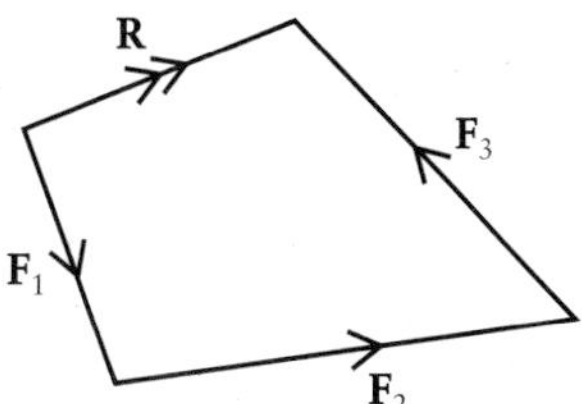

- Draw an accurate diagram, then measure the resultant. This is less accurate than calculation.
- To calculate the resultant, find the resultant of two forces at a time using the trigonometry of triangles. This is time-consuming for more than two forces.

Components

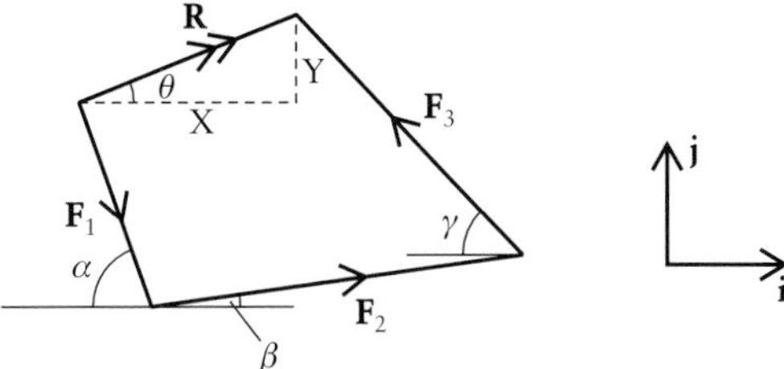

When $\mathbf{R}$ is $X\mathbf{i} + Y\mathbf{j}$

$$X = F_1\cos\alpha + F_2\cos\beta - F_3\cos\gamma$$

$$Y = -F_1\sin\alpha + F_2\sin\beta + F_3\sin\gamma$$

$$|\mathbf{R}| = \sqrt{X^2 + Y^2}$$

$$\tan\theta = \frac{Y}{X}$$

2 **Equilibrium**
When the resultant $\mathbf{R}$ is zero, the forces are in equilibrium.

Three forces in equilibrium can be represented in magnitude and direction by the sides of a triangle, taken in order.

3 When a particle is on a slope, it is usually helpful to resolve in directions parallel and perpendicular to the slope.

Chapter eight

FRICTION

To sleep: perchance to dream: ay, there's the rub.

William Shakespeare, Hamlet

This statement about a road accident was offered to a magistrate's court by a solicitor.

'Briefly the circumstances of the accident are that our client was driving his Porsche motor car. He had just left work at the end of the day. He was stationary at the junction with Plymouth Road when a motorcyclist travelling down the Plymouth Road from Tavistock lost control of his motorcycle due to excessive speed and collided with the front offside of our client's motor car.

'The motorcyclist was braking when he lost control and left a 26 metre skid mark on the road. Our advice from an expert witness is that the motorcyclist was exceeding the speed limit of 30 mph.'

It is the duty of a court to decide whether the motorcyclist was innocent or guilty. Is it possible to deduce his speed from the skid mark? Draw a sketch map and make a list of the important factors that you would need to consider when modelling this situation.

A MODEL FOR FRICTION

Clearly the key information is provided by the skid marks. To interpret it, you need a model for how friction works; in this case between the motorcycle's tyres and the road.

As a result of experimental work Coulomb formulated a model for friction between two surfaces. The following laws are usually attributed to him.

- Friction always opposes relative motion between two surfaces in contact.
- Friction is independent of the relative speed of the surfaces.
- The magnitude of the frictional force has a maximum which depends on the normal reaction between the surfaces and on the roughness of the surfaces in contact.
- If there is no sliding between the surfaces

  $$F \leqslant \mu R$$

  where F is the force due to friction and R is the normal reaction.
  μ is called *the coefficient of friction.*
- When sliding is just about to occur, friction is said to be *limiting* and $F = \mu R$.
- When sliding occurs $F = \mu R$.

According to Coulomb's model, μ is a constant for any pair of surfaces.

Typical values and ranges of values for the coefficient of friction μ are given in this table.

Surfaces in contact	μ
wood sliding on wood	0.2–0.6
metal sliding on metal	0.15–0.3
normal tyres on dry road	0.8
racing tyres on dry road	1.0
sandpaper on sandpaper	2.0
skis on snow	0.02

HOW FAST WAS THE MOTORCYCLIST GOING?

You can now proceed with the problem. As an initial model, you might make the following assumptions:

- that the road is level;
- that the motorcycle was at rest just as it hit the car. (Obviously it was not, but this assumption allows you to estimate a minimum initial speed for the motorcycle);
- that the motorcycle and rider may be treated as a particle, subject to Coulomb's laws of friction with $\mu = 0.8$ (i.e. dry road conditions).

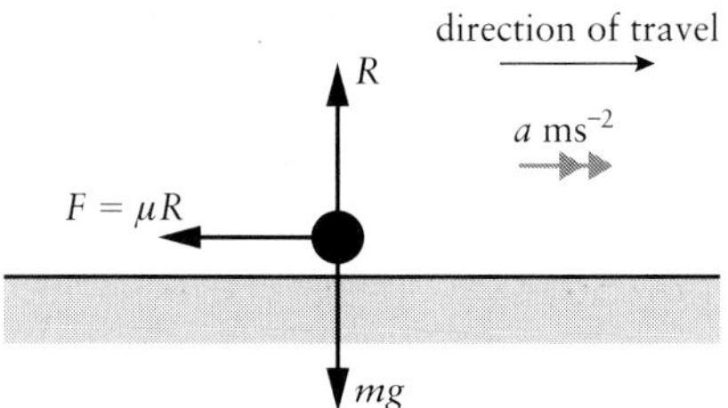

FIGURE 8.1

The calculation then proceeds as follows.

Taking the direction of travel as positive, let the motorcycle and rider have acceleration $a\,\text{ms}^{-2}$ and mass m kg. You have probably realised that the acceleration will be negative. The forces (in N) and acceleration are shown in figure 8.1.

Applying Newton's second law:

perpendicular to the road, since there is no vertical acceleration we have

$$R - mg = 0; \qquad ①$$

parallel to the road, there is a constant force $-\mu R$ from friction, so we have

$$-\mu R = ma. \qquad ②$$

Solving for a gives

$$a = -\frac{\mu R}{m} = -\frac{\mu mg}{m} = -\mu g$$

From ① $R = mg$

Taking $g = 10\,\text{ms}^{-2}$ and $\mu = 0.8$ gives $a = -8\,\text{ms}^{-2}$.

The constant acceleration equation

$$v^2 = u^2 + 2as$$

can be used to calculate the initial speed of the motorcycle. Substituting $s = 26$, $v = 0$ and $a = -8$ gives

$$u = \sqrt{2 \times 8 \times 26} = 20.4\,\text{ms}^{-1}$$

This figure can be converted to miles per hour (using the fact that 1 mile $\approx$ 1600 m):

$$\text{speed} = \frac{20.4 \times 3600}{1600}\ \text{mph}$$
$$= 45.9\ \text{mph}$$

So this first simple model suggests that the motorcycle was travelling at a speed of at least 45.9 mph before skidding began.

MODELLING WITH FRICTION

Whilst there is always some frictional force between two sliding surfaces its magnitude is often very small. In such cases we ignore the frictional force and describe the surfaces as *smooth*.

In situations where frictional forces cannot be ignored we describe the surface(s) as *rough*. Coulomb's law is the standard model for dealing with such cases.

Frictional forces are essential in many ways. For example, a ladder leaning against a wall would always slide if there were no friction between the foot of the ladder and the ground. The absence of friction in icy conditions causes difficulties for road users: pedestrians slip over, cars and motorcycles skid.

Remember that friction always opposes sliding motion.

Historical Note

Charles Augustin de Coulomb was born in Angoulême in France in 1736 and is best remembered for his work on electricity rather than for that on friction. The unit for electric charge is named after him.

Coulomb was a military engineer and worked for many years in the West Indies, eventually returning to France in poor health not long before the Revolution. He worked in many fields, including the elasticity of metal, silk fibres and the design of windmills. He died in Paris in 1806.

EXAMPLE 8.1

A horizontal rope is attached to a crate of mass 70 kg at rest on a flat surface. The coefficient of friction between the floor and the crate is 0.6. Find the maximum force that the rope can exert on the crate without moving it.

Solution

The forces (in N) acting on the crate are shown in figure 8.2.
Since the crate does not move, it is in equilibrium.

Horizontal forces: $T = F$

Vertical forces: $R = mg$

$= 70 \times 9.8 = 686$

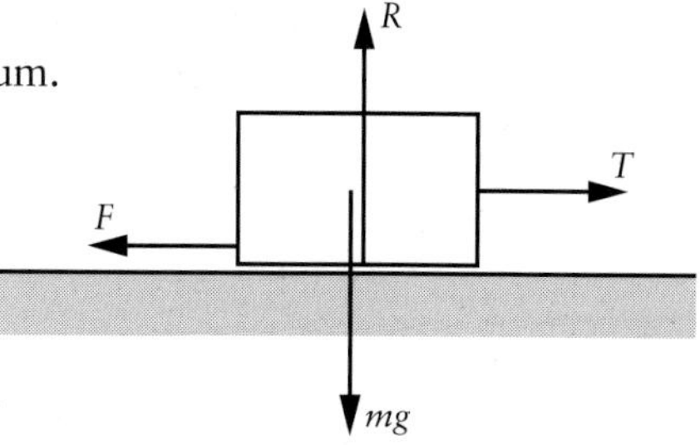

FIGURE 8.2

The law of friction states that:

$F \leqslant \mu R$ for objects at rest.

So in this case $F \leqslant 0.6 \times 686$

$F \leqslant 411.6$

The maximum frictional force is 412 N. As the tension in the rope and the force of friction are the only forces which have horizontal components, the crate will remain in equilibrium unless the tension in the rope is greater than 412 N.

EXAMPLE 8.2

Angus is pulling a sledge of mass 12 kg at steady speed across level snow by means of a rope which makes an angle of 20° with the horizontal. The coefficient of friction between the sledge and the ground is 0.15. What is the tension in the rope?

Solution Since the sledge is travelling at steady speed, the forces acting on it are in equilibrium. They are shown in figure 8.3.

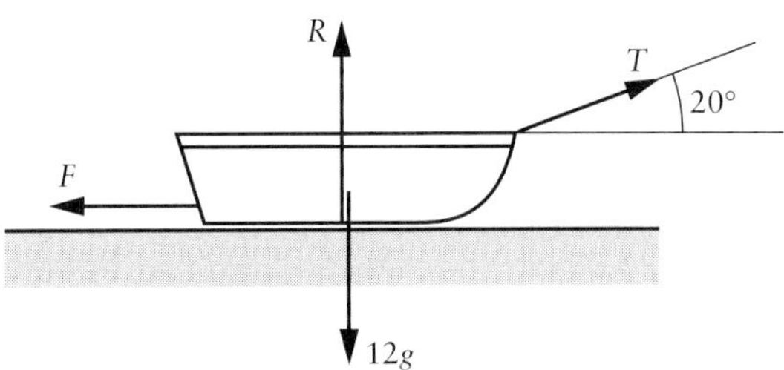

FIGURE 8.3

$$\text{Horizontally:} \quad T\cos 20° = F$$
$$= 0.15R$$

$F = \mu R$ when the sledge slides

$$\text{Vertically:} \quad T\sin 20° + R = 12g$$
$$R = 12 \times 9.8 - T\sin 20°$$

Combining these gives

$$T\cos 20° = 0.15\,(12 \times 9.8 - T\sin 20°)$$
$$T\,(\cos 20° + 0.15\sin 20°) = 0.15 \times 12 \times 9.8$$
$$T = 17.8$$

The tension is 17.8 N.

Notice that the normal reaction is reduced when the rope is pulled in an upwards direction. This has the effect of reducing the friction and making the sledge easier to pull.

EXAMPLE 8.3

A ski slope is designed for beginners. Its angle to the horizontal is such that skiers will either remain at rest on the point of moving or, if they are pushed off, move at constant speed. The coefficient of friction between the skis and the slope is 0.35. Find the angle that the slope makes with the horizontal.

Solution Figure 8.4 shows the forces on the skier.

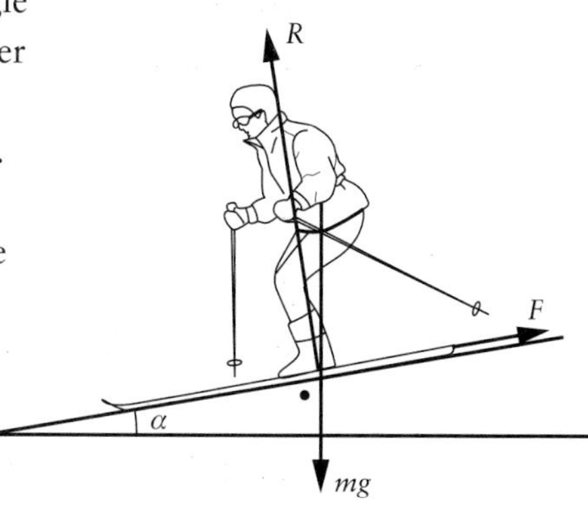

FIGURE 8.4

The weight mg can be resolved into components $mg\cos\alpha$ perpendicular to the slope and $mg\sin\alpha$ parallel to the slope.

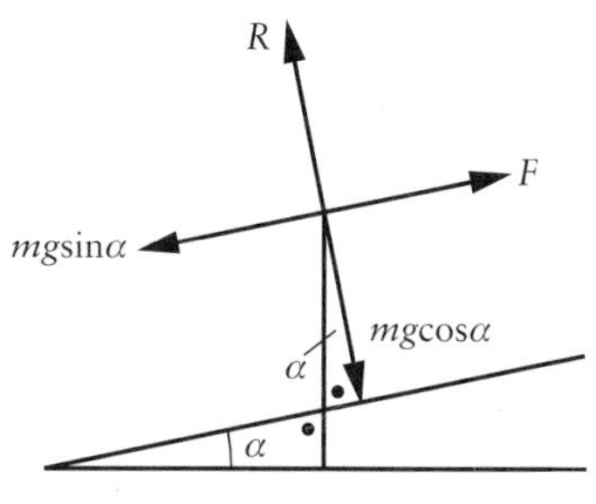

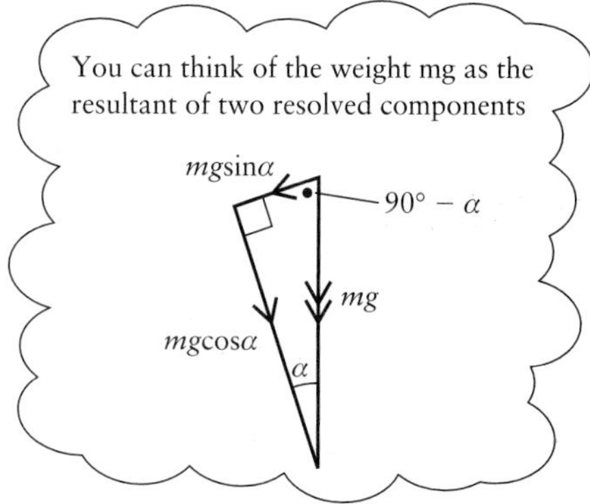

You can think of the weight mg as the resultant of two resolved components
mgsinα
90° − α
mg
mgcosα
α

FIGURE 8.5

Since the skier is in equilibrium (at rest or moving with constant speed) applying Newton's second law:

Parallel to slope: $mg\sin\alpha - F = 0$

$\Rightarrow F = mg\sin\alpha$ ①

Perpendicular to slope: $R - mg\cos\alpha = 0$

$\Rightarrow R = mg\cos\alpha$ ②

In limiting equilibrium or moving at constant speed,

$$F = \mu R$$

$$mg\sin\alpha = \mu\, mg\cos\alpha$$

Substituting for F and R from ① and ②

$$\Rightarrow \quad \mu = \frac{\sin\alpha}{\cos\alpha} = \tan\alpha$$

In this case $\mu = 0.35$, so $\tan\alpha = 0.35$ and $\alpha = 19.3°$

Notes

1 The result is independent of the mass of the skier. This is often found in simple mechanics models. For example, two objects of different mass fall to the ground with the same acceleration. However when such models are refined, for example to take account of air resistance, mass is often found to have some effect on the result.

2 The angle for which the skier is about to slide down the slope is called the angle of friction. The angle of friction is often denoted by λ (lambda) and defined by $\tan\lambda = \mu$.

When the angle of the slope (α) is equal to the angle of the friction (λ), it is just possible for the skier to stand on the slope without sliding. If the slope is slightly steeper, the skier will slide immediately, and if it is less steep he or she will find it difficult to slide at all without using the ski poles.

EXAMPLE 8.4

A block of mass 3 kg rests on a rough plane inclined at an angle θ to the horizontal, where $\tan\theta = \frac{3}{4}$. The coefficient of friction between the block and the plane is 0.4. The block is connected to a light string which passes over a small smooth pulley fixed at the top of the plane. The other end of the string is connected to another block of mass m which hangs freely. The block of mass 3 kg is just prevented from sliding down the plane. Find m.

Solution

Figure 8.6 shows the forces in the system.

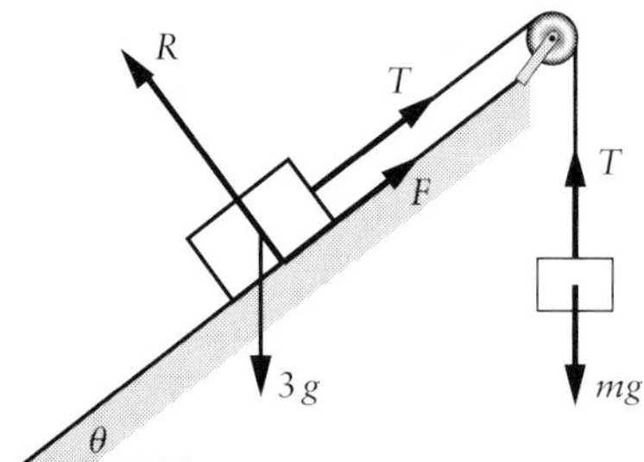

FIGURE 8.6

For the 3 kg block, resolving perpendicular to the plane (↖):

$$R - 3g\cos\theta = 0 \qquad ①$$

Resolving parallel to the plane (↗):

$$T + F - 3g\sin\theta = 0 \qquad ②$$

Since it is about to slide, friction is limiting and $F = \mu R$.

Substituting from ①: $F = 0.4 \times 3g\cos\theta = 9.408\text{ N}$

From ②: $T = 3g\sin\theta - F = 8.232\text{ N}$

As the hanging mass is in equilibrium, $T = mg$

and $m = \dfrac{T}{g} = 0.84\text{ kg}$

EXERCISE 8A

You will find it helpful to draw diagrams when answering these questions.

1 A block of mass 10 kg is resting on a horizontal surface. It is being pulled by a horizontal force T (in N), and is on the point of sliding. Draw a diagram showing the forces acting and find the coefficient of friction when

(a) $T = 9.8$ **(b)** $T = 49$.

2 The brakes on a caravan of mass 700 kg have seized so that the wheels will not turn. What force must be exerted on the caravan to make it move horizontally? (The coefficient of friction between the tyres and the road is 0.7.)

3 A box of mass 50 kg is being moved across a room. To help it to slide a suitable mat is placed underneath the box.

(a) Explain why the mat makes it easier to slide the box.

A force of 98 N is needed to slide the mat at a constant velocity.

(b) What is the value of the coefficient of friction between the box and the floor?

A child of mass 20 kg climbs on to the box.

(c) What force is now needed to slide the mat at constant velocity?

4 Shona, whose mass is 30 kg, is sitting on a sledge of mass 10 kg which is being pulled at constant speed along horizontal ground by her older brother, Aloke. The coefficient of friction between the sledge and the snow-covered ground is 0.15. Find the tension in the rope from Aloke's hand to the sledge when

(a) the rope is horizontal

(b) the rope makes an angle of 30° with the horizontal.

5 In each of the following situations a brick is about to slide down a rough inclined plane. Find the unknown quantity.

(a) The plane is inclined at 30° to the horizontal and the brick has mass 2 kg. Find μ.

(b) The brick has mass 4 kg and the coefficient of friction is 0.7. Find the angle of the slope.

(c) The plane is at 65° to the horizontal and the brick has mass 5 kg. Find μ.

(d) The brick has mass 6 kg and μ is 1.2. Find the angle of the slope.

6 The coefficient of friction between the skis and an artificial ski slope for learners is 0.3. During a run the angle, α, which the slope makes with the horizontal varies so that initially the skier accelerates, then travels at constant speed and then slows down. What can you say about the values of α in each of these three parts of the run?

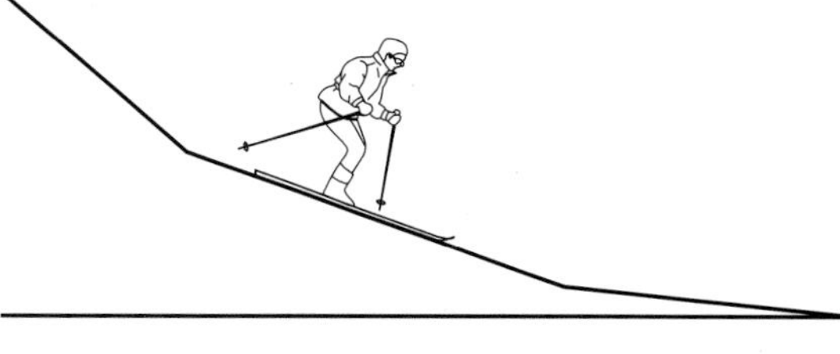

7 The diagram shows a mop being used to clean the floor. The coefficient of friction between the mop and the floor is 0.3.

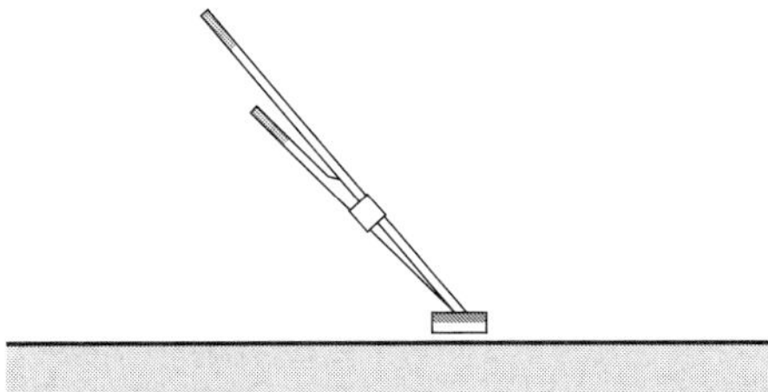

(a) Draw a diagram showing the forces acting on the head of the mop.

In an initial model the weight of the mop is assumed to be negligible.

(b) Find the angle between the handle and the horizontal when the mop head is moving across the floor at constant velocity. Explain briefly why this angle is independent of how much force is exerted on the mop.

In a more refined model the weight of the head of the mop is taken to be 5 N, but the weight of the handle is still ignored.

(c) Use this model to calculate the thrust in the handle if it is held at 70° to the horizontal while the head moves at constant velocity across the floor.

(d) Could the same model be applied to a carpet cleaner on wheels? Explain your reasoning.

8 The diagram shows a block of mass 0.5 kg resting on a rough inclined plane. The block is attached to a fixed point by a stretched elastic string, parallel to the plane. The coefficient of friction is 0.7 and the angle which the plane makes with the horizontal is given by $\alpha = \arcsin 0.6$.

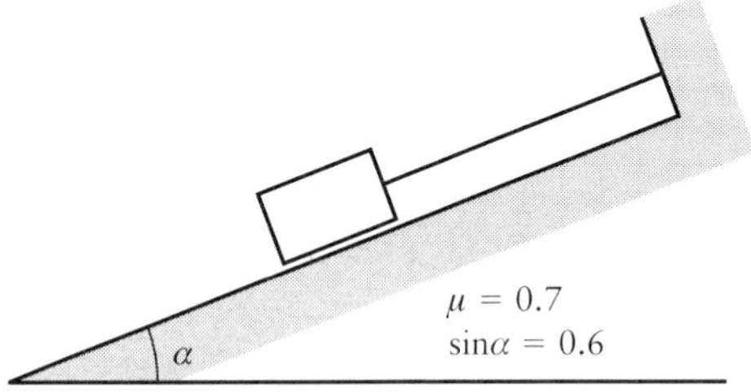

(a) Find the tension in the string when the block is on the point of sliding up the plane.

The block is pulled further down the plane from this position so that the tension is greater. It is then released and it slides up the plane for some distance before coming momentarily to rest with the string slack.

(b) What happens next?

9 A box of weight 100 N is pulled at steady speed across a rough horizontal surface by a rope which makes an angle α with the horizontal. The coefficient of friction between the box and the surface is 0.4. Assume that the box slides on its underside and does not tip up.

(a) Find the tension in the string when the value of α is

(i) $10°$ **(ii)** $20°$ **(iii)** $30°$

(b) Find an expression for the value of T for any angle α.

DYNAMIC FRICTION

When relative motion is actually happening, the friction is always limiting, so $F = \mu R$. This makes calculating its value quite easy. The coefficient of friction often drops slightly, and is then called the *coefficient of dynamic friction*, but this effect is quite small and is usually ignored in a first model. There will usually be an acceleration, so we must use $F = ma$. The acceleration usually turns out to be constant, so we can use the constant acceleration equations.

EXAMPLE 8.5

A book is pushed across a table with an initial velocity of $2\,\text{ms}^{-1}$. The coefficient of friction between the book and the table is 0.2. Find how far the book travels before coming to rest.

Solution This is a very common case where we are not given the mass of the book, which might be important. We must therefore give it a letter.

Let the mass of the book be m kg. The diagram shows the forces on the system.

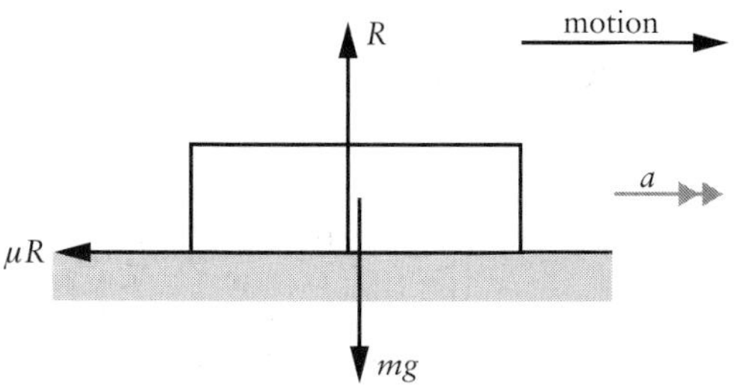

FIGURE 8.7

Vertically, the system is in equilibrium, so $R = mg$

Friction is limiting, so $F = 0.2R = 0.2mg$

Horizontally, $F = ma$ $\quad -0.2mg = ma$

m cancels, and $a = -1.96\,\text{ms}^{-2}$

Using $v^2 = u^2 + 2as$ $\quad 0 = 4 - (2 \times 1.96s)$

$s = 1.02\,\text{m}$

The book travels 1.02 m.

EXAMPLE 8.6

Figure 8.8 shows a block of mass 5 kg on a rough table. It is connected by light inextensible strings passing over smooth pulleys to masses of 4 kg and 7 kg which hang vertically. The coefficient of friction between the block and the table is 0.4.

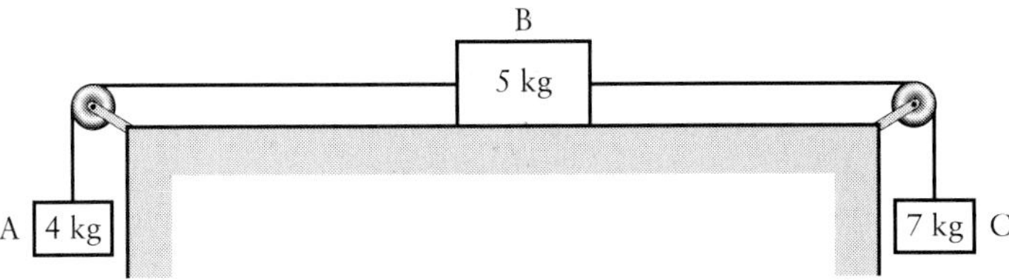

FIGURE 8.8

(a) Draw a diagram showing the forces acting on the three blocks and the direction of acceleration if the system moves.

(b) Show that acceleration does take place.

(c) Find the acceleration of the system and the tensions in the strings.

Solution **(a)**

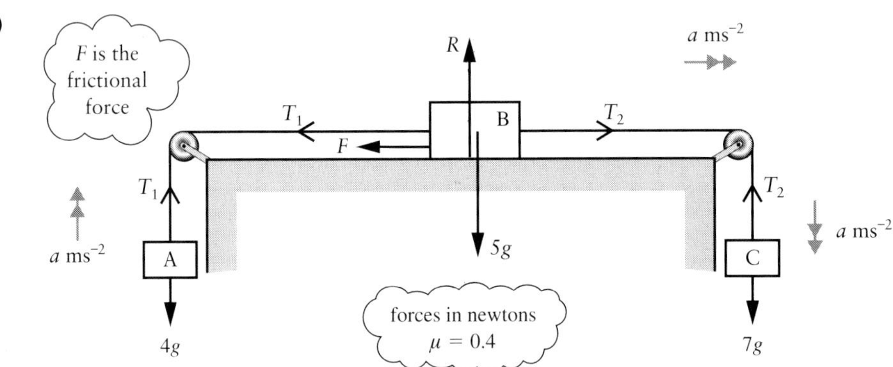

FIGURE 8.9

If acceleration takes place it is in the direction shown and $a > 0$.

(b) When the acceleration is a ms^{-2} ($\geqslant 0$), Newton's second law gives

for B, horizontally $\quad T_2 - T_1 - F = 5a$ ①

for A, vertically upwards: $\quad T_1 - 4g = 4a$ ②

for C, vertically downwards: $\quad 7g - T_2 = 7a$ ③

Adding ①, ② and ③, $\quad 3g - F = 16a$ ④

B has no vertical acceleration so $\quad R = 5g$

The maximum possible value of F is $\mu R = 0.4 \times 5g = 2g$

In ④, a can be zero only if $F = 3g$, so $a > 0$ and sliding occurs.

(c) When sliding occurs, $F = 2g$.

Equation ④ gives $\quad 3g - 2g = g = 16a$

$$a = 0.6125$$

Back-substituting gives $\quad T_1 = 41.65$ and $T_2 = 64.3125$

The acceleration is 0.61 ms^{-2} and the tensions are 42 N and 64 N.

EXERCISE 8B

1 In each of the following situations, use the equation of motion for each object to decide whether the block moves. If so, find the magnitude of the acceleration and if not, write down the magnitude of the frictional force.

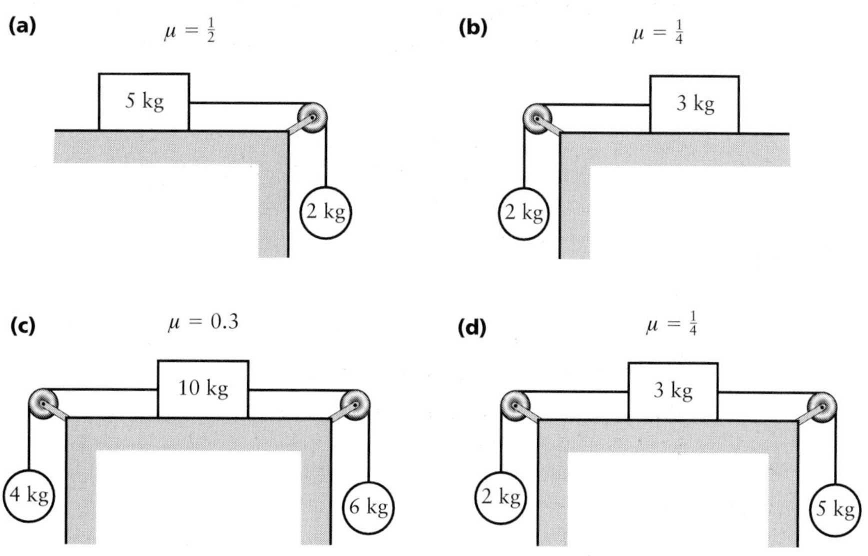

2 A boy slides a piece of ice of mass 100 g across the surface of a frozen lake. Its initial speed is $10\,\mathrm{ms^{-1}}$ and it takes 49 m to come to rest.

(a) Find the deceleration of the piece of ice.

(b) Find the frictional force acting on the piece of ice.

(c) Find the coefficient of friction between the piece of ice and the surface of the lake.

(d) How far will a 200 g piece of ice travel if it, too, is given an initial speed of $10\,\mathrm{ms^{-1}}$?

3 Jasmine is cycling at $12\,\mathrm{ms^{-1}}$ when her bag falls off the back of her cycle. The bag slides a distance of 9 m before coming to rest. Calculate the coefficient of friction between the bag and the road.

4 A car of mass 1200 kg is travelling at $20\,\mathrm{ms^{-1}}$ when it is forced to perform an emergency stop. Its wheels lock as soon as the brakes are applied so that they slide along the road without rotating. For the first 15 m the coefficient of friction between the wheels and the road is 0.75 but then the road surface changes and the coefficient of friction becomes 0.8.

(a) Find the deceleration of the car immediately after the brakes are applied.

(b) Find the speed of the car when it comes to the change of road surface.

(c) Find the total distance the car travels before it comes to rest.

5 The diagram shows a boy on a simple playground slide. The coefficient of friction between a typically clothed child and the slide is 0.25 and it can be assumed that no speed is lost when changing direction at B. The section AB is 3 m long and makes an angle of 40° with the horizontal. The slide is designed so that a child, starting from rest, stops at just the right moment of arrival at C.

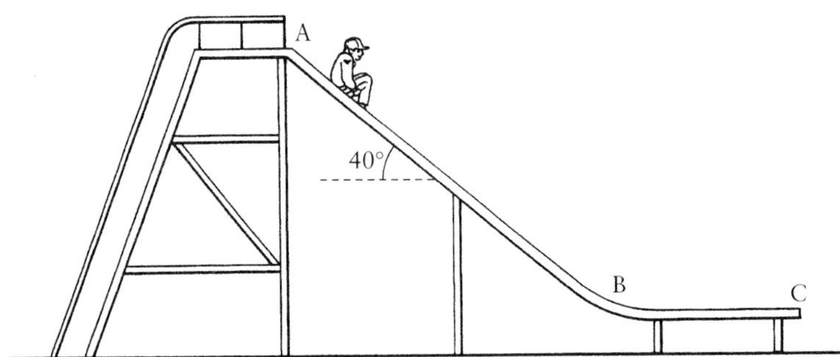

(a) Draw a diagram showing the forces acting on the boy when on the sloping section AB.

(b) Calculate the acceleration of the boy when on the section AB.

(c) Calculate the speed on reaching B.

(d) Find the length of the horizontal section BC.

6

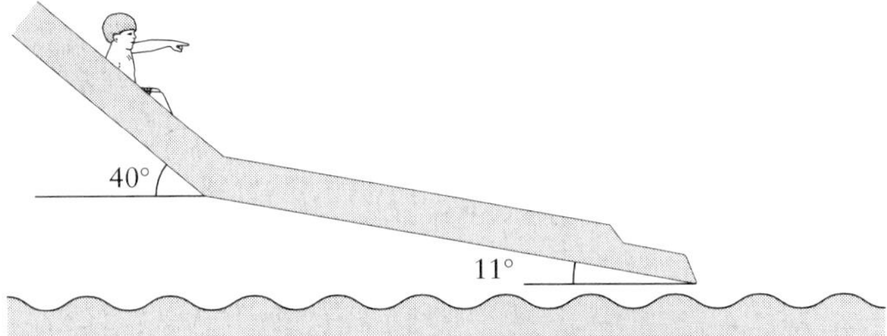

A chute at a water sports centre has been designed so that swimmers first slide down a steep part which is 10 m long and at an angle of 40° to the horizontal. They then come to a 20 m section with a gentler slope, 11° to the horizontal, where they travel at constant speed.

(a) Find the coefficient of friction between a swimmer and the chute.

(b) Find the acceleration of a swimmer on the steep part.

(c) Find the speed at the end of the chute of a swimmer who starts at rest. (You may assume that no speed is lost at the point where the slope changes.)

An alternative design of chute has the same starting and finishing points but has a constant gradient.

(d) With what speed do swimmers arrive at the end of this chute?

EXERCISE 8C **Examination-style questions**

1 A sledge of mass 15 kg is being pulled at constant velocity across level snow by a light rope which is at an angle of 30° to the horizontal. The coefficient of friction between the sledge and the snow is 0.1. Find the tension in the rope.

2 A boat of mass 100 kg is being pulled at constant velocity up a beach which is at 5° to the horizontal by a light rope which is parallel to the beach. The coefficient of friction between the boat and the beach is 0.4. Find the tension in the rope.

3 A high-speed train is travelling on level track at its top speed of $300\,\text{km}\,\text{h}^{-1}$ when it has to make an emergency stop. The coefficient of friction between the wheels and the rails is 0.3. Find

(a) the shortest time at which it can come to a halt

(b) how far it would travel in that time.

4 A particle of mass 1.5 kg rests on a rough slope, and is connected by a light string which passes over a smooth pulley to a block of mass of m kg, which hangs freely. The slope is at an angle of 40° to the horizontal, and the coefficient of friction between the particle and the slope is 0.2. The particle is on the point of moving up the plane. Find m.

5 The diagram shows a block of mass 4 kg resting on a rough table. The coefficient of friction between the table and the block is 0.4. The block is connected by a light inextensible string, which passes over a smooth pulley at the end of the table, to a particle of mass of 2 kg, which hangs vertically.

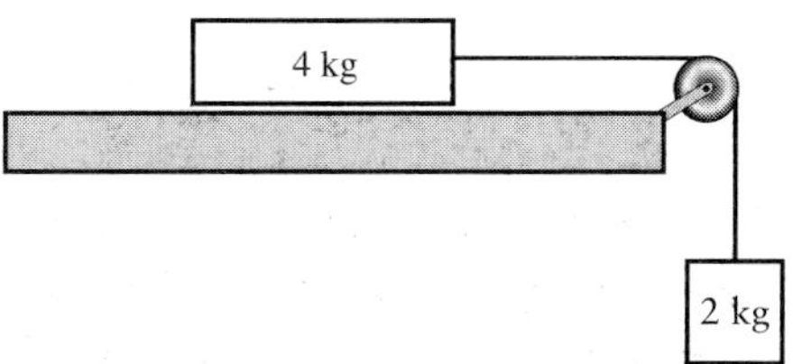

(a) Show that acceleration takes place.

(b) Find the value of the acceleration.

(c) Find the tension in the string.

6 A mop may be modelled as a particle of mass 2 kg attached to a light rod. The mop is pushed across a horizontal floor at constant speed.

(a) When the rod is at an angle of 70° to the horizontal, the force required to move the mop is 25 N. Find the coefficient of friction between the mop and the floor.

(b) The angle of the rod is changed to 50° to the horizontal. Find the new force required to move the mop.

7 The diagram shows two planes. Plane AB is at angle α to the horizontal, where $\tan\alpha = \frac{4}{3}$, and is rough. Plane BC is at angle β to the horizontal, where $\tan\beta = \frac{3}{4}$, and is smooth. A particle of mass 4 kg rests on plane AB and is connected by a light string, which passes over a smooth pulley at B, to a particle of mass 2 kg which rests on plane BC.

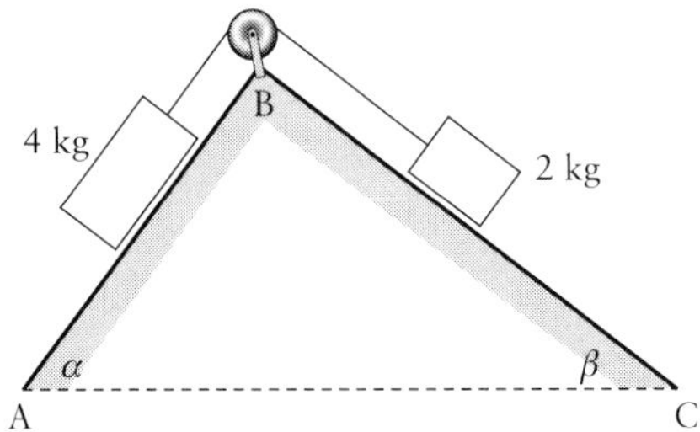

(a) The system is on the point of sliding, with the particle of mass 4 kg sliding down. Find the coefficient of friction between it and the plane AB.

(b) Both planes are now replaced by rough planes with the same coefficient of friction. The system is still on the point of sliding the same way. Find the new coefficient of friction.

8 A crate is pushed down a ramp which is at an angle of 25° to the horizontal. The crate starts with a velocity of $2\,\mathrm{ms}^{-1}$, and stops after a distance of 0.4 m.

(a) Find the coefficient of friction between the crate and the ramp.

(b) At what angle should the ramp be for the crate to maintain a constant speed?

9 A ski slope is at a constant angle of 3° to the horizontal. The coefficient of friction between the skis and the slope is 0.03.

(a) A skier of mass 70 kg starts from rest. Find the skier's velocity after 200 m.

(b) The skier returns to the top using a drag lift. The skier is connected to a light rope which makes an angle of 10° with the slope, and is pulled up the slope at constant speed. Find the tension in the rope.

10 A teacher is making a pile of ring binders. The cross-section of one may be modelled as an isosceles trapezium with parallel sides of 50 mm and 10 mm. The perpendicular distance between the parallel sides is 260 mm. The coefficient of friction between any two binders is 0.5.

(a) Find the angle between the non-parallel sides of the binders.

(b) Assuming that each binder is put the same way round, and that equilibrium is broken by sliding and not by toppling, find which binder causes equilibrium to fail.

(c) Comment on the assumption that equilibrium is broken by sliding and not by toppling.

(d) If the binders are placed alternate ways round, how high can the pile get?

11 The diagram shows two particles, A and B. A is of mass $3m$ kg and rests on a rough plane with coefficient of friction $\frac{1}{3}$. A is connected to B by a light inextensible string which passes over a smooth pulley. B is of mass $2m$ and hangs freely. The system is released from rest with the string taut.

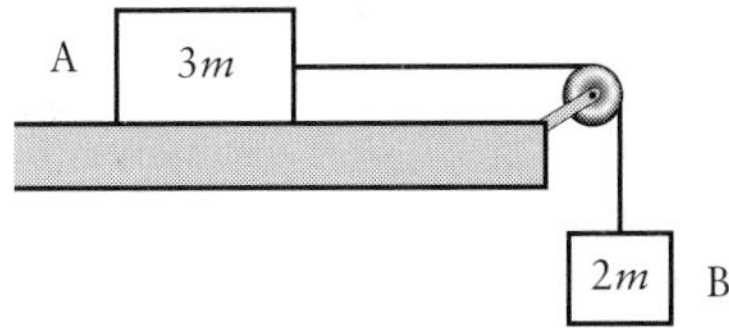

(a) Find the initial acceleration of the system in terms of g.

The system is released with B 1 m above the ground. When B hits the ground the string goes slack.

(b) Find the total distance moved by A before coming to rest again, assuming that it does not hit the pulley.

(c) State where you have used the assumption that the pulley is smooth.

12 The diagram shows two particles, A of mass m kg and B of mass $2m$ kg. A lies on a rough plane which is at angle α to the horizontal, where $\tan\alpha = \frac{3}{4}$, and is connected by a light inextensible string which passes over a smooth pulley to B, which hangs freely. The coefficient of friction between A and the plane is 0.5. The system is released from rest with the string taut.

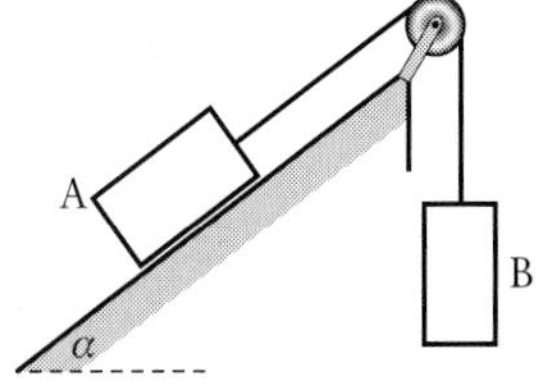

(a) Find the initial acceleration of the system in terms of g.

After both particles have moved a distance of 0.5 m, B hits the ground and the string goes slack.

(b) Find the total distance moved by A before coming to rest.

(c) Does A start to slide down the plane again?

13 The diagram shows two particles A and B joined by a light inextensible string which passes over a smooth light pulley. A is of mass m kg and rests on a rough horizontal plane. B is of mass $2m$ kg and rests on a rough plane inclined at an angle α to the horizontal, where $\tan\alpha = \frac{4}{3}$. The coefficient of friction between each particle and the plane is $\frac{1}{3}$. The system is released from rest with the string taut.

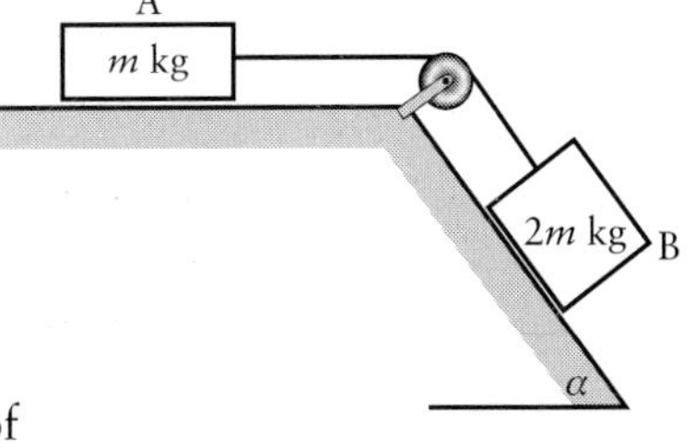

(a) Show that the frictional force on B has magnitude $\frac{2}{5}mg$.

(b) Find **(i)** the magnitude of the acceleration of the system

(ii) the magnitude of the tension in the string.

(c) State where you have used the fact that the string is inextensible.

14 The diagram shows two particles A and B lying on inclined rough planes. A is of mass m kg and lies on a plane with coefficient of friction $\frac{1}{4}$ which is inclined at angle of α to the horizontal, where $\tan\alpha = \frac{5}{12}$. B is of mass $2m$ kg and lies on a plane with coefficient of friction $\frac{1}{2}$ which is inclined at angle of β to the horizontal, where $\tan\beta = \frac{4}{3}$. The system is released from rest with the string taut.

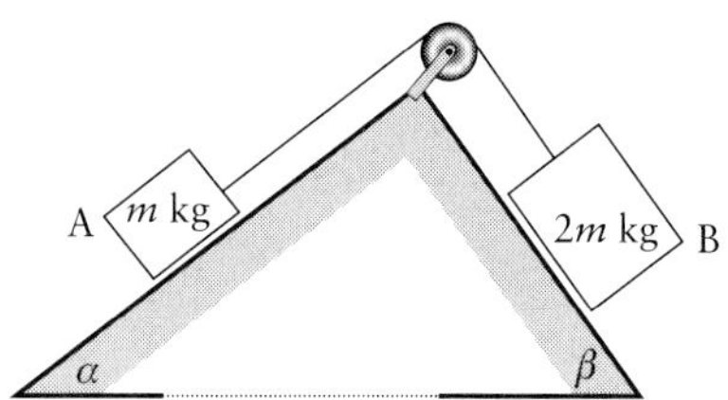

(a) Show that the magnitude of the frictional force on A is $\frac{3}{13}mg$.

(b) Find **(i)** the acceleration of the system in terms of g

(ii) the tension in the string in terms of m and g.

15 A parcel of mass 5 kg lies on a rough plane inclined at an angle α to the horizontal, where $\tan\alpha = \frac{3}{4}$. The parcel is held in equilibrium by the action of a horizontal force of magnitude 20 N, as shown in the diagram. The force acts in a vertical plane through a line of greatest slope of the plane. The parcel is on the point of sliding down the plane. Find the coefficient of friction between the parcel and the plane.

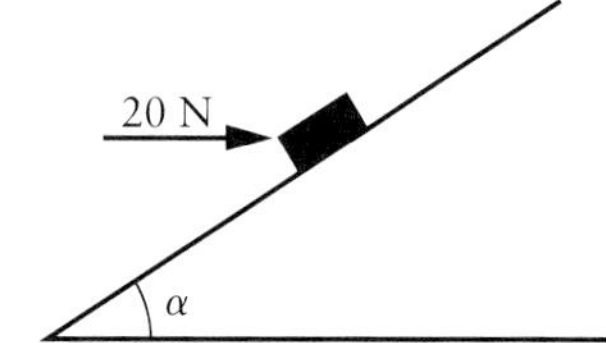

[Edexcel]

16 A particle P of mass 3 kg is projected up a line of greatest slope of a rough plane inclined at an angle of 30° to the horizontal. The coefficient of friction between P and the plane is 0.4. The initial speed of P is 6 ms^{-1}. Find

(a) the frictional force acting on P as it moves up the plane

(b) the distance moved by P up the plane before P comes to instantaneous rest.

[Edexcel]

17 Particles A and B, of mass $2m$ and m respectively, are attached to the ends of a light inextensible string. The string passes over a small smooth pulley fixed at the edge of a rough horizontal table. Particle A is held on the table, while B rests on a smooth plane inclined at 30° to the horizontal, as shown in the diagram. The string is in the same vertical plane as a line of greatest slope of the inclined plane. The coefficient of friction between A and the table is μ. The particle A is released from rest and begins to move.

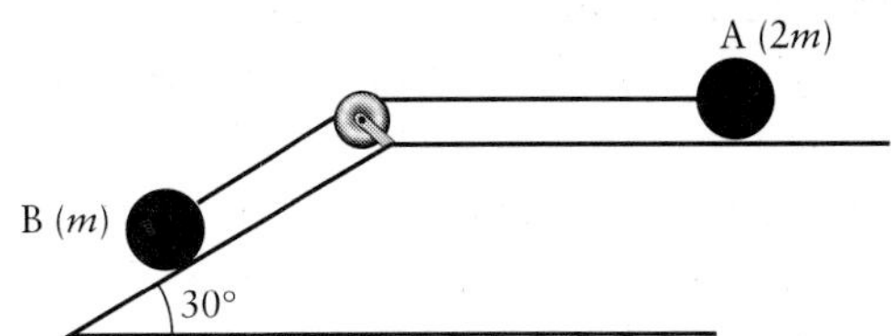

By writing down an equation of motion for each particle

(a) show that, while both particles move with the string taut, each particle has an acceleration of magnitude $\frac{1}{6}(1 - 4\mu)g$.

When each particle has moved a distance h, the string breaks. The particle A comes to rest before reaching the pulley. Given that $\mu = 0.2$

(b) find, in terms of h, the total distance moved by A.

For the model described above

(c) state two physical factors, **apart** from air resistance, which could be taken into account to make the model more realistic.

[Edexcel]

18 Two particles P and Q have masses $3m$ and $5m$ respectively. They are connected by a light inextensible string which passes over a small smooth light pulley fixed at the edge of a rough horizontal table. Particle P lies on the table and particle Q hangs freely below the pulley, as shown in the diagram.

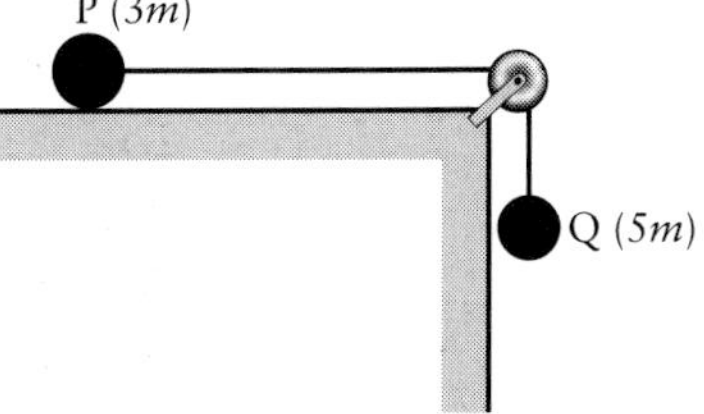

The coefficient of friction between P and the table is 0.6. The system is released from rest with the string taut. For the period before Q hits the floor or P reaches the pulley

(a) write down an equation of motion for each particle separately

(b) find, in terms of g, the acceleration of Q

(c) find, in terms of m and g, the tension in the string.

When Q has moved a distance h, it hits the floor and the string becomes slack. Given that P remains on the table during the subsequent motion and does not reach the pulley

(d) find, in terms of h, the distance moved by P after the string becomes slack until P comes to rest.

[Edexcel]

KEY POINTS

Coulomb's law

The frictional force, F, between two surfaces is given by

$F \leqslant \mu R$ when there is no sliding,

$F = \mu R$ when sliding occurs.

The frictional force always acts in the direction to oppose sliding.

Chapter nine

MOMENTS OF FORCES

i shall show you how
a solar system
pivots on the nubbin
of a flageolet bean

don marquis, the return of archy

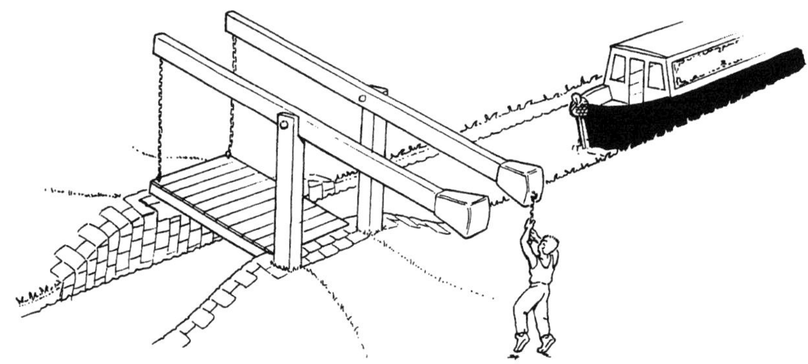

FIGURE 9.1

The illustration shows a lift bridge over a canal. It can be raised to allow barges and boats to pass. It is operated by hand, even though it is very heavy. How is this possible?

The bridge depends on the turning effects or *moments* of forces. To understand these you might find it helpful to look at a simpler situation.

Two children sit on a simple see-saw, made of a plank balanced on a fulcrum as in figure 9.2. Will the see-saw balance?

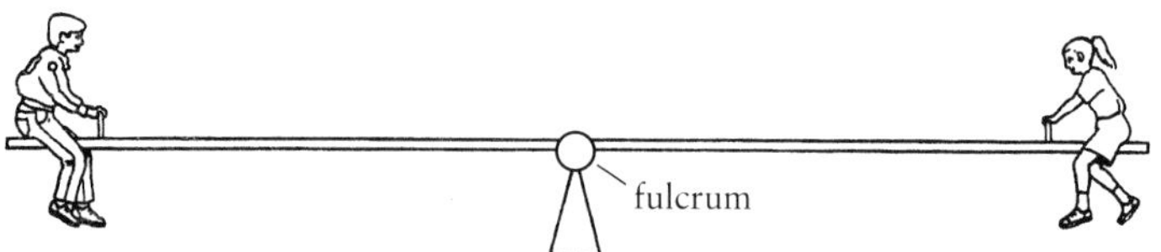

FIGURE 9.2

If both children have the same mass and sit the same distance from the fulcrum, then you expect the see-saw to balance.

Now consider possible changes to this situation:

- If one child is heavier than the other then you expect the heavier one to go down.
- If one child moves nearer the centre you expect that child to go up.

You can see that both the weights of the children and their distances from the fulcrum are important.

What about this case? One child has mass 35 kg and sits 1.6 m from the fulcrum and the other has mass 40 kg and sits on the opposite side 1.4 m from the fulcrum (see figure 9.3).

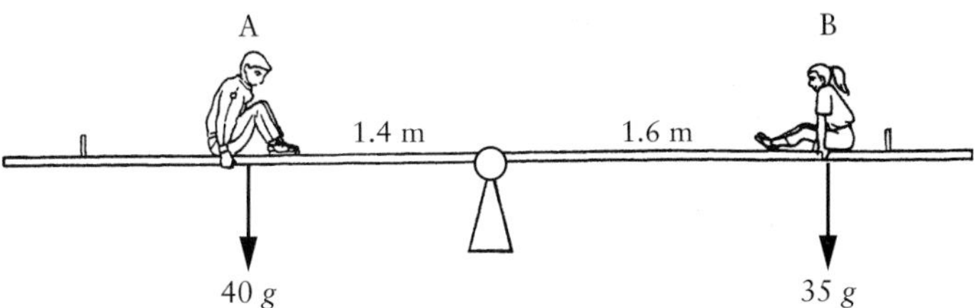

FIGURE 9.3

Taking the products of their weights and their distances from the fulcrum, gives

A: $40g \times 1.4 = 56g$

B: $35g \times 1.6 = 56g$

So you might expect the see-saw to balance and this indeed is what would happen.

RIGID BODIES

Until now the particle model has provided a reasonable basis for the analysis of the situations you have met. In examples like the see-saw however, where turning is important, this model is inadequate because the forces do not all act through the same point.

In such cases you need the *rigid body model* in which an object, or *body*, is recognised as having size and shape, but is assumed not be deformed when forces act on it.

Suppose that you push a tray lying on a smooth table with one finger so that the force acts parallel to one edge and through the centre of mass (figure 9.4).

FIGURE 9.4

The particle model is adequate here: the tray travels in a straight line in the direction of the applied force.

If you push the tray equally hard with two fingers as in figure 9.5, symmetrically either side of the centre of mass, the particle model is still adequate.

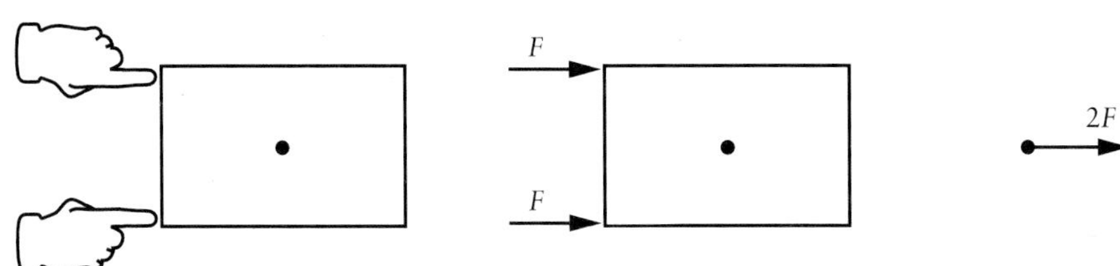

FIGURE 9.5

However, if the two forces are not equal or are not symmetrically placed, or as in figure 9.6 are in different directions, the particle model cannot be used.

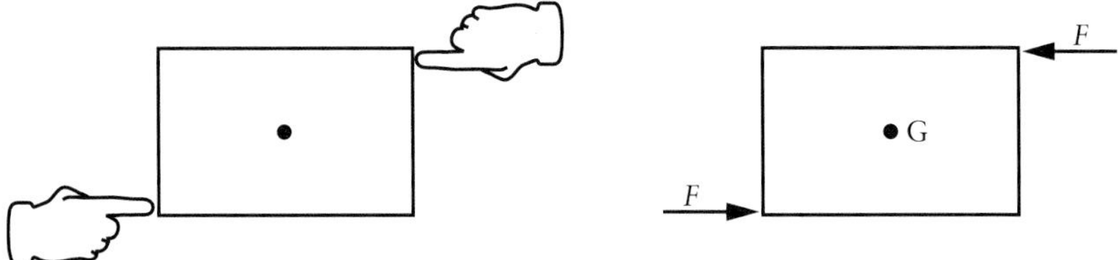

FIGURE 9.6

The resultant force is now zero, since the individual forces are equal in magnitude but opposite in direction. What happens to the tray? Experience tells us that it starts to rotate about G. How fast it starts to rotate depends, among other things, on the magnitude of the forces and the width of the tray. The rigid body model allows you to analyse the situation.

MOMENTS

In the example of the see-saw we looked at the product of each force and its distance from a fixed point. This product is called the *moment* of the force about the point. The see-saw balances because the moments of the forces on either side of the fulcrum are the same magnitude and in opposite directions. One would tend to make the see-saw turn clockwise, the other anticlockwise. By contrast, the moments about G of the forces on the tray in the last situation do not balance. They both tend to turn it anticlockwise, so rotation occurs.

CONVENTIONS AND UNITS

The moment of a force F about a point O is defined by

$$\text{moment} = Fd$$

where d is the perpendicular distance from the point O to the line of action of the force (figure 9.7).

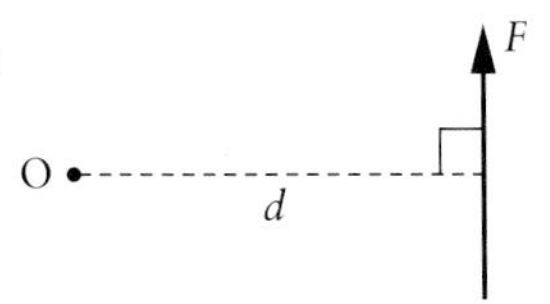

FIGURE 9.7

The line of the force and its perpendicular make a T (for 'turning')

In two dimensions, the sense of a moment is described as either positive (anticlockwise) or negative (clockwise) as shown in figure 9.8.

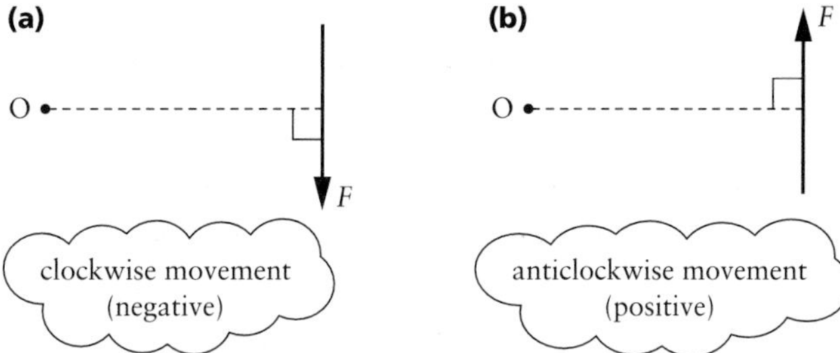

FIGURE 9.8

If you imagine putting a pin at O and pushing along the line of F, your page would turn clockwise for (a) and anticlockwise for (b).

In the S.I. system the unit for moment is the newton metre (Nm), because a moment is the product of a force, the unit of which is the newton, and distance, the unit of which is the metre.

Remember that moments are always taken about a point and that you must always specify what that point is. A force acting through the point will have no moment about that point because in that case $d = 0$.

Figure 9.9 shows two tools for undoing wheel nuts on a car. A tool as shown in figure 9.9(a) is often supplied with a car, but many people buy a tool as shown in figure 9.9(b). Why?

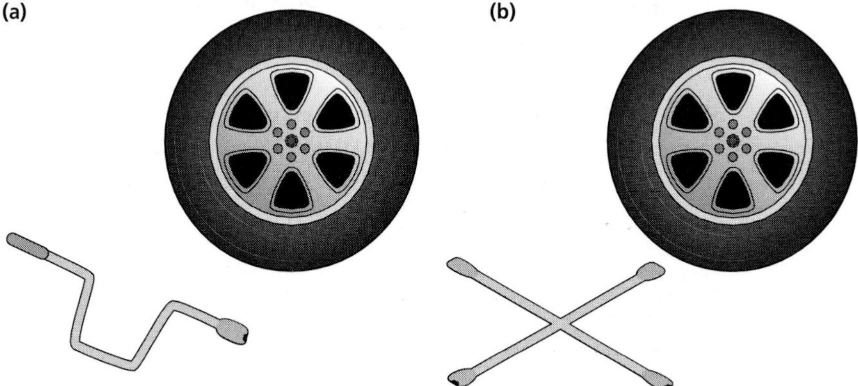

FIGURE 9.9

When using the spider wrench (the tool with two 'arms'), you apply equal and opposite forces either side of the nut. These produce moments in the same direction. One advantage of this method is that there is no resultant force and hence no tendency for the nut to snap off.

Couples

Whenever two forces of the same magnitude act in opposite directions along different lines, they have a zero resultant force, but do have a turning effect. In fact the moment will be Fd about any point, where d is the perpendicular distance between the forces. This is demonstrated in figure 9.10.

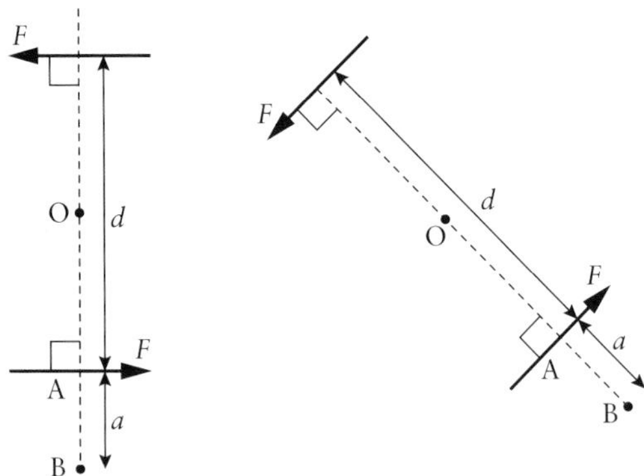

Figure 9.10

In each of these situations:

Moment about O $\quad F\frac{d}{2} + F\frac{d}{2} = Fd$ ← anticlockwise is positive

Moment about A $\quad 0 + Fd = Fd$

Moment about B $\quad -aF + (a + d)F = Fd$

Any set of forces like these with a zero resultant but a non-zero total moment is known as a *couple*. The effect of a couple on a rigid body is to cause rotation.

Equilibrium revisited

In Chapter 7 we said that an object is in equilibrium if the resultant force on the object is zero. This definition is adequate provided all the forces act through the same point on the object. However, we are now concerned with forces acting at different points, and in this situation even if the forces balance there may be a resultant moment.

Figure 9.11 shows a tray on a smooth surface being pushed equally hard at opposite corners.

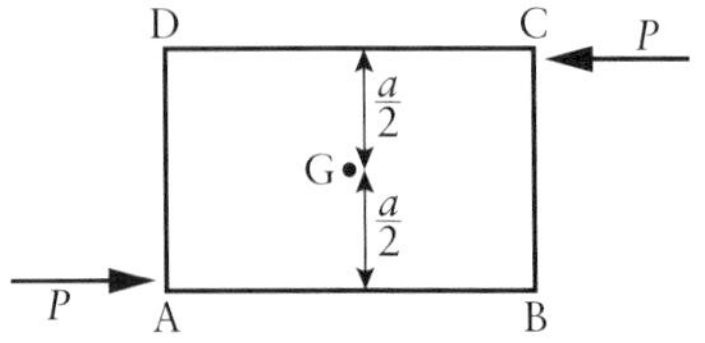

Figure 9.11

The resultant force on the tray is clearly zero, but the resultant moment about its centre point, G, is

$$P \times \frac{a}{2} + P \times \frac{a}{2} = Pa.$$

The tray will start to rotate about its centre and so it is clearly not in equilibrium.

Note You could have taken moments about any of the corners, A, B, C or D, or any other point in the plane of the paper and the answer would have been the same, *Pa* anticlockwise.

So we now tighten our mathematical definition of equilibrium to include moments.

For an object to remain at rest (or moving at constant velocity) when a system of forces is applied, both the resultant force and the total moment must be zero.

To check that an object is in equilibrium under the action of a system of forces, you need to check two things:

- that the resultant force is zero
- that the resultant moment about any point is zero. (You only need to check one point.)

EXAMPLE 9.1

Two children are playing with a door. Kerry tries to open it by pulling on the handle with a force 50 N at right angles to the plane of the door, at a distance 0.8 m from the hinges. Peter pushes at a point 0.6 m from the hinges, also at right angles to the door and with sufficient force just to stop Kerry opening it.

(a) What is the moment of Kerry's force about the hinges?
(b) With what force does Peter push?
(c) Describe the resultant force on the hinges.

FIGURE 9.12

Solution Looking down from above, the line of the hinges becomes a point, H. The door opens clockwise. Anticlockwise is taken to be positive.

(a)

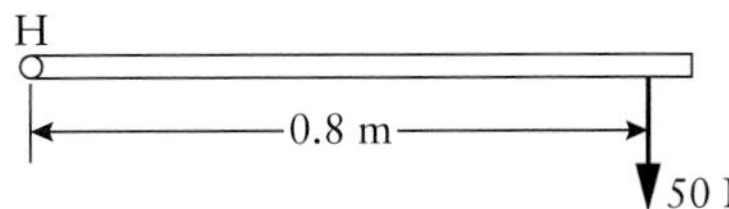

FIGURE 9.13

Kerry's moment about H = -50×0.8

$= -40$ Nm

The moment of Kerry's force about the hinges is -40 Nm. (Note that it is a clockwise moment and so negative.)

(b)

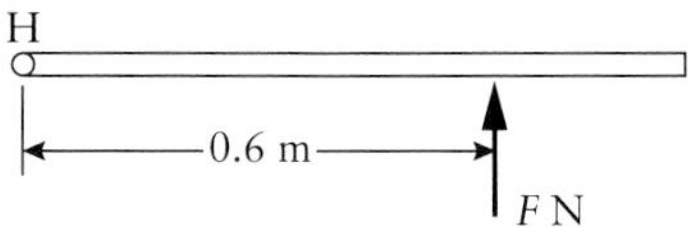

H

0.6 m

F N

Figure 9.14

Peter's moment about H = $+F \times 0.6$

Since the door is in equilibrium, the total moment on it must be zero, so

$$F \times 0.6 - 40 = 0$$

$$F = \frac{40}{0.6}$$

$$= 66.7$$

Peter pushes with a force of 66.7 N.

(c) Since the door is in equilibrium the overall resultant force on it must be zero.

All the forces are at right angles to the door, as shown in the diagram.

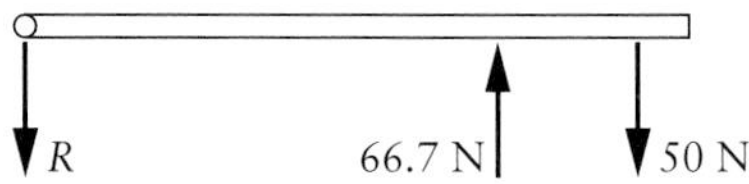

Figure 9.15

Resolve perpendicular to door:

$$R + 50 = 66.7$$
$$R = 16.7$$

The reaction at the hinge is a force of 16.7 N in the same direction as Kerry is pulling.

Note

The reaction force at a hinge may act in any direction, according to the forces elsewhere in the system. A hinge can be visualised in cross section as shown in figure 9.16. If the hinge is well oiled, and the friction between the inner and outer parts is negligible, the hinge cannot exert any moment. In this situation the door is said to be 'freely hinged'.

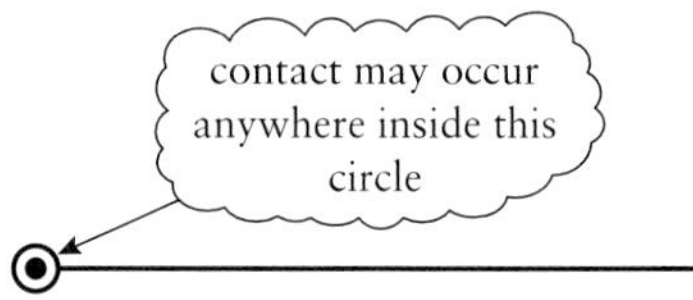

Figure 9.16

EXAMPLE 9.2

The diagram shows a man of weight 600 N standing on a footbridge that consists of a uniform wooden plank just over 2 m long of weight 200 N. Find the reaction forces exerted on each end of the plank.

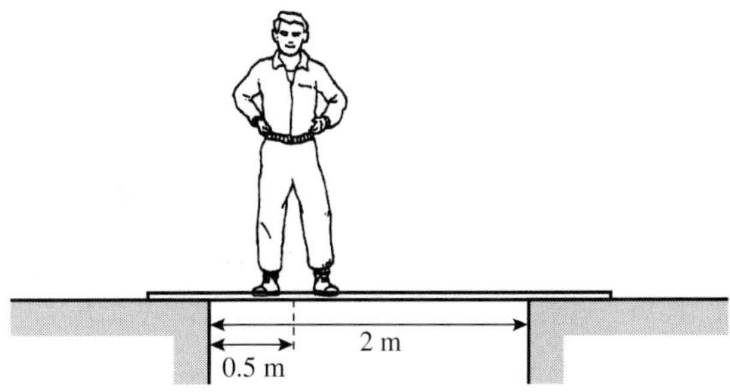

FIGURE 9.17

Solution The diagram shows the forces acting on the plank.

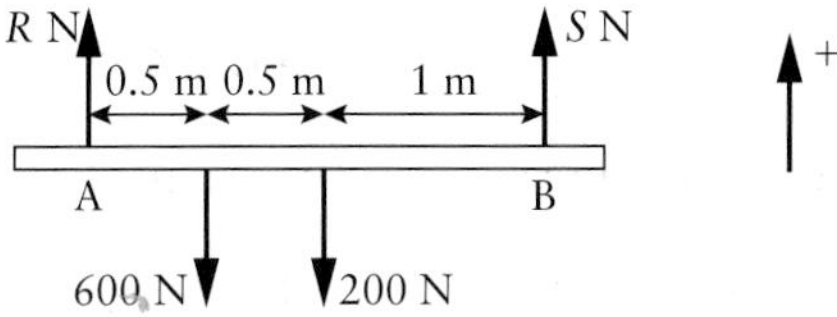

FIGURE 9.18

For equilibrium both the resultant force and the total moment must be zero.

As all the forces act vertically we have

$$R + S - 800 = 0 \quad ①$$

Taking moments about the point A gives

$$R \times 0 - 600 \times 0.5 - 200 \times 1 + S \times 2 = 0 \quad ②$$

From equation ② $S = 250$ and so equation ① gives $R = 550$.

The reaction forces are 550 N at A and 250 N at B.

Notes

1 You cannot solve this problem without taking moments.

2 You can take moments about any point and can, for example, show that by taking moments about B you get the same answer.

3 The whole weight of the plank is being considered to act at its centre.

4 When a force acts through the point about which moments are being taken, its moment about that point is zero.

Levers

A lever can be used to lift or move a heavy object using a relatively small force. Levers depend on moments for their action.

Two common lever configurations are shown below. In both cases a load W is being lifted by an applied force F, using a lever of length l. The calculations assume equilibrium.

Case 1

The fulcrum is at one end of the lever, figure 9.19.

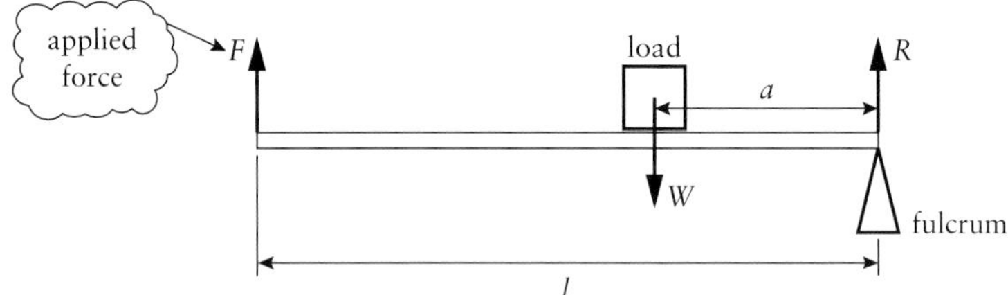

Figure 9.19

Taking moments about the fulcrum:

$$F \times l - W \times a = 0$$

$$F = W \times \frac{a}{l}$$

Since a is much smaller than l, the applied force F is much smaller than the load W.

Case 2

The fulcrum is within the lever, figure 9.20.

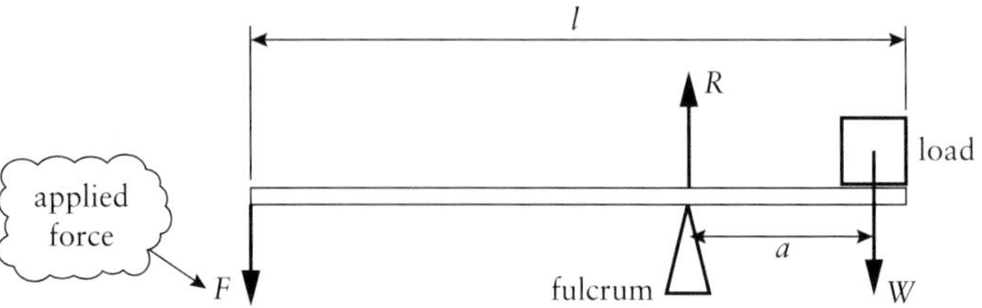

Figure 9.20

Taking moments about the fulcrum:

$$F \times (l - a) - W \times a = 0$$

$$F = W \times \frac{a}{l - a}$$

Provided that the fulcrum is nearer the end with the load, the applied force is less than the load.

EXERCISE 9A

1 In each of the situations shown below, find the moment of the force about the point and state whether it is positive (anticlockwise) or negative (clockwise).

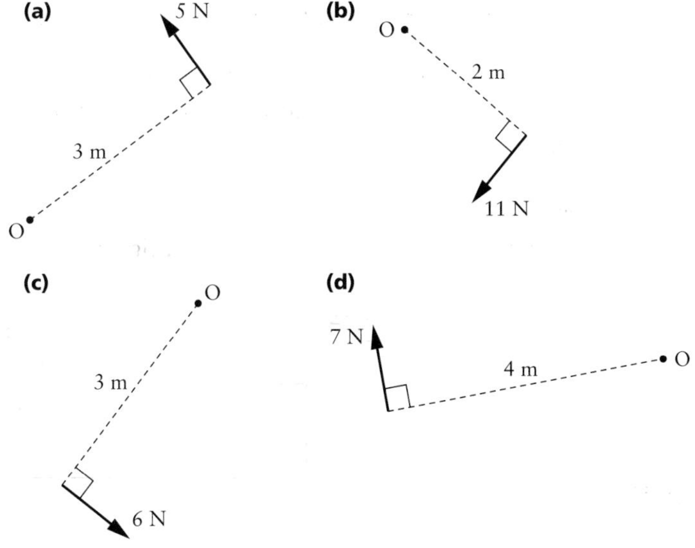

2 A uniform horizontal bar of mass 5 kg has length 30 cm and rests on two vertical supports, 10 cm and 22 cm from its left-hand end. Find the magnitude of the reaction force at each of the supports.

3 Find the reaction forces on the hi-fi shelf shown below. The shelf itself has weight 25 N and its centre of mass is midway between A and D.

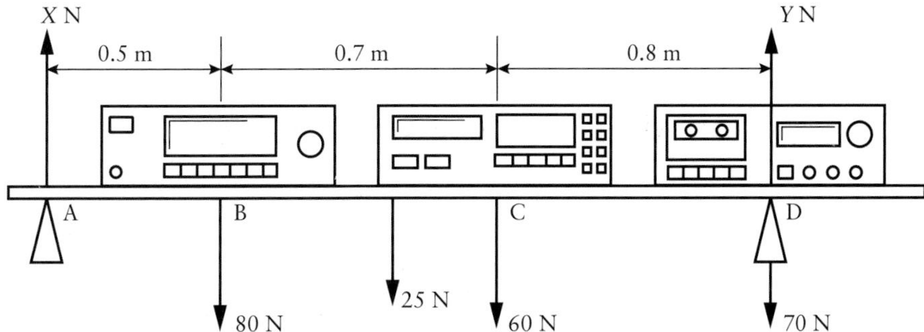

4 The diagram shows a motorcycle of mass 250 kg, and its rider whose mass is 80 kg. The centre of mass of the motorcycle lies on a vertical line midway between its wheels. When the rider is on the motorcycle, his centre of mass is 1 m behind the front wheel. Find the vertical reaction forces acting through the front and rear wheels when

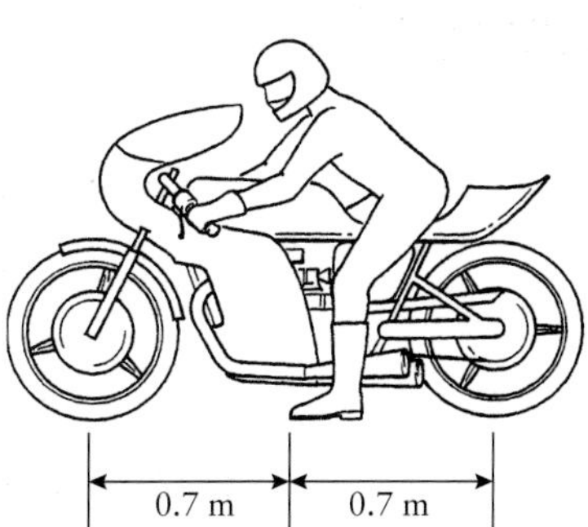

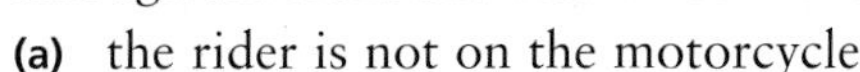

(a) the rider is not on the motorcycle

(b) the rider is on the motorcycle.

5 Karen and Jane are trying to find the positions of their centres of mass. They place a uniform board of mass 8 kg symmetrically on two bathroom scales whose centres are 2 m apart. When Karen lies flat on the board, Jane notes that scale A reads 37 kg and scale B reads 26 kg.

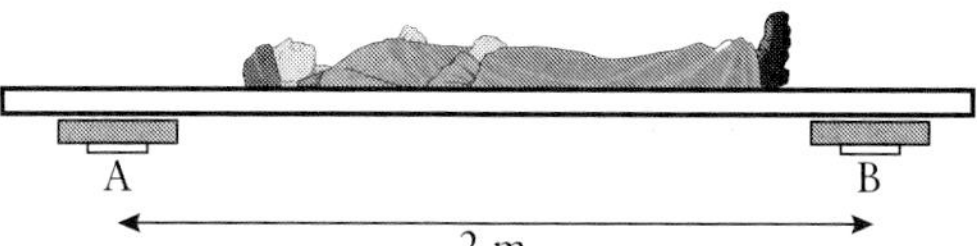

(a) Draw a diagram showing the forces acting on Karen and the board and calculate Karen's mass.

(b) How far from the centre of scale A is her centre of mass?

6 The diagram shows two people, an adult and a child, sitting on a uniform bench of mass 40 kg; their positions are as shown. The mass of the child is 50 kg, that of the adult is 85 kg.

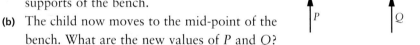

(a) Find the reaction forces, P and Q (in N), from the ground on the two supports of the bench.

(b) The child now moves to the mid-point of the bench. What are the new values of P and Q?

(c) Is it possible for the child to move to a position where $P = 0$? What is the significance of a zero value for P?

(d) What happens if the child leaves the bench?

7 The diagram shows a diving board which some children have made. It consists of a uniform plank of mass 20 kg and length 3 m, with 1 m of its length projecting out over a pool. They have put a boulder of mass 25 kg on the end over the land; and there is a support at the water's edge.

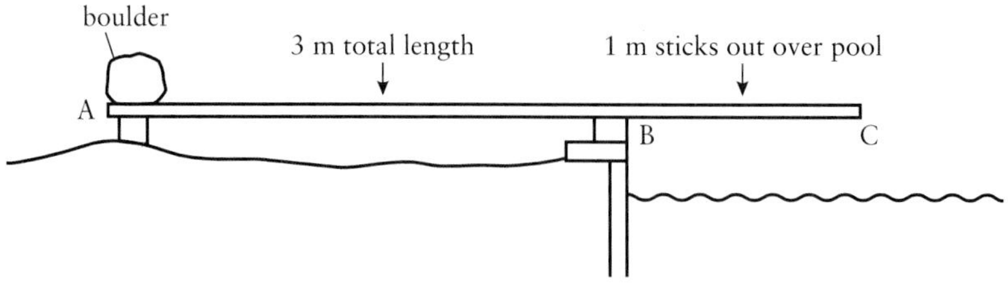

(a) Find the forces at the two supports (A and B) when nobody is using the diving board.

(b) A child of mass 50 kg is standing on the end of the diving board over the pool. What are the forces at the two supports?

(c) Some older children arrive and take over the diving board. One of these is a heavy boy of mass 90 kg. What is the reaction at A if the board begins to tip over?

(d) How far can the boy walk from B before the board tips over?

8 A lorry of mass 5000 kg is driven across a Bailey bridge of mass 20 tonnes. The bridge is a roadway of length 10 m which is supported at both ends.

(a) Find expressions for the reaction forces at each end of the bridge in terms of the distance x in metres travelled by the lorry from the start of the bridge.

(b) From what point of the lorry is the distance x measured?

Two identical lorries cross the bridge at the same speed, starting at the same instant, from opposite directions.

(c) How do the reaction forces of the supports on the bridge vary as the lorries cross the bridge?

9 A simple suspension bridge across a narrow river consists of a uniform beam, 4 m long and of mass 60 kg, supported by vertical cables attached at a distance 0.75 m from each end of the beam.

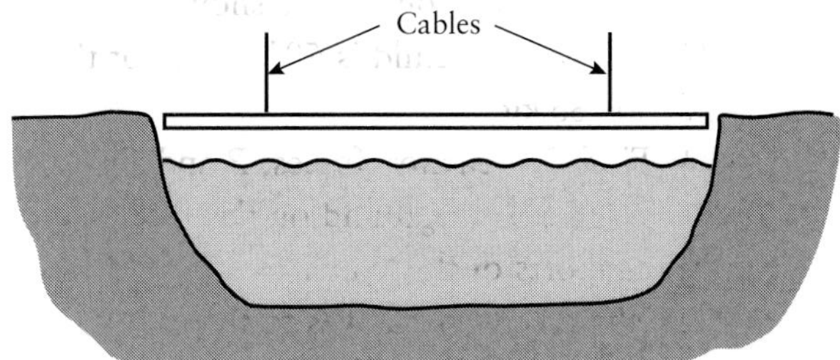

(a) Find the tension in each cable when a boy of mass 50 kg stands 1 m from the end of the bridge.

(b) Can a couple walking hand-in-hand cross the bridge safely, without it tipping, if their combined mass is 115 kg?

(c) What is the mass of a person standing on the end of the bridge when the tension in one cable is four times that in the other cable?

10 The diagram shows a stone slab AB of mass 1 tonne resting on two supports, C and D. The stone is uniform and has length 3 m. The supports are at distances 1.2 m and 0.5 m from the end.

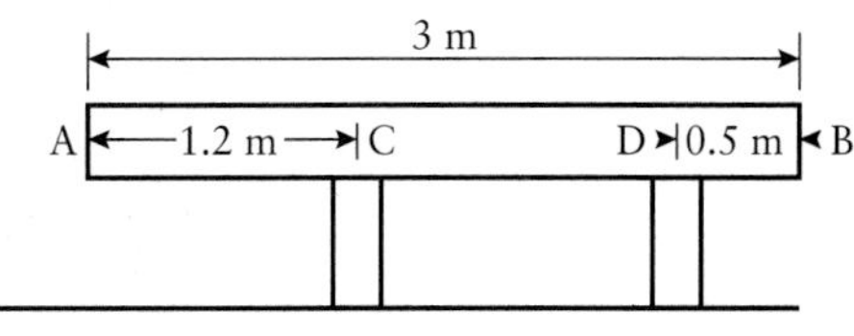

(a) Find the reaction forces at the two supports.

Local residents are worried that the arrangement is unsafe since their children play on the stone.

(b) How many children each of mass 50 kg would need to stand at A in order to tip the stone over?

The stone's owner decides to move the support at C to a point nearer to A. To take the weight of the slab while doing this, he sets up the lever system shown in the diagram overleaf. The distance XF is 1.25 m and FY is 0.25 m.

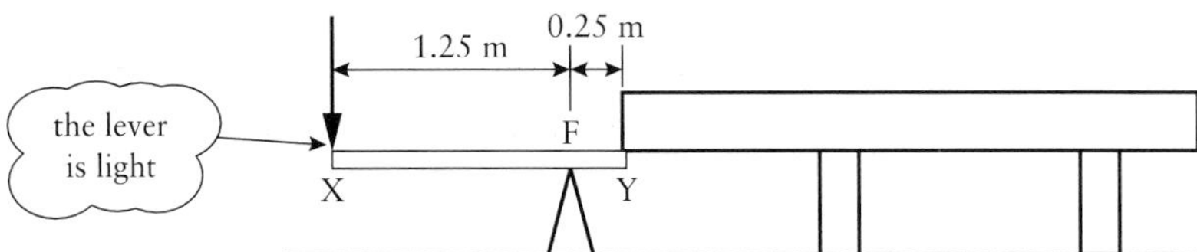

(c) What downward force applied at X would reduce the reaction force at C to zero (and so allow the support to be moved)?

Exercise 9B Examination-style questions

1 A teacher wishing to demonstrate the principle of moments is having a push-of-war with a pupil. They are standing on opposite sides of a freely hinged door of width 80 cm, and each is pushing horizontally at the same height. The teacher is pushing at a distance of 80 cm from the line of the hinges, while the pupil is pushing at a distance of 10 cm from the hinges. The pupil is exerting a force of 200 N, and the door is in equilibrium.

(a) What force is the teacher exerting?

(b) What force are the hinges exerting?

2 An asymmetric see-saw consists of a uniform plank AB of length 3 m and mass 20 kg. It is smoothly supported at a point 1 m from A.

(a) A child sitting at A will balance the see-saw. Find the mass of the child.

(b) The child now moves to B, and another child sits at A. The see-saw is again balanced. Find the mass of the second child.

3 Two removal men are carrying a package across rough ground. The front removal man complains that he has got the heavy end. In fact, he is carrying 1.2 times the load of the rear man. The two men are separated by 2 m, and the package has mass 88 kg.

(a) Find the load carried by each man.

(b) Find the position of the centre of mass of the package.

4 A cycle is of mass 10 kg. The two axles are separated by a distance of 105 cm horizontally and are at the same height. The centre of mass may be assumed to be exactly half-way between the axles, and the points of contact with the ground to be vertically below the axles. A rider of mass 60 kg has centre of mass 20 cm in front of the back axle. Find the forces exerted by the ground on each wheel.

5 A large white board of weight 100 N has been set up on an easel. The white board is of width 2.4 m and height 1.2 m and may be assumed to be in a vertical plane. The easel may be modelled as two smooth pegs at the same height and 0.5 m apart horizontally. Unfortunately, the white board has been placed 10 cm to the left of the symmetrical position. Find the force exerted by each peg.

6 A uniform plank AB of mass 10 kg and length 3 m is being used as a see-saw. It is smoothly supported at a point 1.2 m from A. A child of mass 40 kg sits at A, and is balanced by another child sitting at B.

(a) Suggest suitable models for the plank and the children.

(b) Find the mass of the child sitting at B.

(c) Find the force exerted by the pivot.

7 A diving board consists of a uniform plank AB of mass 20 kg and length 4 m supported by two supports. One is on top of the plank at A, and the other is under the plank 0.8 m from A, as shown below.

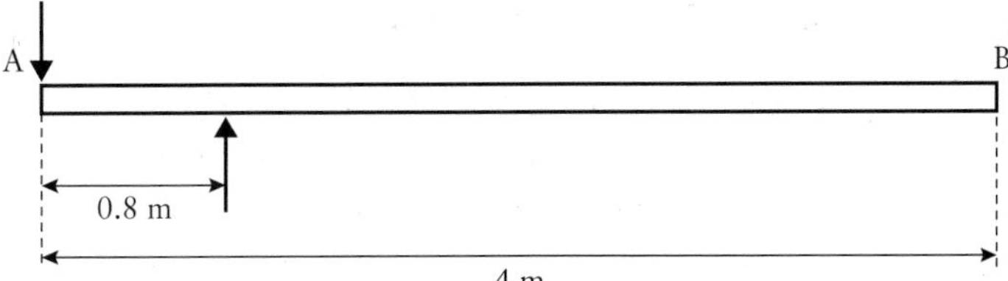

(a) A diver of mass 50 kg is standing stationary at B just before starting a dive. Find the forces exerted by the two supports.

(b) The support at A will break if subjected to a force of 2500 N. Find the maximum mass of a diver who can stand at B.

8 As part of an initiative exercise, a group of cadets have put a uniform scaffold plank on top of two parallel walls as shown below. The plank is of length 5 m and mass 15 kg. The walls are separated by a distance of 2 m. The end A is 1 m from the nearer wall.

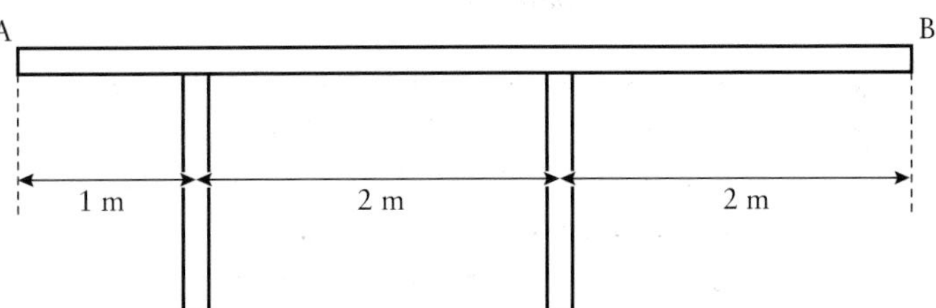

A cadet of mass 50 kg is standing on the plank at a distance x m from end A.

(a) Find the reaction on each wall in terms of x.

(b) Hence show that $0.55 \leqslant x \leqslant 3.15$.

9 A uniform plank AB of length 2.5 m and mass 5 kg is resting on two smooth supports, C and D. The distance AC is 0.5 m and the distance CD is 1 m, as shown below.

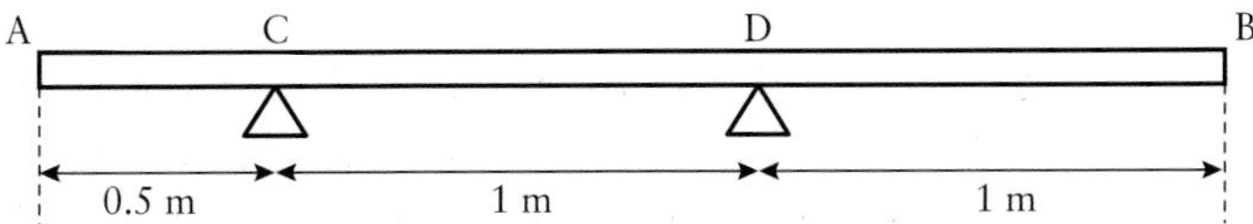

A particle of mass 10 kg is placed at A, and another particle of mass X kg is placed at B. The plank remains in equilibrium.

Find, in terms of X

(a) the reaction at C

(b) the reaction at D.

(c) Hence show that $\frac{5}{8} \leqslant X \leqslant \frac{65}{4}$.

10 The diagram shows two stacking chairs in a stacked position. Each chair has mass 3 kg, and its front and back legs are separated by a distance of 40 cm. The centre of mass of each chair may be assumed to be 15 cm in front of the point of contact of the back legs with the ground.

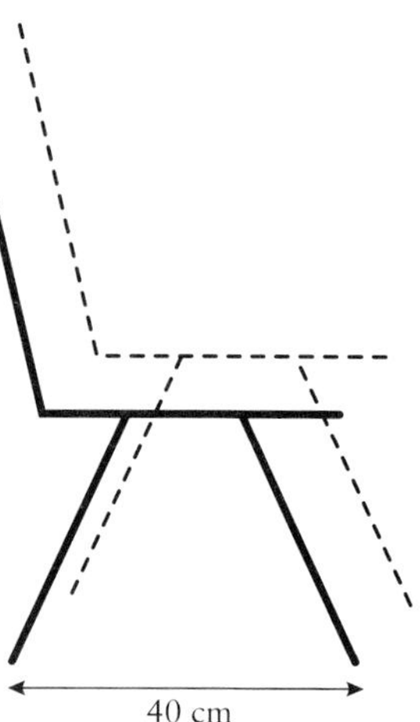

When the chairs are stacked, each is 5 cm in front of the one below, and 5 cm above it.

(a) When there is only one chair, find the reactions of the front legs and the back legs on the ground.

(b) When there are n chairs in the stack, show that the reaction of the front legs on the ground is

$$\frac{3ng}{80}(5n + 25)\,\text{N}$$

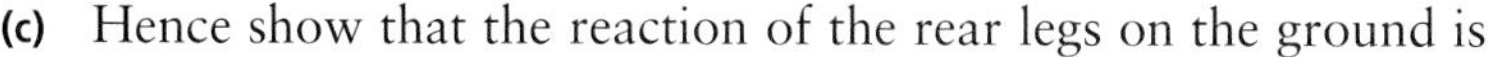

(c) Hence show that the reaction of the rear legs on the ground is

$$\frac{3ng}{16}(11 - n)\,\text{N}$$

(d) How many chairs can be stacked before the stack falls over?

11 A uniform plank AB has mass 40 kg and length 4 m. It is supported in a horizontal position by two smooth pivots, one at the end A, the other at the point C of the plank where AC = 3 m, as shown in the diagram. A man of mass 80 kg stands on the plank which remains in equilibrium.

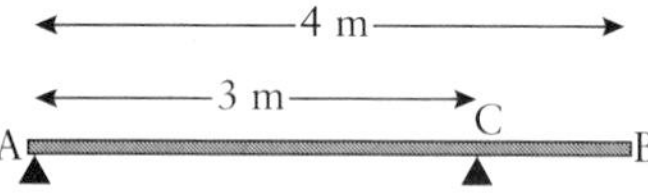

The magnitudes of the reactions at the two pivots are each equal to R newtons. By modelling the plank as a rod and the man as a particle, find

(a) the value of R

(b) the distance of the man from A.

[Edexcel]

12 A uniform plank AB has weight 80 N and length x metres. The plank rests in equilibrium horizontally on two smooth supports at A and C, where AC = 2 m, as shown in the diagram. A rock of weight 20 N is placed at B and the plank remains in equilibrium. The reaction on the plank at C has magnitude 90 N. The plank is modelled as a rod and the rock as a particle.

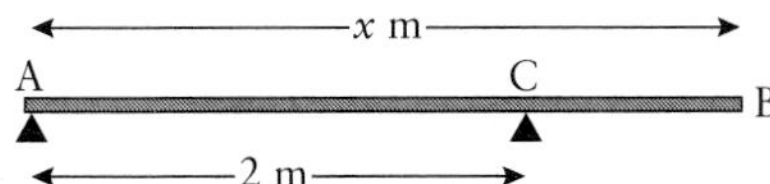

(a) Find the value of x.

(b) State how you have used the model of the rock as a particle.

The support at A is now moved to a point D on the plank and the plank remains in equilibrium with the rock at B. The reaction on the plank at C is now three times the reaction at D.

(c) Find the distance AD.

[Edexcel]

13 A heavy uniform steel girder AB has length 10 m. A load of weight 150 N is attached to the girder at A and a load of weight 250 N is attached to the girder at B. The loaded girder hangs in equilibrium in a horizontal position, held by two vertical steel cables attached to the girder at the points C and D, where AC = 1 m and DB = 3 m, as shown in the diagram. The girder is modelled as a uniform rod, the loads as particles and the cables as light inextensible strings. The tension in the cable at D is three times the tension in the cable at C.

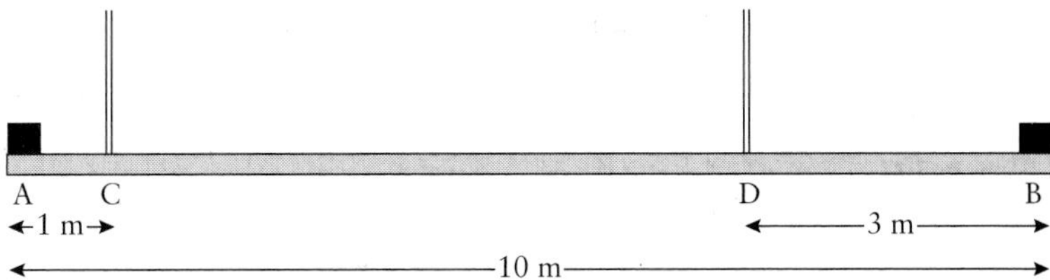

(a) Draw a diagram showing all the forces acting on the girder.

(b) Find the tension in the cable at C.

(c) Find the weight of the girder.

(d) Explain how you have used the fact that the girder is uniform.

[Edexcel]

KEY POINTS

The **moment** of a force F about a point O is given by the product Fd where d is the perpendicular distance from O to the line of action of the force.

If a body is in **equilibrium** the sum of the moments of the forces acting on it, about any point, is zero.

The **S.I. unit** for moment is the newton metre (Nm).

Answers

Chapter 1

Exercise 1A (Page 5)

1 particle, ignore air resistance
2 particle, include air resistance
3 monkeys – particles, rope – light string, pulley – light, smooth
4 ship – rigid body, ropes – light strings
5 particle, ignore air resistance
6 particle moving under variable gravity
7 tray – uniform lamina, glasses – particles
8 particle sliding down a rough plane
9 particle sliding on a smooth plane
10 yo-yo – rigid body, string – light string, ignore air resistance, include rotation

Chapter 2

Exercise 2A (Page 12)

1 c = –b, d = –a, e = a, f = 1.5a, g = –2b, |a| = |b|
2 3 m, +50°; 3 m, –40°; 1 m, horizontal
3 32 ms^{-1} and 28 ms^{-1}
4 **(a)** 8 ms^{-1} downstream
(b) 2 ms^{-1} upstream
(c) 3 ms^{-1} downstream
5

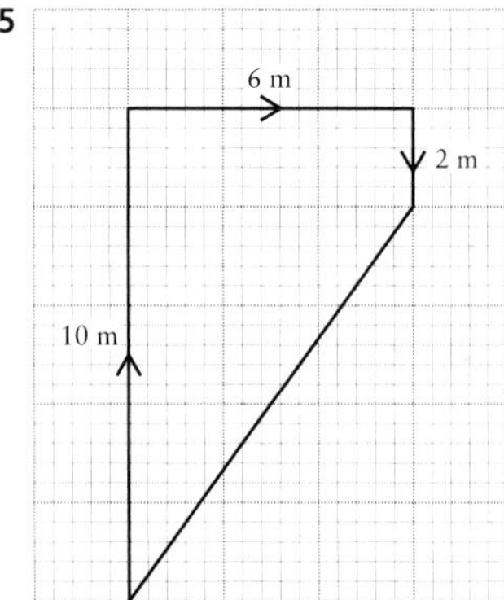

10 m at 53° to the horizontal

Exercise 2B (Page 15)

1 **(a)** 0 m E, 2 m N
(b) 6 m E, 0 m N
(c) 6 m E, 4 m N
2 a = –2i, b = j, c = –3i, d = 3j, e = 2i, f = i + j, g = –2i – j, h = i – 2j, k = i – j
3 (4, –11)
4 **(a)** 9i – 3j
(b) 4i – 2j
(c) –7i + 2j
(d) 4i – 6j
(e) –3i + 11j
(f) –8i + 8j
5 **(a)** i + 2j, 5i + j, 7i + 8j
(b) 4i – j, 2i + 7j, –6i – 6j
(c)

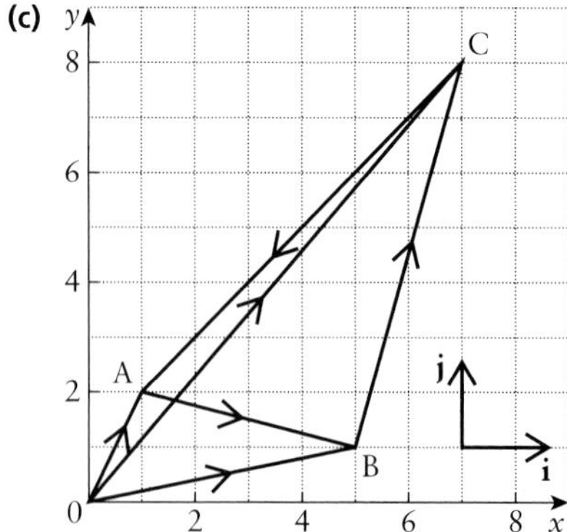

6 **(a)** –3j, 2i + 5j, 3i + 9j
(b) 2i + 8j, i + 4j
(c) BC is parallel to AB.
7 **(a)** $d = 9$
(b) BC is equal and parallel to AD so ABCD is a parallelogram.
8 9i + 6j
9 **(a)** $\frac{1}{2}$(8i – 11j)
(b) $\frac{19}{3}$i – 16j
10 –4.5, 10.5

EXERCISE 2C (Page 18)

1 (a) 3.61 at 56.3°
(b) 13 at −67.4°
(c) 4.12 at 166°
(d) 6.71 at −117°

2 (a) 10 at −53.1°
(b) 8.94 at −117°
(c) 2.24 at −117°

3 30i + 30j, 42.4 at 45°

4 −i + 2j, 2.24 at 117°

EXERCISE 2D (Page 20)

1 (a) 5.64i + 2.05j **(b)** −5.36i + 4.50j
(c) 1.93i − 2.30j **(d)** −1.45i − 2.51j

2 (a) 113i + 65j **(b)** 192i − 161j

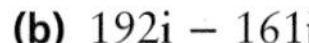

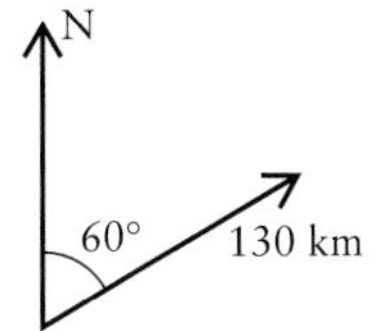

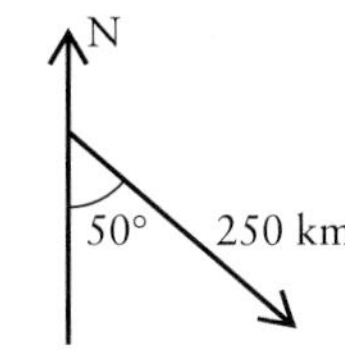

(c) −200i − 346j **(d)** −43i + 25j

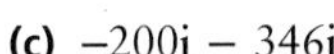

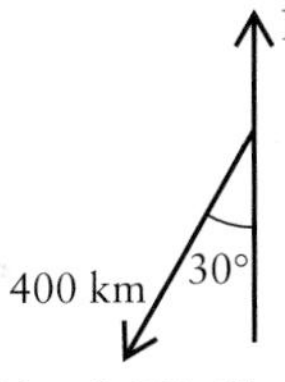

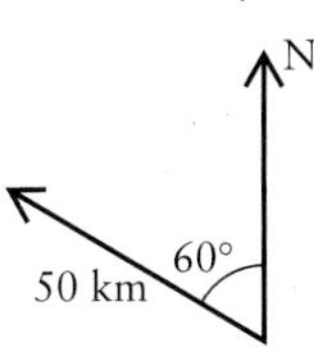

3 2.83i + 2.83j, 3i, 6.48 km h^{-1} at 064°

4 (a)

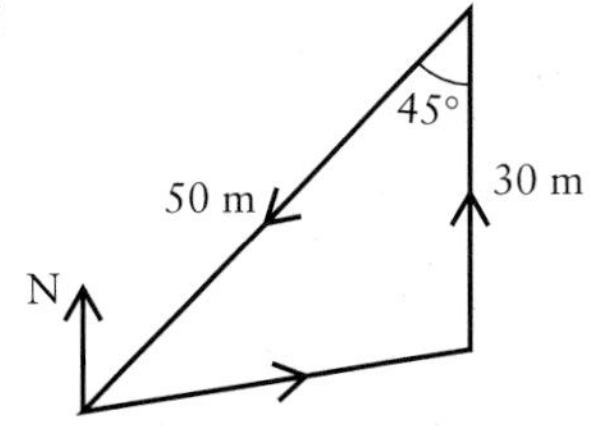

(b) 30j, −35.4i − 35.4j
(c) 081°

5 (a) (i) p = −0.92i + 2.54j, q = 2.30i + 1.93j,
r = 1.7i − 2.94j, s = −2.42i − 1.4j
(ii) 0.66i + 0.12j
(b) (i) t = 1.35i + 2.34j, u = 2.68i − 1.55j,
v = −0.35i − 1.97j, w = −2i
(ii) 1.69i − 1.18j

6 (a) 1449 m, 046°
(b) 0 m

7 64.3i + 76.6j, −153.2i + 128.6j, −88.9i + 205.2j

8 (a)

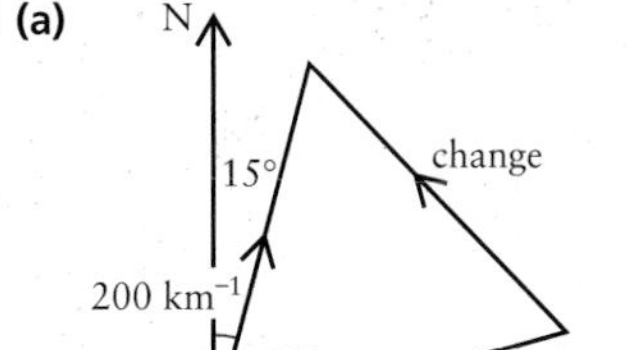

(b) −141i + 141j

9 5544 km, 051°

EXERCISE 2E (Page 24)

1 4.8i − 6.4j
2 5i + 2j ms^{-1}
3 (b) 0.5i − 5j ms^{-1}
4 no
5 $\lambda = -1.25$, $\mu = -1.25$
6 15.6 s

EXERCISE 2F (Page 24)

1 (a) 124°
(c) $\lambda = 4$, $\mu = 1$

2 (a) −34°
(c) 7.28

3 (a) 13.1i − 15.1j, −14.6i − 3.37j
(b) 005°, 18.5 nautical miles

4 (a) 46.0i + 19.5j, −37.1i − 59.4j, −92.0i + 39.1j
(b) −83.1i − 0.75j
(c) 83.1 m on 269°

5 (a) −j
(c) i − $\frac{2}{3}$j

6 (a) −0.02i + 0.01j ms^{-2}
(b) 153.4°

7 (a) $3t$i − $5t$j, $(10 + 2t)$i + $(15 + 6t)$j
(c) 3.14 hr (3 hr 8 min)

8 (a) $(2 + t)$i + $(-2 + 2t)$j, $2t$i + tj
(c) −i + j ms^{-1}

9 (a) 59.0°
(b) $3t$i + $5t$j
(c) $-2(t - 10)$i + $6(t - 10)$j
(d) 14.7 s

10 (a)

(c) 4i ms^{-1}

11 **(a)** 63°

(c) 4.47 N

12 **(a)** $2\mathbf{i} + \mathbf{j}\ \text{m s}^{-1}$

(b) 26.6°

(c) 12.6 m

13 **(a)** $60\mathbf{i} - 120\mathbf{j}\ \text{km h}^{-1}$

(b) $(20 + 60t)\mathbf{i} + (35 - 120t)\mathbf{j}$

(c) $96t\mathbf{i} - 72t\mathbf{j}$

(d) 80 km

(c)

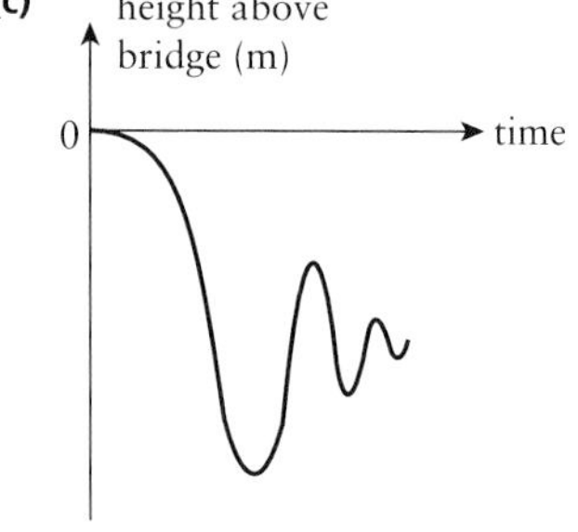

CHAPTER 3

EXERCISE 3A (Page 30)

1 **(a)** +1 m

(b) +2.25 m

2 **(a)** 3.8 m, 6 m, 6.8 m, 6 m, 3.8 m, 0 m

(b) 0 m, 2.2 m, 3 m, 2.2 m, 0 m, −3.8 m

(c) **(i)** 3 m

(ii) 9.8 m

3 **(a)** 2 m, 0 m, −0.25 m, 0 m, 2 m, 6 m, 12 m

(b)

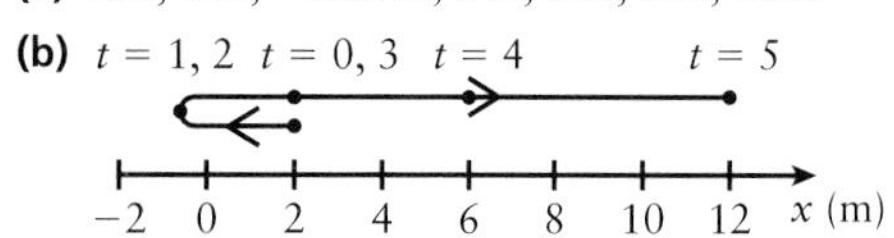

(c) 10 m

(d) 14.5 m

4 **(a)**

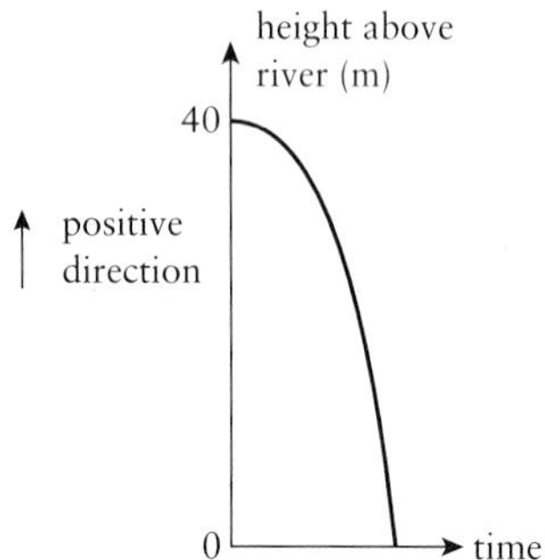

(b)

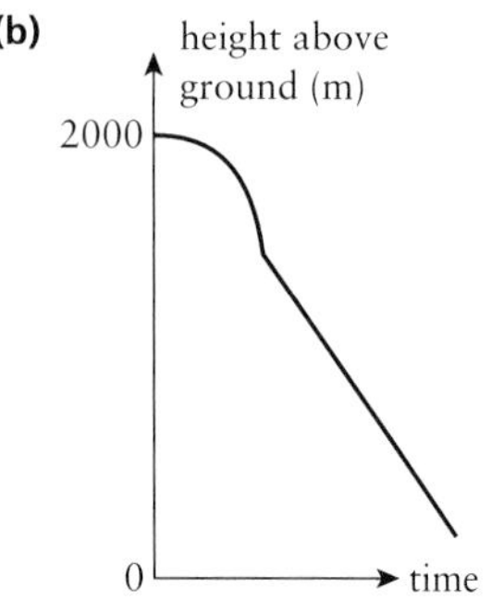

EXERCISE 3B (Page 34)

1

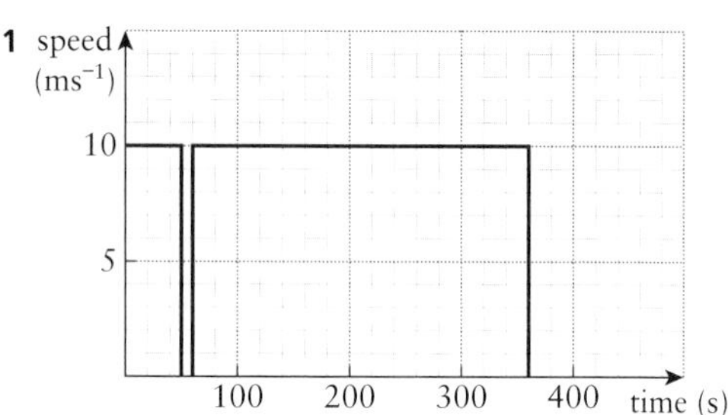

2 **(a)** The person is waiting at the bus stop.

(b) It is faster.

(c)

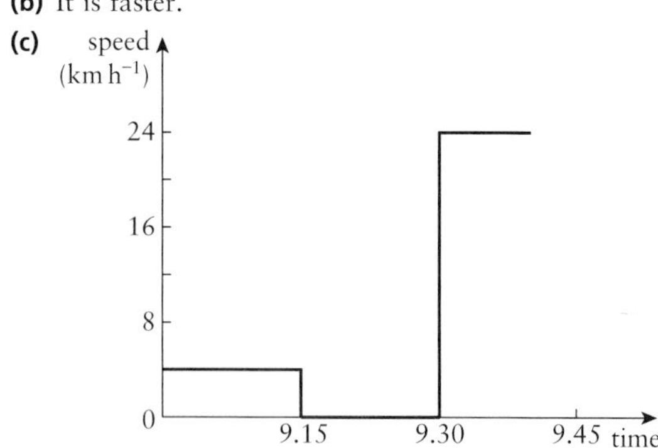

(d) constant speeds, infinite acceleration

3 **(a)** **(i)** 2 m, 8 m

(ii) 6 m

(iii) 6 m

(iv) $2\ \text{m s}^{-1}$, $2\ \text{m s}^{-1}$

(v) $2\ \text{m s}^{-1}$

(vi) $2\ \text{m s}^{-1}$

(b) **(i)** 60 km, 0 km

(ii) −60 km

(iii) 60 km

(iv) $-90\ \text{km h}^{-1}$, $90\ \text{km h}^{-1}$

(v) $-90\ \text{km h}^{-1}$

(vi) $90\ \text{km h}^{-1}$

(c) **(i)** 0 m, −10 m

(ii) −10 m

(iii) 50 m

(iv) OA $10\,ms^{-1}$, $10\,ms^{-1}$; AB $0\,ms^{-1}$, $0\,ms^{-1}$; BC $-15\,ms^{-1}$, $15\,ms^{-1}$
(v) $-1.67\,ms^{-1}$
(vi) $8.33\,ms^{-1}$

(d) (i) 0 km, 25 km
(ii) 25 km
(iii) 65 km
(iv) AB $-10\,km\,h^{-1}$, $10\,km\,h^{-1}$; BC $11.25\,km\,h^{-1}$, $11.25\,km\,h^{-1}$
(v) $4.167\,km\,h^{-1}$
(vi) $10.83\,km\,h^{-1}$

4 774.2 mph

EXERCISE 3C (Page 37)

1 (a) (i) $+0.8\,ms^{-2}$
(ii) $-1.4\,ms^{-2}$
(iii) $+0.67\,ms^{-2}$
(iv) 0
(v) $+0.5\,ms^{-2}$

(b) 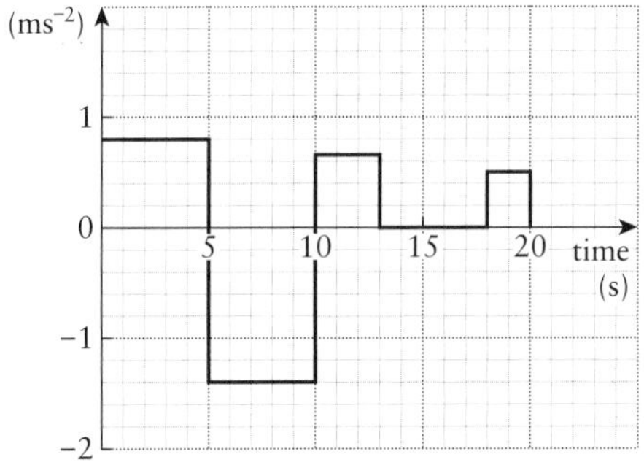

2 (a) 0 m, −16 m, −20 m, 0 m, 56 m.

(b) 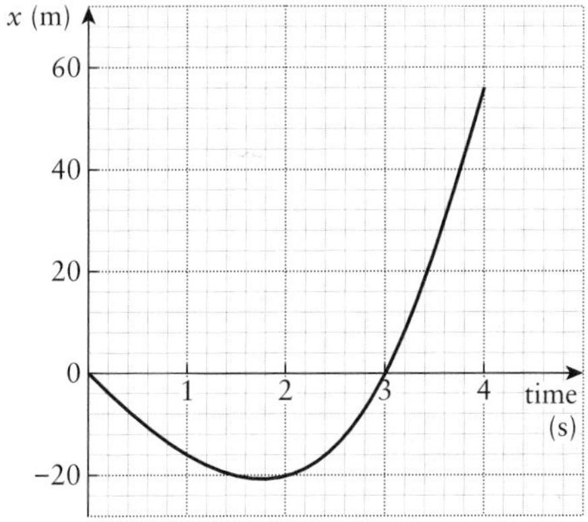

(c) after 0 s (negative direction) and 3 s (positive direction).

3 (a) 20 mph
(b) 23.7 mph

4 (a) (i) 36 mph
(ii) 58.5 mph
(iii) 30 mph

(b) The average speed is not equal to the mean value of the two speeds unless the same time is spent at the two speeds. In this case the ratio of distances must be 3:1.

5 (a) 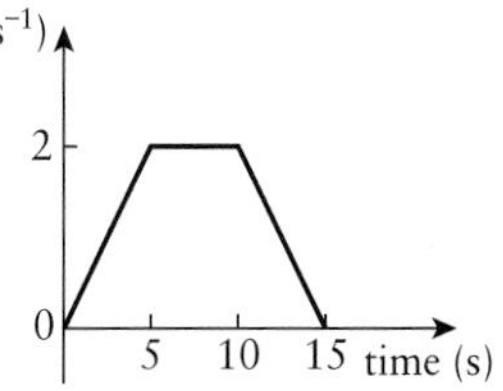

(b) 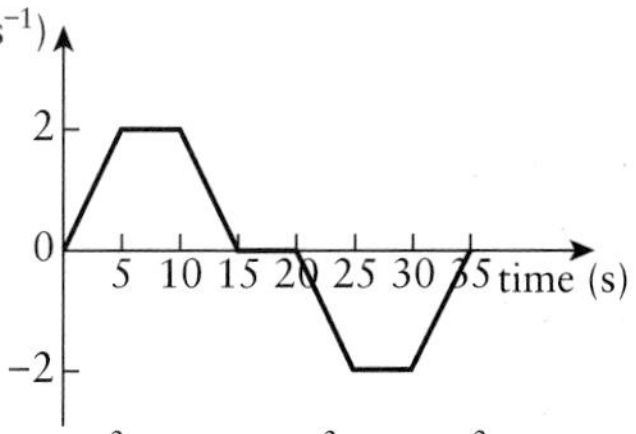

(c) $+0.4\,ms^{-2}$, $0\,ms^{-2}$, $-0.4\,ms^{-2}$, $0\,ms^{-2}$, $-0.4\,ms^{-2}$, $0\,ms^{-2}$, $+0.4\,ms^{-2}$

(d) 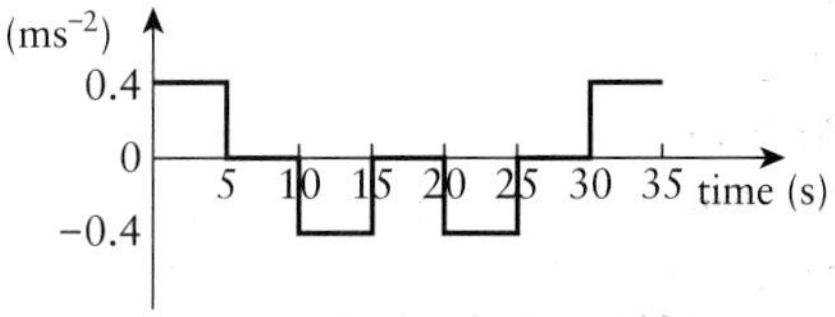

6 (a) 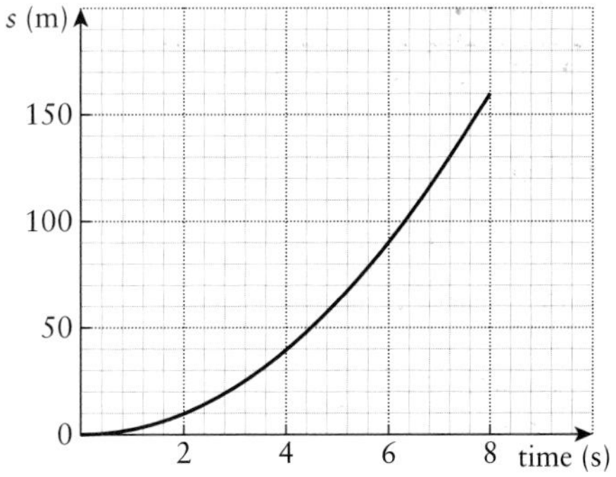

(b) (i) 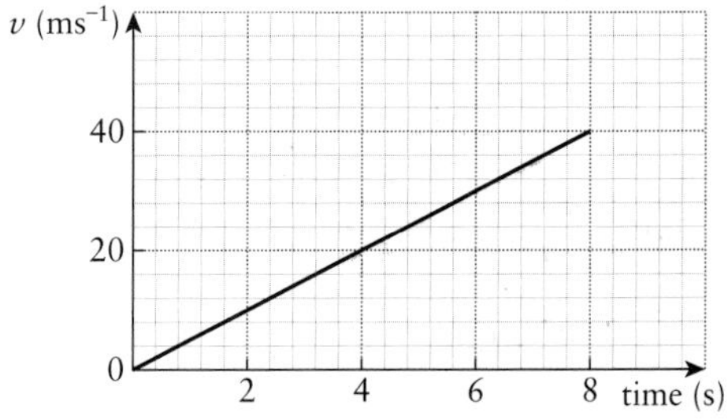

(ii) 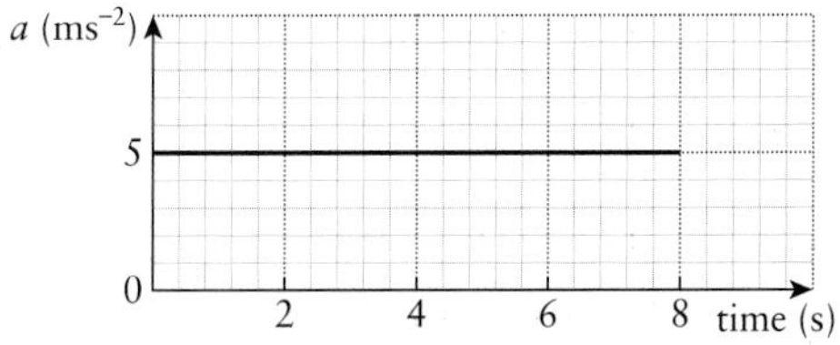

EXERCISE 3D (Page 41)

1 Car A

(a) $0.4\,\text{ms}^{-2}$, $0\,\text{ms}^{-2}$, $3\,\text{ms}^{-2}$

(b) 62.5 m

(c) $4.17\,\text{ms}^{-1}$

Car B

(a) $-1.375\,\text{ms}^{-2}$, $-0.5\,\text{ms}^{-2}$, $0\,\text{ms}^{-2}$, $2\,\text{ms}^{-2}$

(b) 108 m

(c) $3.6\,\text{ms}^{-1}$

2 (a) Enters motorway at $10\,\text{ms}^{-1}$, accelerates to $30\,\text{ms}^{-1}$ and maintains this speed for about 150 s. Slows down to stop after a total of 400 s.

(b) approx. $0.4\,\text{ms}^{-2}$, $-0.4\,\text{ms}^{-2}$

(c) approx. 9.6 km, $24\,\text{ms}^{-1}$

3 (a)

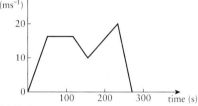

speed (ms^{-1})
20
10
0
100 200 300 time (s)

(b) 3562.5 m

4 (a)

speed (ms^{-1})
30
20
10
0
20 40 60 time (s)

(b) 558 m

5 (a)

speed (ms^{-1})
50
40
30
20
10
0
20 40 60 80 time (s)

(b) after 60 s

(c) 6.6 km

(d) $v = 20 + 0.5t$ for $0 \leqslant t \leqslant 60$,
$v = 50$ for $t \geqslant 60$

6 (a)

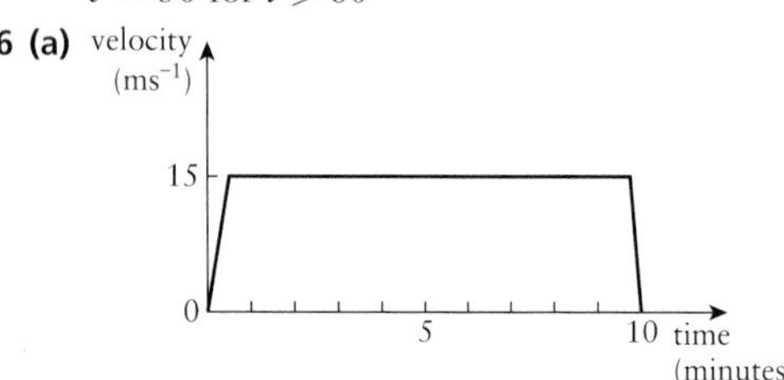

(b) $15\,\text{ms}^{-1}$, $1\,\text{ms}^{-2}$, 8.66 km

7 (a) BC constant deceleration, CD stationary, DE constant acceleration

(b) $-0.5\,\text{ms}^{-2}$, 2500 m

(c) $0.2\,\text{ms}^{-2}$, 6250 m

(d) 325 s

(e)

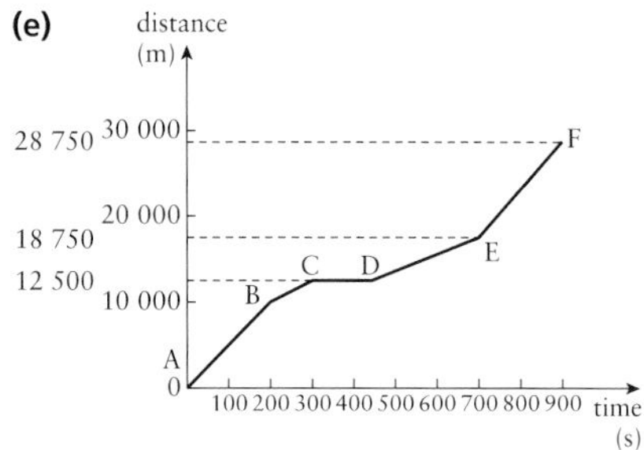

8 (a) $10\,\text{ms}^{-1}$, 0.7 s

(b)

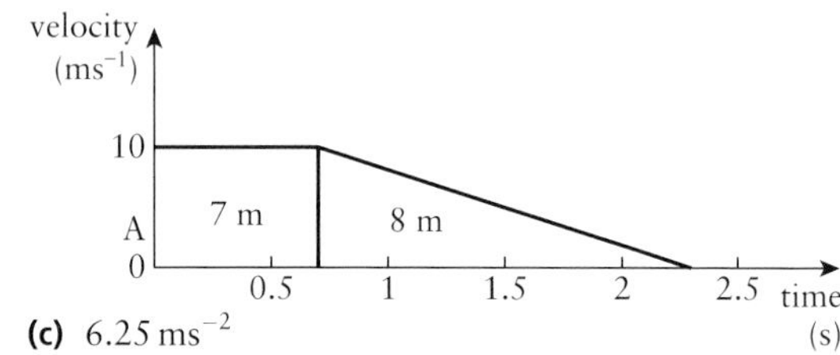

(c) $6.25\,\text{ms}^{-2}$

(d) 33.9 m

EXERCISE 3E (Page 49)

1 (a) 22

(b) 120

(c) 0

(d) -10

2 (a) $v^2 = u^2 + 2as$

(b) $v = u + at$

(c) $s = ut + \frac{1}{2}at^2$

(d) $s = \frac{1}{2}(u + v)t$

(e) $v^2 = u^2 + 2as$

(f) $s = ut + \frac{1}{2}at^2$

(g) $v^2 = u^2 + 2as$

(h) $s = vt - \frac{1}{2}at^2$

3 (a) $9.8\,\text{ms}^{-1}$, $98\,\text{ms}^{-1}$

(b) 4.9 m, 490 m

(c) 2 s.

(d) speed and distance after 10 s, both over-estimates

4 $2.08\,\text{ms}^{-2}$, 150 m. Assume constant acceleration.

5 $4.5\,\text{ms}^{-2}$, 9 m

6 $-8\,\text{ms}^{-2}$, 3 s

7 (a) $s = 16t - 4t^2$, $v = 16 - 8t$

(b) (i) 2 s

(ii) 4 s

(c)

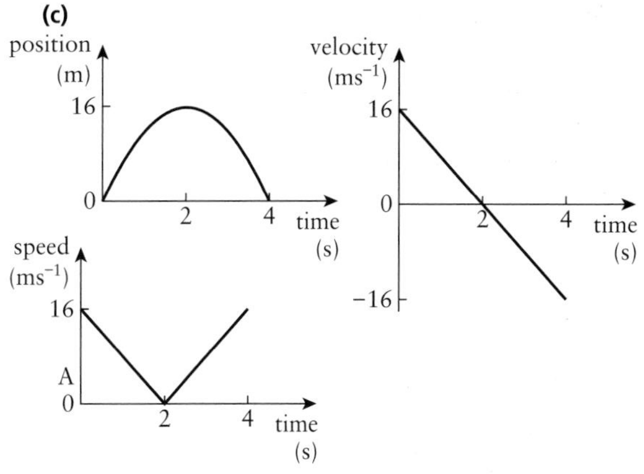

EXERCISE 3F (Page 53)

1 604.9 s, 9037 m or 9.04 km

2 (a) $v = 2 + 0.4t$

(b) $s = 2t + 0.2t^2$

(c) 18 ms^{-1}

3 No, he is 10 m behind when Sabina finishes.

4 (a) $h = 2t - 4.9t^2 + 4$

(b) 1.13 s

(c) 9.08 ms^{-1}

(d) t greater, v less

5 (a) 12 ms^{-1}

(b) 8.45 m

(c) 13 ms^{-1}

(d) 5.41 m

(e) underestimate

6 (a)

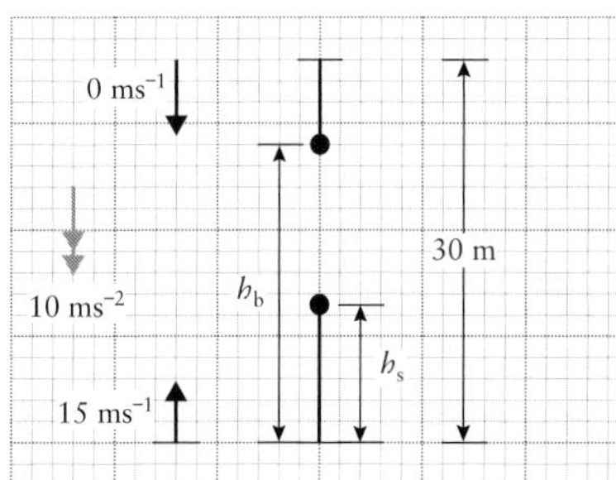

(b) $h_s = 15t - 5t^2$

(c) $h_b = 30 - 5t^2$

(d) $t = 2$ s

(e) 10 m

7 (a) 5.4 ms^{-1}

(b) –4.4 ms^{-1}

(c) 1 ms^{-1} increase

(d) 9 ms^{-1}

(e) too fast

8 3 m

9 43.75 m

EXERCISE 3G (Page 55)

1 (a) 30.6 m

(b) air resistance

(c) The well would appear shallower.

2 0.191 ms^{-2}

3 (a)

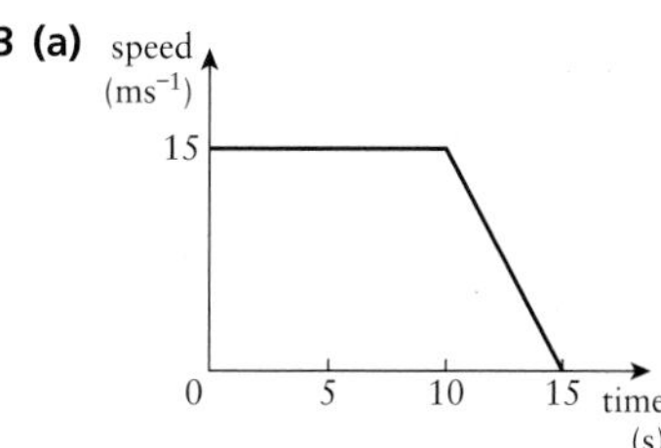

(b) 187.5 m

4 6.86 s

5 (a) 4 m

(b) yes, 1 s

6 (a) 4 m

(b) 0.667 s

7 0.877 m, 0.599 s

8 (a) 0.5 ms^{-2}

(b) yes

9 (a) 10^{17} ms^{-2}

(b) 10^7 ms^{-1}

10 (a) 26.6 s after cyclist starts

(b) 425 m

11 (a) 3.75 ms^{-2}

(b) $116\frac{2}{3}$ m

12 (a) 10.7 ms^{-1}

(b) 1.50 s

(c) Two from air resistance, height of diver, rotation of diver

13 (a)

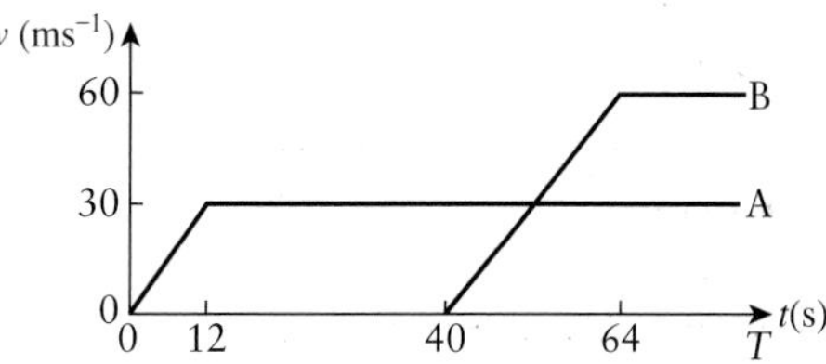

(b) 98

CHAPTER 4

EXERCISE 4A (Page 66)

In these diagrams, W represents a weight, N a normal reaction with another surface, F a friction force, R air resistance and P another force.

1

2

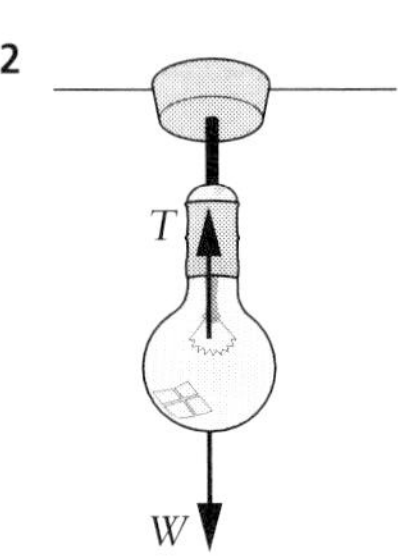

3

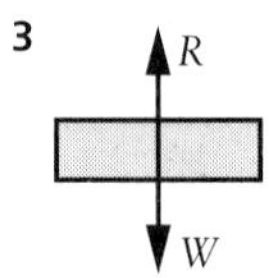

4

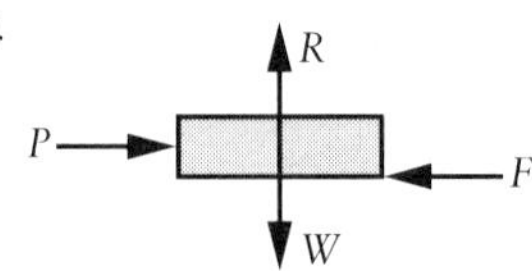

5

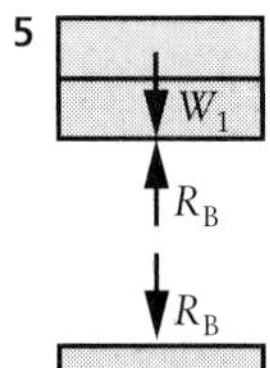

6

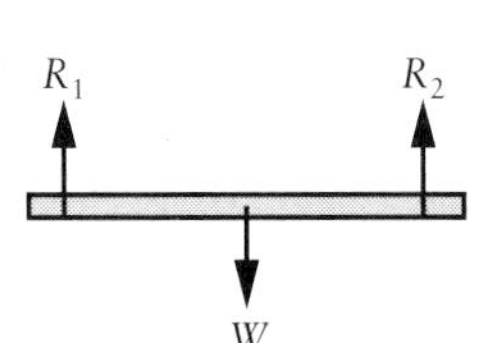

7 (a)

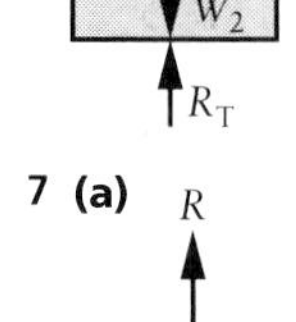

(b)

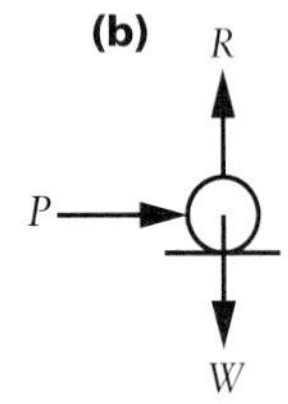

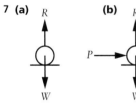

8 (a)

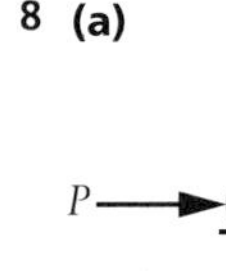

(b)

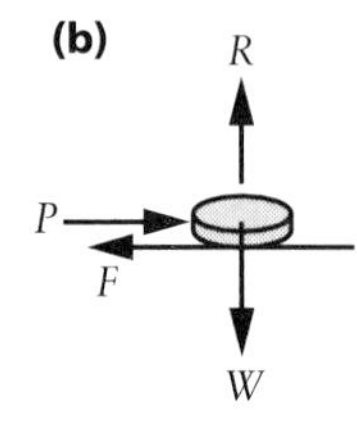

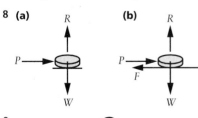

9

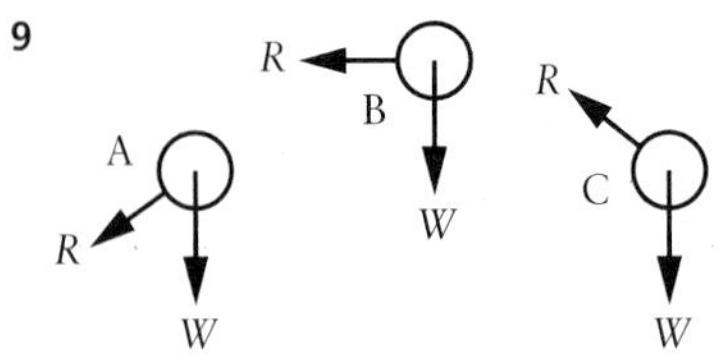

10 (a)

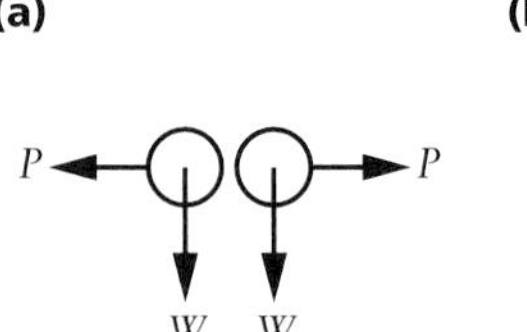

(b)

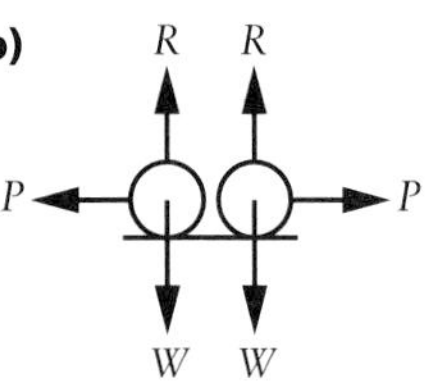

11 **12**

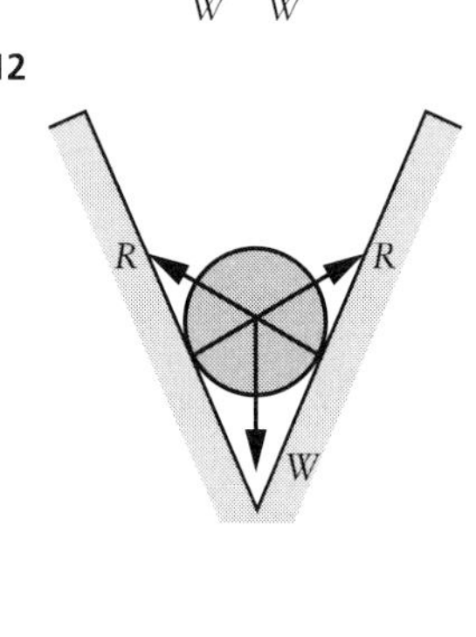

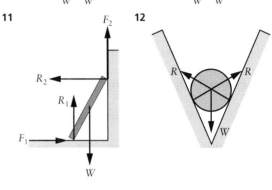

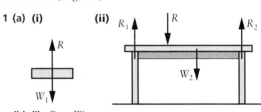

EXERCISE 4B (Page 69)

1 (a) (i) **(ii)**

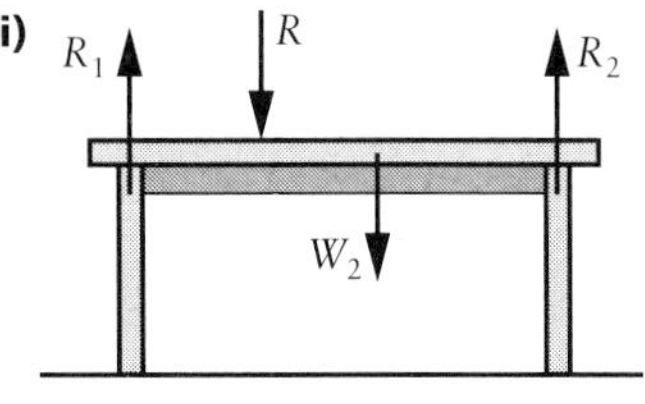

(b) (i) $R = W_1$

(ii) $R_1 + R_2 = W_2 + R$

2 (a) $R = W, 0$

(b) $W > R$, $W - R$ down

(c) $R > W$, $R - W$ up

3 (a) no

(b) yes

(c) yes

(d) no

(e) yes

(f) yes

(g) yes

(h) no

4 Forces are required to give passengers the same acceleration as the car.

(a) A seat belt provides a backwards force.

(b) The seat provides a forwards force on the body and the head rest is required to make the head move with the body.

EXERCISE 4C (Page 74)

1 (a) 147 N

(b) 11 760 N = 11.76 kN

(c) 0.49 N

2 (a) 61.2 kg
(b) 1120 kg = 1.12 tonne

3 (a) 637 N
(b) 637 N

4 112 N

5 (a) Both hit the ground together.
(b) The balls take longer to hit the ground on the moon, but still do so together.

6 Answers for 60 kg
(b) 588 N
(c) 96 N
(d) Its mass is 4 kg.

In the diagrams for questions 7–12, mg represents a weight, N a normal reaction with another surface, F a friction force, R air resistance, T a tension or thrust, D a driving force and P another force.

7 (a)

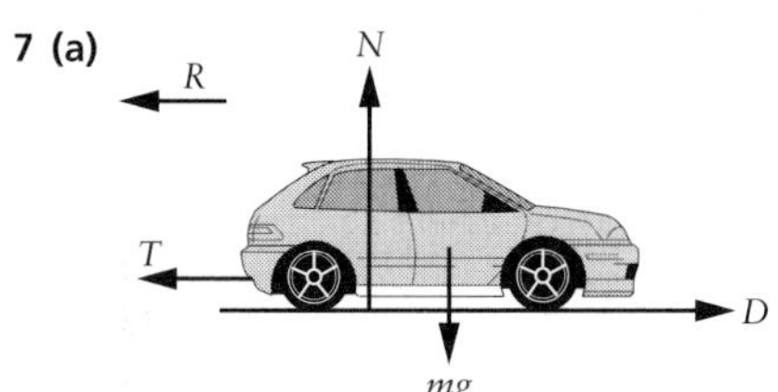

(b)

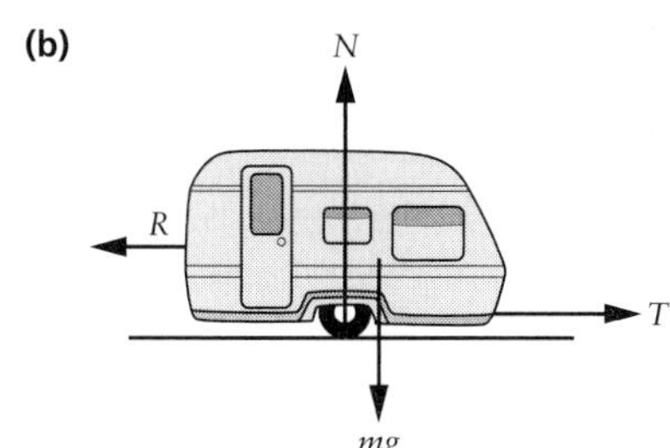

(c)

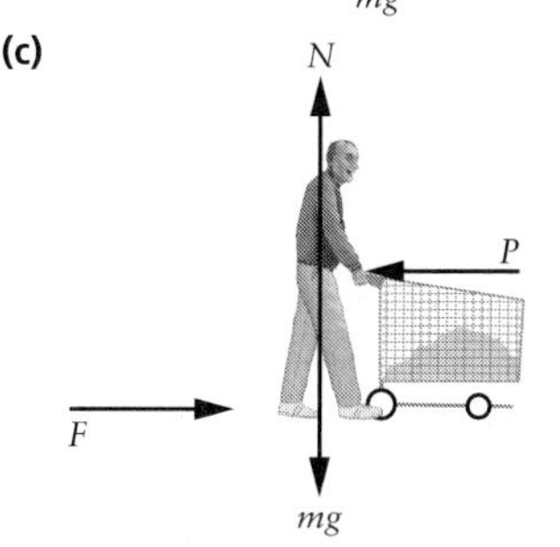

(d) (i) **(ii)**

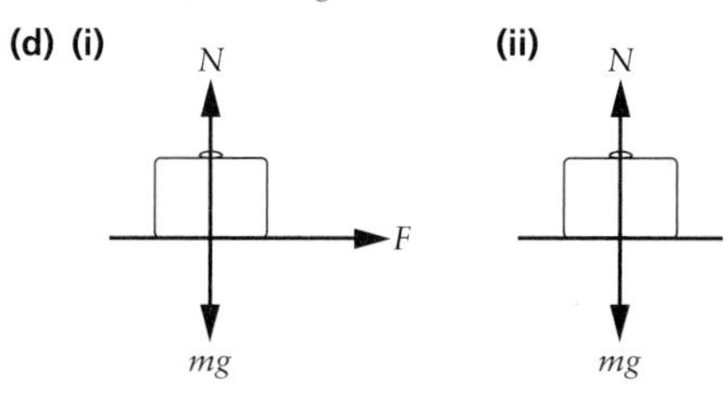

(e)

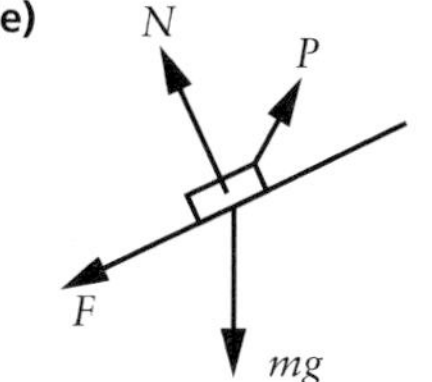

8 (a) weight $5g$ down and reaction ($=5g$) up
(b) weight $5g$ down, reaction with box above ($=45g$ down) and reaction with ground ($=50g$ up)

9 (a) 10 N
(b) $15 - F_2$ N

10 (a) towards the left
(b)

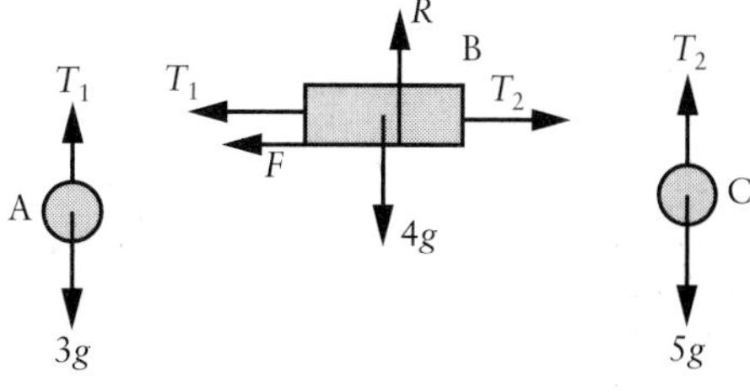

(c) $3g$ N, $5g$ N
(d) $2g$ N
(e) $T_1 - 3g$ N ↑, $T_2 - T_1 - F$ N →, $5g - T_2$ N ↓

11 All forces are in newtons.
(a) greater **(b)** less

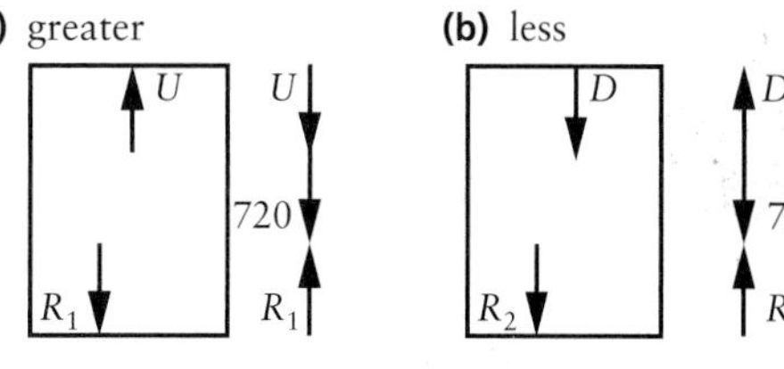

(c) greater **(d)** less

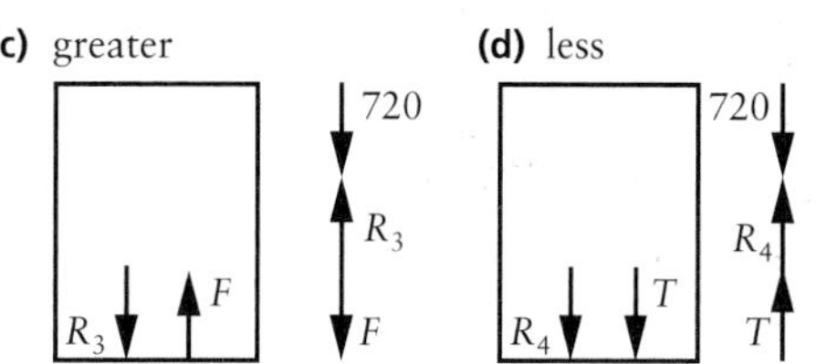

12 (a) 2400 N

2400 N
D N
B
A

(b)

2000 N
D N
2400 N
200 N
T_1 N
T_2 N
B

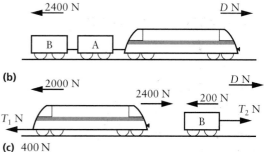

(c) 400 N
(d) 200 N

EXERCISE 4D (Page 78)

1 (a) 1600 N
(b) 88 500 N
(c) 0.0225 N
(d) 84 000 N
(e) 8×10^{-20} N
(f) 548.8 N
(g) 8.75×10^{-5} N
(h) 10^{30} N
2 (a) 200 kg
(b) 50 kg
(c) 10 000 kg
(d) 1.02 kg
3 (a) 7.6 N
(b) 7.84 N

EXERCISE 4E (Page 82)

1 (a) 0.5 ms^{-2}
(b) 25 m
2 (a) 1.67 ms^{-2}
(b) 16.2 s
3 (a) 325 N
(b) 1764 N
4 (a) 13 N
(b) 90 m
(c) 13 N
5 (a)

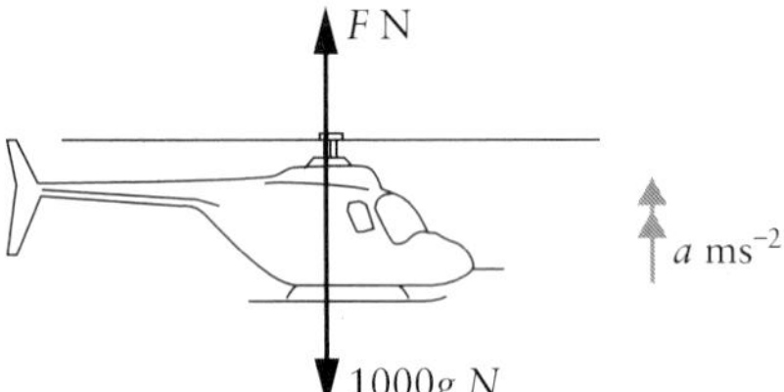

(b) 11 300 N
6 (a) $400 - 250 = 12\,000a$, 0.0125 ms^{-2}
(b) 0.5 ms^{-1}, 40 s
(c) (i) 15 s
(ii) 13.75 m
(iii) 55 s
7 (a) 60 ms^{-1}
(b) continues at 60 ms^{-1}
(c) 1.25 N
(d) the first by 655 km
8 (a) 6895 N, 6860 N, 6790 N, 1960 N
(b) 815 kg
(c) max $T < 9016$ N
9 (a) 7.84 ms^{-2}
(b) 13.7 ms^{-1}
(c) It is just over 30 mph

EXERCISE 4F (Page 86)

1 (a) $1.5\mathbf{i} - \mathbf{j}$
(b) 1.8 ms^{-2}
2 (a) $4\mathbf{i} + 11\mathbf{j}$
(b) $8\mathbf{i} + 8\mathbf{j}$, $2\mathbf{i} + 2\mathbf{j}$
3 (a)

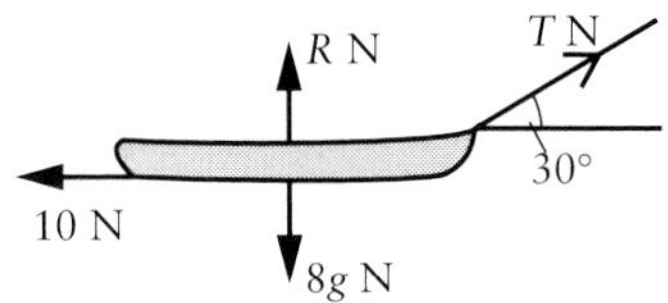

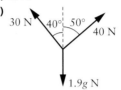

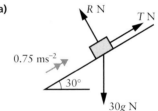

(b) 11.55 N
(c) 1 ms^{-2}
(d) 0.4 s
4 (a)
(b) Davies $-19.3\mathbf{i} + 23\mathbf{j}$; Jones $30.6\mathbf{i} + 25.7\mathbf{j}$; Total $11.4\mathbf{i} + 30\mathbf{j}$
(c) $5.98\mathbf{i} + 15.8\mathbf{j}$ ms^{-2}
(d) It has an acceleration of $16.1\mathbf{i} + 3.73\mathbf{j}$ ms^{-2}.
5 (a)
(b) $T\mathbf{i} + 0\mathbf{j}$; $0\mathbf{i} + R\mathbf{j}$; $-30g\sin 30°\mathbf{i} - 30g\cos 30°\mathbf{j}$
(c) 169.5 N
(d) The crate slows down to a stop and then starts sliding down the slope.
6 (a) 98.5 N, 17.4 N
(b) the reaction of the rails
(c) 98.5 N
(d) All the forces are constant. 109.3 N, 11.25 m
(e) $ma = T\cos\theta - (100 + 44\sin\theta)$. Each term decreases as θ increases, so a decreases.

EXERCISE 4G (Page 88)

1 178 kN
2 1.51 ms^{-2}, no
3 (a) 2.11 ms^{-2} down
(b) 10.2 ms^{-2} up
4 (a) 2550 tonnes
(b) 546 tonnes
(c) 1.87 ms^{-2}

5 (a) $2\mathbf{i} - 0.5\mathbf{j}\ \text{ms}^{-2}$
(b) $6\mathbf{i} - 1.5\mathbf{j}\ \text{ms}^{-1}$
6 $-180\mathbf{i} + 120\mathbf{j}$ N
7 (a) $3\mathbf{i} - 0.5\mathbf{j}\ \text{ms}^{-2}$
(b) $11\mathbf{i} - 1.5\mathbf{j}\ \text{ms}^{-1}$
8 (a) $\mathbf{i} + 0.2\mathbf{j}$
(b) $0.6\mathbf{i}$
9 (a) $0.4\mathbf{i} + 10.2\mathbf{j}$
(b) $-0.2\mathbf{i} + 11.4\mathbf{j}$
10 84.9 N
11 (a) $5.39\ \text{ms}^{-2}$
(b) $10\mathbf{i} - 17\mathbf{j}\ \text{ms}^{-1}$
12 (a) 153°
(b) $2\mathbf{i} - 3\mathbf{j}\ \text{ms}^{-2}$
(c) 7.21 N
(d) $(-5 + 2t)\mathbf{i} + (7 - 3t)\mathbf{j}\ \text{ms}^{-1}$
(e) 2.4 s

CHAPTER 5

EXERCISE 5A (Page 97)

1 (a)

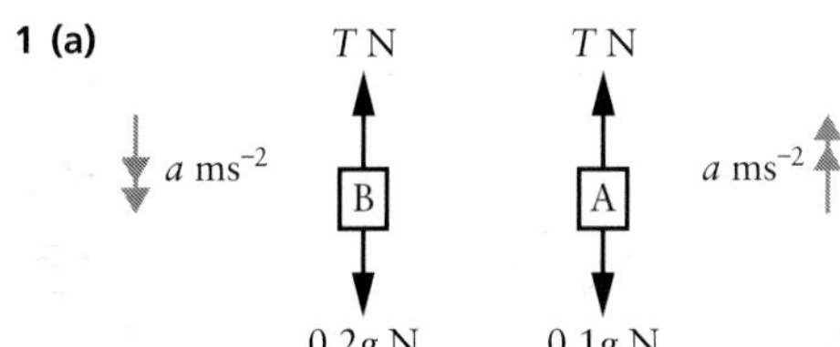

(b) $0.2g - T = 0.2a,\ T - 0.1g = 0.1a$
(c) $3.27\ \text{ms}^{-2}$, 1.31 N
(d) 1.11 s
2 (a)

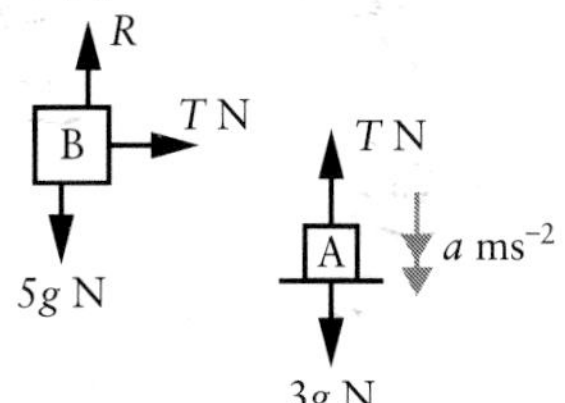

(b) $T = 5a,\ 3g - T = 3a$
(c) $3.68\ \text{ms}^{-2}$, 18.4 N
(d) 9.4 N
3 (b) 750 N
(c) tension, 44 N
(d) 170 N
4 (a) $0.767\ \text{ms}^{-2}$
(b) 18.1 N
5 (a) $2.1\ \text{ms}^{-2}$
(b) 8.4 N
(c) by giving both particles the same acceleration
6 (a)

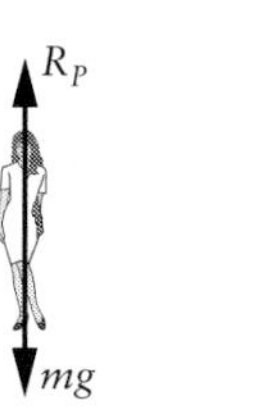

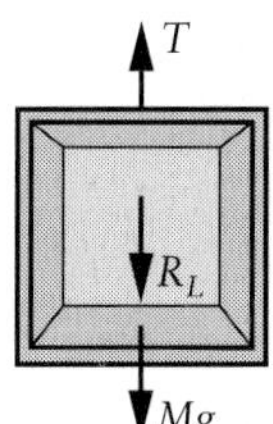

(b) 4900 N, 490 N, 490 N
(c) 5300 N, 530 N, 530 N

EXERCISE 5B (Page 99)

1 (a) $2.45\ \text{ms}^{-2}$
(b) 36.75 N
(c) 73.5 N
2 (a) 67.2 N
(b) 8
(c) 134.4 N
(d) by making the tensions the same at both ends of the string
3 (a) $\frac{7}{13}g$
(b) 0.7 m
(c) by giving both particles the same acceleration
4 (a) $T - 10 = 3a,\ 8g\sin 30° - T = 8a$
(b) $2.65\ \text{ms}^{-2}$, 18.0 N
(c) by making the tensions the same at both ends of the string
5 (a) 3.12
(b) $1.43\ \text{ms}^{-2}$
6 (a) 6000 N
(b) 2600 N
(c) 200 N, tension
7 (a) $\dfrac{21mg}{5}$
(b) The string is inextensible.
(c) 7
(d) By making the tension the same throughout the string.
8 (a) $0.582\ \text{ms}^{-2}$
(b) 938 N
(c) $-0.09\ \text{ms}^{-2}$; decreases
9 (a) $0.7\ \text{ms}^{-2}$
(b) 960 N
(c) Old time was 11.43 s, new time is 5.33 s so time difference is 6.1 s

CHAPTER 6

EXERCISE 6A (Page 105)

1 (a) 500 Ns
(b) 20 000 Ns
(c) 2.8×10^8 Ns
(d) 2×10^{-22} Ns
2 (a) 18 200 Ns
(b) 2.25×10^{-3} Ns
(c) 3 Ns
(d) 10 Ns
3 (a) 15 N
(b) 20 m
(c) 20 ms^{-1}
(d) 30 Ns, impulse = change in momentum
4 (a) 1.2 Ns upwards
(b) 2 s
(c) 0 Ns
(d) 1.2 Ns
5 (a) 2.125 Ns
(b) (i) 21.25 N
(ii) 42.5 N
(c) smaller force
6 (a) 11 900 Ns
(b) 99 000 N
(c) 11g
(d) much lower maximum deceleration
7 (a) 5.42 ms^{-1}
(b) 108 Ns
(c) 108 Ns
(d) 542 N
8 (a) +30 000 Ns
(b) −15 000 Ns
(c) −45 000 Ns
(d) the impulse
(e) 450 000 N

EXERCISE 6B (Page 112)

1 195 ms^{-1}
2 2 ms^{-1}
3 (a) 25.6 ms^{-1}
(b) 4440 Ns forwards
(c) 4440 Ns backwards
4 (a) $1\frac{2}{3}$ ms^{-1}
(b) 1670 Ns forwards on car, backwards on lorry
5 (a) 0.623 ms^{-1}
(b) 9.97 Ns
(c) 997 N
6 (a) 4990 ms^{-1}
(b) 5000.001 ms^{-1}
7 (a) 3 ms^{-1}
(b) Impulse 1500 Ns is too great
8 (a) 0
(b) M −0.75 ms^{-1}, A 1.05 ms^{-1}
(c) M −52.5 Ns, A +52.5 Ns
(d) 0
9 (a) 10 ms^{-1}
(b) 24 000 Ns
(c) 24 000 Ns
(d) 966 000 N
(e) 0.5 m
10 (a) $\frac{2}{3}$ ms^{-1}
(c) True in general

EXERCISE 6C (Page 113)

1 $\frac{1}{3}$
2 10 ms^{-1}
3 7501.9 ms^{-1}
4 (a) 7
5 (a) 3 ms^{-1}
(b) 12 Ns
(c) 480 N
6 (a) 3.78 ms^{-1}
(b) 2.14 m
7 (a) 0.6 ms^{-1}, 0.3 ms^{-1}
(b) 0.0036 Ns
(c) 0.054 m
8 (a) 0.25 ms^{-1}
(b) 1875 Ns
(c) 0.057 s
(d) 7 mm
9 (a) 3.75 kg
(b) 15 Ns
(c) 0.938 s
(d) 1.41 m
10 (a) 4.9 ms^{-1}
(b) 3.81 ms^{-1}
(c) 7.62 Ns
(d) 0.061 s
(e) 0.116 m
11 (a) 0.36 Ns
(b) 2.7 ms^{-1}
(c) 0.216 Ns
12 (a) 2.2 ms^{-1}
(b) 1.8 or 0.9
13 (a) Momentum is conserved
(b) 24 m
(c) 79.2 m
14 (a) 2.4 ms^{-1}
(b) 900 N

CHAPTER 7

EXERCISE 7A (Page 118)

1 (a)

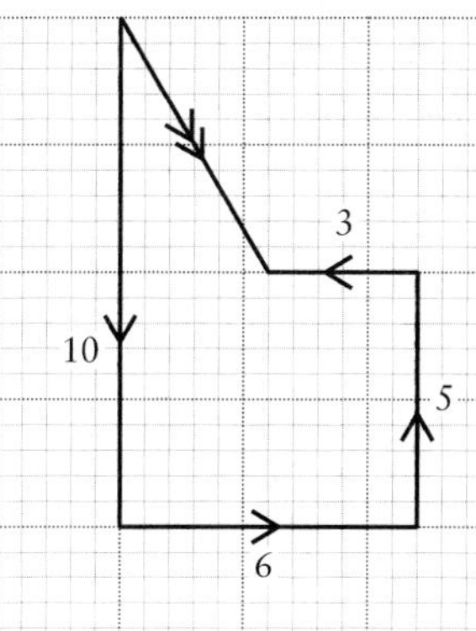

2 (a)

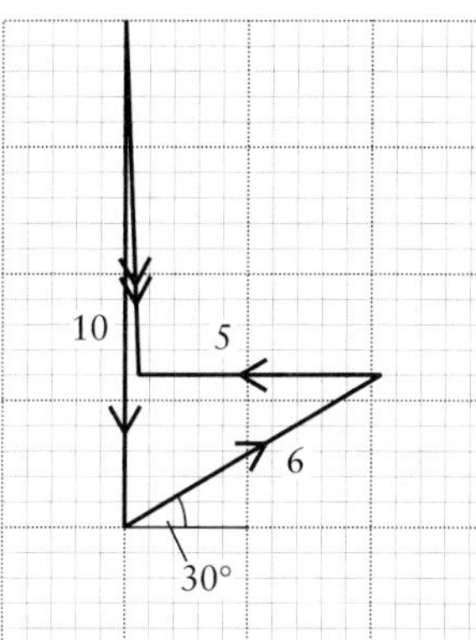

3 (a)

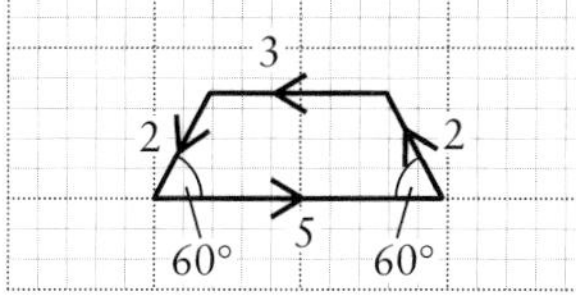

4 (a)

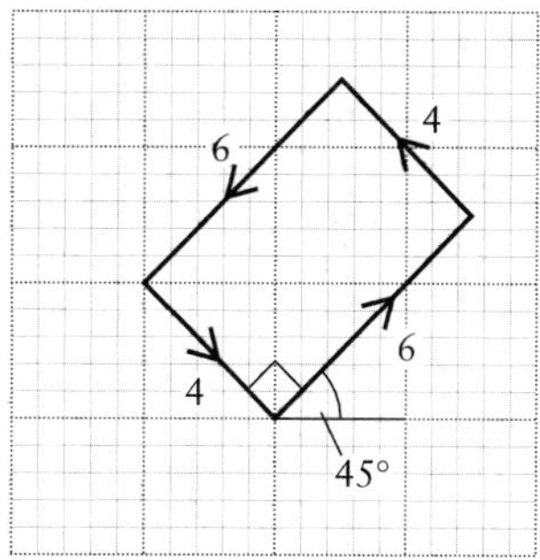

5 (a)

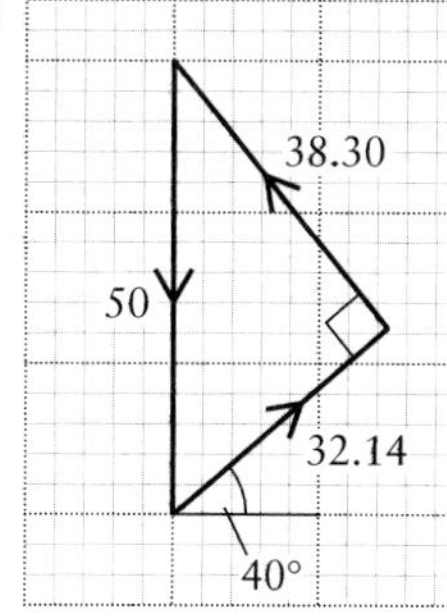

6 (a)

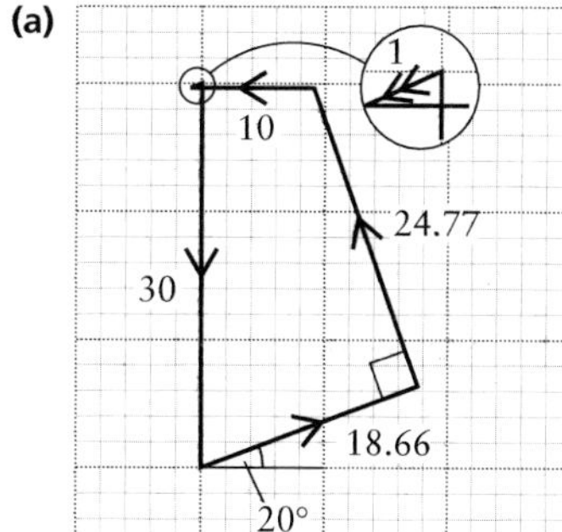

For resultants, see Exercise 7B.

EXERCISE 7B (Page 119)

1 3**i** – 5**j**, 5.83 N at –59.0°
2 0.196**i** – 7**j**, 7.00 N at –88.4°
3 equilibrium
4 equilibrium
5 equilibrium
6 –**i**, 1 N down slope

EXERCISE 7C (Page 122)

1 (a) 30 N, 36.9°; 65 N, 67.4°

(b)

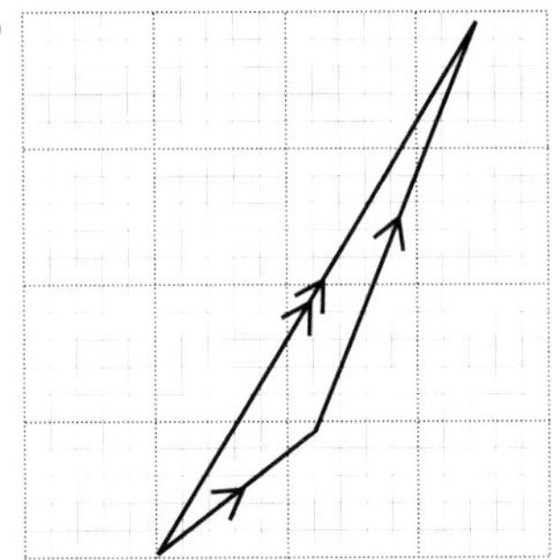

(c) 49**i** + 78**j**; 92.1 N, 57.9°

2 (a)

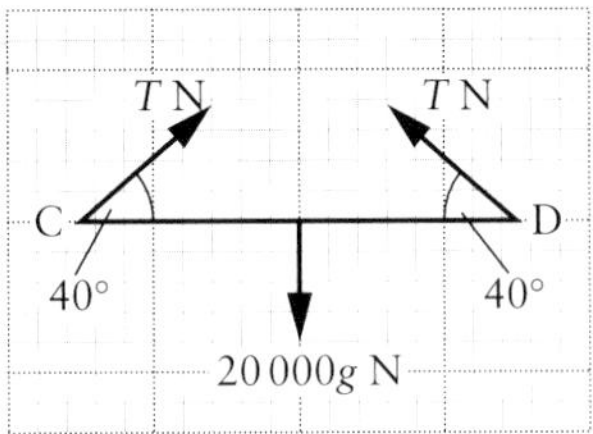

(b) $T\cos 40°$, $T\sin 40°$; $-T\cos 40°$, $T\sin 40°$

(d)

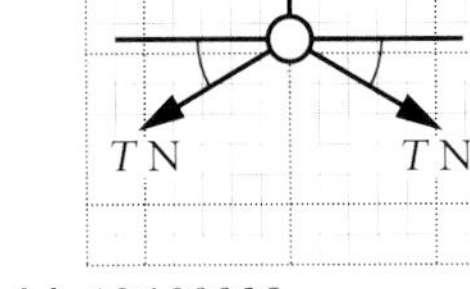

(e) 196 000 N

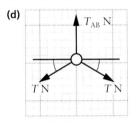

(f) resolve vertically for the whole system

3 (a) (i)

T_2 N

load

30 N

(ii)

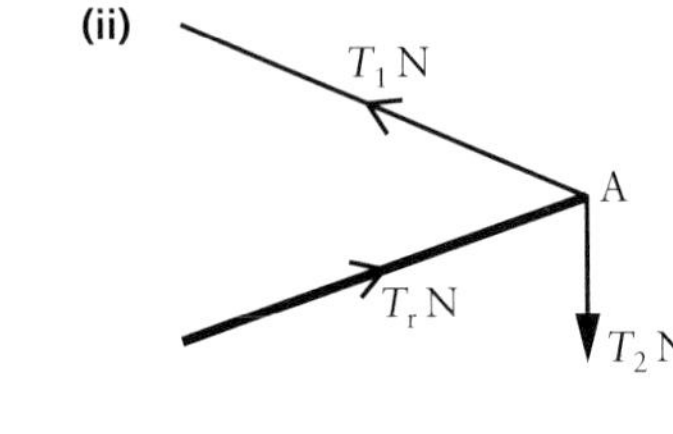

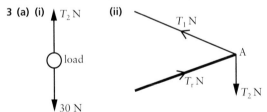

(b) rod 56.4 N, compression; cable 1 59.1 N, tension

4 (a) 15.04 kg

(b) Both read 10 kg.

(c) Both read 7.64 kg.

(d) method A or C

5 (a)

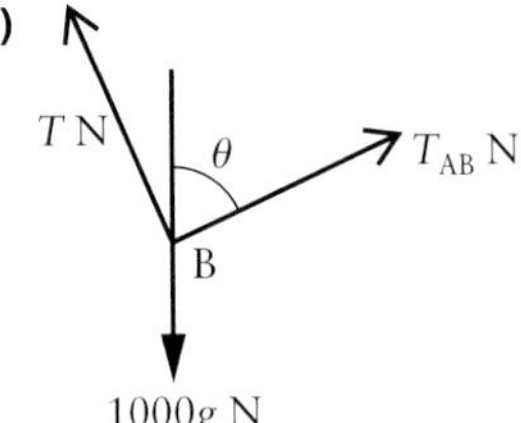

(b) By resolving horizontally. A component to the right is required.

(c)

T N

1000g N

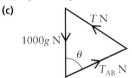

θ

T_{AB} N

(d) (i) 9800 N, 13 859 N, 9800 N

(ii) 9800 N, 9800 N, 9800 N

6 (a) Cable 1 (5638, 2052); Cable 2 ($T_2\cos 30°$, $T_2\sin 30°$)

(b) 4100 N

(c) 9190 N

7 (a)

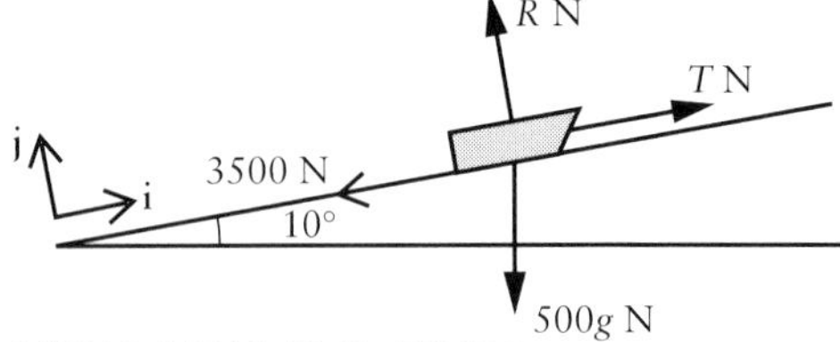

(b) 3500 N, 851 N, T; R, 4826 N

(c) 4351 N

(d) 4351 N

(e) no

8 (a)

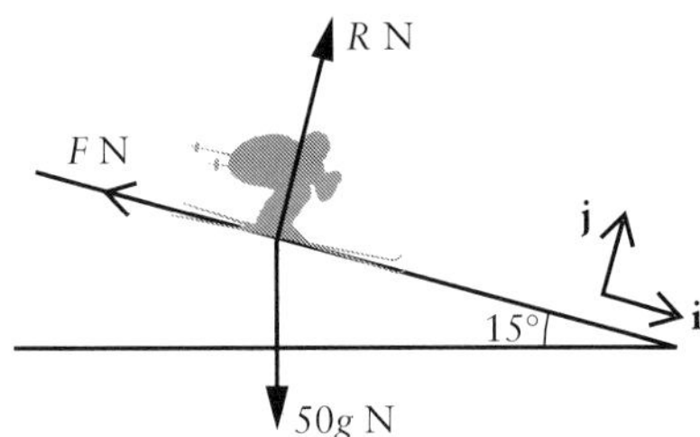

(b) 127 N, 473 N

(c) 473 N, 127 N

(d) 254 N

9 (a)

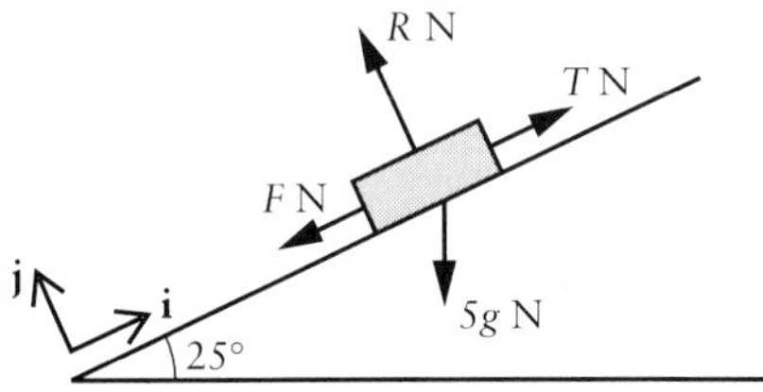

(b) T**i**, $-F$**i**, R**j**, -20.7**i** $-$ 44.4**j**

(c) T = 29.4, 8.69 N

(d) 1.23 kg

10 (a) 58**i** + 15.5**j**; 59**i** $-$ 10.4**j**

(b) (i) 117 N

(ii) 5.11 N

(c) 97 N forwards

(d) 3 N

11 (a) 11.0 N, 63.43°

(b) A circle with centre B, radius 1 m. No; two parallel forces and a third not parallel cannot form a triangle.

EXERCISE 7D (Page 127)

1 68.4 N, 153 N
2 (a) 2.78 N, 3.08 N
(b) reasonable assumption
3 14.5°
4 (a) 38.1 N
(b) 71.6 N
5 (a) 63.8 N
(b) 52.0 N
6 (a) 84.9 N
(b) 32.7 N
7 (a) 29.2°
(b) 15.5 kN
8 (a) particles
(b) 0.196 N
(c) BC 0.235 N, BD 0.183 N
9 (a) garments – particles, line – light string
(b) 75.7 N
(c) 73.1 N
(d) 78.8 N, 21.9°
10 (a) 0.551 kN
(b) 1.74 kN
11 (a) 19.9 N
(b) 3.46 N
12 (a) 6.93 N
(b) 3.46 N
13 (a) 52.6°
(b) 24.7 N

CHAPTER 8

EXERCISE 8A (Page 139)

1

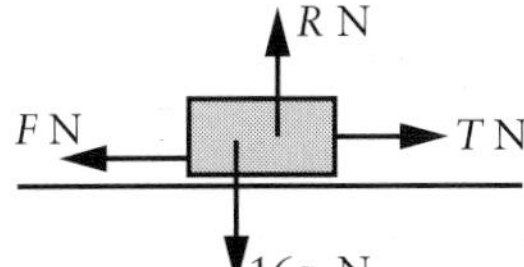

(a) 0.1
(b) 0.5
2 4.80 kN
3 (a) There is a lower coefficient of friction between the mat and the floor.
(b) 0.2
(c) 137 N
4 (a) 58.8 N
(b) 62.5 N
5 (a) 0.577
(b) 35°
(c) 2.14
(d) 50.2°
6 greater than, equal to, less than 16.7°, respectively
7 (a)

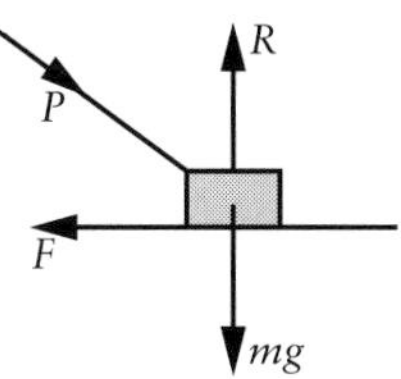

(b) 73.3° $\frac{F}{R}$ does not change
(c) 25.0 N
(d) No, the wheels roll rather than slide.
8 (a) 5.68 N
(b) It starts to slide down again.
9 (a) (i) 37.9 N
(ii) 37.2 N
(iii) 37.5 N
(b) $\dfrac{40}{(\cos\alpha + 0.4\sin\alpha)}$

EXERCISE 8B (Page 143)

1 (a) $F = 2g$
(b) 2.45 ms^{-2}
(c) $F = 2g$
(d) 2.205 ms^{-2}
2 (a) 1.02 ms^{-2}
(b) 0.102 N
(c) 0.104
(d) 49 m; independent of mass
3 0.816
4 (a) 7.35 ms^{-2}
(b) 13.4 ms^{-2}
(c) 26.5 m
5 (a)

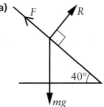

(b) 4.42 ms^{-2}
(c) 5.15 ms^{-1}
(d) 5.42 m
6 (a) 0.194
(b) 4.84 ms^{-2}
(c) 9.84 ms^{-1}
(d) 9.85 ms^{-1}

EXERCISE 8C (Page 145)

1 16.0 N
2 476 N
3 (a) 28.3 s
(b) 1181 m
4 1.19 kg
5 (b) 0.653 ms^{-2}
(c) 18.3 N
6 (a) 0.198
(b) 7.92 N
7 (a) 0.833
(b) 0.5
8 (a) 1.03
(b) 45.8°
9 (a) 9.37 ms^{-1}
(b) 57.0 N
10 (a) 8.8°
(b) the fifth binder
(c) reasonable for a small number
(d) no theoretical limit
11 (a) $\frac{1}{5}g$
(b) 1.6 m
(c) by making the tensions at each end of the string equal
12 (a) $\frac{1}{3}g$
(b) $\frac{2}{3}$ m
(c) yes
13 (b) (i) 2.83 ms^{-2}
(ii) $6.10m$ N
(c) by making the accelerations of the two particles equal
14 (b) (i) $\frac{5}{39}g$
(ii) $\frac{29}{39}mg$
15 0.262
16 (a) 10.2 N
(b) 5.3 m
17 (a) For A: $T - F = 2ma$ where $F = 2\mu mg$
For B: $\frac{mg}{2} - T = ma$
(b) $\dfrac{13h}{12}$
(c) Two from mass of string, stretch of string, friction at pulley, friction at B
18 (a) For P: $T - 1.8\,mg = 3ma$
For Q: $5\,mg - T = 5ma$
(b) $0.4\,g$
(c) $3mg$
(d) $\dfrac{2h}{3}$

EXERCISE 9A (Page 159)

1 (a) 15 Nm
(b) −22 Nm
(c) 18 Nm
(d) −28 Nm
2 28.6 N, 20.4 N
3 96.5 N, 138.5 N
4 (a) 1225 N, 1225 N
(b) 1449 N, 1785 N
5 (a) 55 kg

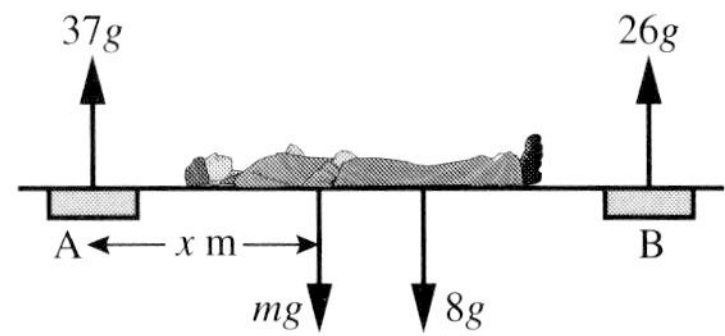

(b) 0.8 m
6 (a) $P = 269.5$ N, $Q = 1445.5$ N
(b) $P = 24.5$ N, $Q = 1690.5$ N
(c) Yes. The bench is balanced on the other support.
(d) The bench tips if A is not anchored.
7 (a) 294 N, 147 N
(b) 49 N, 882 N
(c) 0 N
(d) 0.67 m
8 (a) $0.5g(30 - x)$ kN, $0.5g(20 + x)$ kN
(b) its centre of mass
(c) They remain constant at 147 kN each.
9 (a) 735 N, 343 N
(b) No
(c) 36 kg
10 (a) 7538 N, 2262 N
(b) 6
(c) 784 N

EXERCISE 9B (Page 162)

1 (a) 25 N
(b) 175 N
2 (a) 10 kg
(b) 30 kg
3 (a) 392 N, 470 N
(b) 91 cm from the front
4 525 N, 161 N
5 70 N, 30 N
6 (a) plank – uniform rod, children – particles
(b) 25 kg
(c) 735 N
7 (a) 2254 N, 2940 N
(b) 56.3 kg

8 (a) $S = 245x - 134.75$, $R = 771.75 - 245x$

9 (a) $(16.25 - X)g$

(b) $(2X - 1.25)g$

10 (a) $\frac{9}{8}g$ N, $\frac{15}{8}g$ N

(d) 11

11 (a) $60g$ N = 588 N

(b) 1.25 m

12 (a) 3

(b) By putting the weight of it at a single point at the end of the plank.

(c) 1.2 m

13 (a)

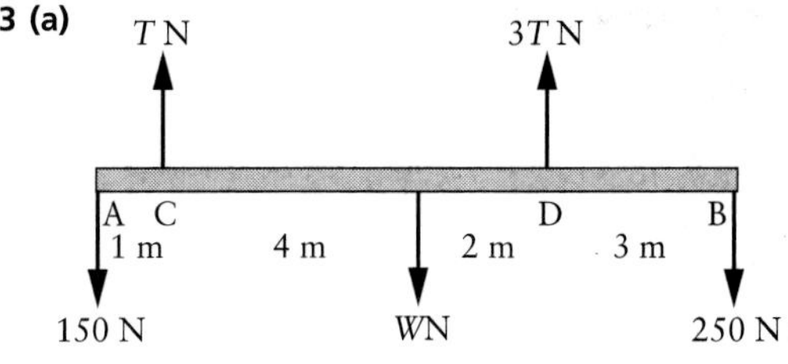

(b) 250 N

(c) 600 N

(d) By putting the weight in the middle.

INDEX